W9-BSW-441

# AMERICAN CLOCKS
# AND CLOCKMAKERS

BOOKS

*by Carl W. Drepperd*

AMERICAN CLOCKS AND CLOCKMAKERS

FIRST READER FOR ANTIQUE COLLECTORS

THE PRIMER OF AMERICAN ANTIQUES

# AMERICAN CLOCKS & CLOCKMAKERS

CARL W. DREPPERD

ENLARGED EDITION

BOSTON 59, MASSACHUSETTS

CHARLES T. BRANFORD COMPANY

1958

PRINTED IN THE UNITED STATES

SECOND EDITION, 1958

*In Memory of*

ROBERT CARR LANPHIER

*President of Hamilton-Sangamo Clock Company Who Introduced Me to the Clock Business as a Friend and Associate, 1928–1931.*

# AMERICAN CLOCKS AND CLOCKMAKERS

# CHAPTER I

THIS story begins many thousands of years ago. Before recorded history, man measured his life span by alternating periods of light and darkness and by alternating changes in season. Measurement by "moons" was probably one of late prehistoric man's ways of keeping time. After the apparent rising and setting of the sun, the rise and set of the moon, and its mystifying waxing and waning from day to day, was, in all likelihood, a phenomenon by which Og and Oggie from Neanderthal kept track of time. Then some master mathematician of a later day, on the verge of history (he could probably count up to twenty and do simple sums in division, et cetera), noticed that the sun cast a shadow that moved. He forthwith invented the sundial. This assumption is, of course, prosaic license. It probably took several thousand years for man to develop the sundial. That his dial was incorrect as a timekeeper save on but few days a year never entered the heads of our remote ancestors.

Timekeeping, by some device or other, is required by all people. But the degree of accuracy demanded is something else again. Once, when we were in the clock business, we arranged with a well-known writer to carry a chronometer and go around the city of New York asking, of various types of people, this simple question: "What time is it, please?" One individual asked near the steps of the public library was obviously a man of affairs. His watch was within three seconds of being right with the chronometer. A fish peddler was three minutes off. A cloak-and-suit worker had no watch. He guessed the time within thirteen minutes. On a park bench at the Battery, a down-and-outer answered the question with a dirty look. "Daytime!" he growled.

The civilizations of Sumaria, Egypt, China, the Cycladic Greek islands, and our own Incas, Aztecs, and Mayans reveal evidence of knowledge of sundials and their use. Certainly the Aztecs knew the pole star and its significance in the days when the stars around Polaris circled it at a speed obvious to the observer. It is said that the swastika, as an emblem, derives from noticing this heavenly display. Egypt, and perhaps also China, had timekeeping machines of another sort as early as 2000 B.C. They had a device with a controlled leak, filled with water. The escape of the water told the time. They had gotten hold of a great truth. Timekeeping is nothing more nor less than the controlled leaking away of either sand, water, or some other weight, or a similar control over the leaking away of another source of power, as that of a coiled or compressed spring.

It is said that the Chinese had a clock made from a smoldering rope of punk-like stuff that burned away at a fairly steady rate. Just as soon as man invented the candle he began to notice that a candle of a certain size, when lighted, was consumed in a given space of time. King Alfred the Great invented a time candle which he placed within a horn case to protect it from draught. There is a record, or memorial, in medieval Latin, citing this invention and crediting Alfred with it. Whether Hero of Alexandria, first man of record to build a steam engine, also made a mechanical timepiece is still a moot question. Aristotle, Archimedes, Euclid, and other great philosophers seem to have known something of the mechanics and the mathematics involved in timekeeping. But knowing something about a science is not proof that its applications were in use by those who knew the principles involved.

Our own Aztecs developed a calendar system of amazing accuracy. They carved their perpetual calendar on a huge stone that was set in the ceiling of a great temple. The Aztec calendar stone is an almost precise circle. Its divisions reveal a knowledge of mathematics on a parity with the parallax of astronomers. Yet with that beautifully conceived circle of stone as proof the Aztecs knew the circle, will someone rise and go to the head of the class with the answer to this question: Knowing the circle, why did they not use the wheel as a means of mechanics and of conveyance? The Aztecs transported stuff on the backs of humans, animals, and on two poles dragged behind a beast or a man. They knew how to build a keyed wall of great stones. They knew how to calculate a calendar system well in advance of that used by

Europeans. Yet apparently they lacked the wheel. Why? The answer is shrouded in mystery.

From about the middle of the seventeenth century to the early eighteenth century clocks, by their makers, were often called "Artificial Timepieces." In calling their devices artificial timepieces and their timepieces "Artificial Clocks," these men displayed a depth of knowledge that we of this day and age may not always appreciate. That word "artificial" is the clue that tells us the makers knew there is only one real timepiece, the earth itself. The earth, spinning on its axis, is our master clock. That the earth does not revolve once in twenty-four hours need concern us only as a curiosity. Yet the fact is that any artificial timepiece or clock, no matter how precise, that measures time in seconds,. sixty to the minute, sixty minutes to the hour, and twenty-four hours to the day, will not be "right" in time. Our "day" is not twenty-four hours long, but twenty-three hours, fifty-six minutes, four and one-tenth seconds long. So that master clock would be three minutes and fifty-five and nine-tenths seconds "fast" in our day.

We do not measure the rotation of the earth accurately by observing the sun. We measure it by taking our bearings from what are called "fixed" stars, whose position, in relation to the earth, is uniform. We do not check up on the stars. We check the rotation of the earth by the stars.

These facts about the earth and its rotation demonstrate that the art of clockmaking and timekeeping is not simply a matter of making a machine that will tick off seconds, minutes, and hours. The ticking off must *measure* against the only standard we have, a rotation of our own earth. A second is not 1/86.400 of twenty-four hours, but 1/86.400 of 86,164.1 seconds.

"It is precisely twelve o'clock when the sun is overhead" is a truism you can laugh at on all but four days a year, generally on December 24, April 15, June 15, and August 31. Why? Because the earth has another known movement in addition to revolution on its axis. It follows a path around the sun. Hence timekeeping involves a bit of complicated mathematical calculation to include that motion and what it does to our apparent time. All of which will probably cause you to say that clockmaking and timekeeping are almost as complicated as atomic fission or the fourth dimension. That is quite true. Yet, when the science is reduced to its least common denominator for human use, we have clocks; some very lovely clocks, amusing clocks, expensive clocks, cheap clocks, clocks as small as a dime, and some clocks as big as whales.

What is a clock? is a simple question. It deserves a simple, direct answer. A clock is a bell. The terms cloche, clocke, clock, glocken, all mean bell. Just when the first mechanical clock was made may never be known. The monk Liutprand, of Chartres, and builder of the cathedral at Montferrat, Italy, is sometimes credited with inventing a machine to ring the hours in the eighth century. Other experts credit him with inventing the sand glass. Chances are he invented neither. The sand glass was a simplification, not an advance over the clepsydra, or water-thief. This machine, using the escape of water as motive power, was known in many complicated forms in Greek and Roman times. The machinery only wanted another kind of weight and an escapement device comparable to the dropping of water from a reservoir through an orifice. That is precisely what happened. Somebody, somewhere, put geared wheels together, tied a great weight to them and, noting that the falling weight actually caused the gearing to turn as expected, devised an escapement to regulate the fall of the weight. There was a time-measuring machine! More machinery and another weight was added. The extra machinery was designed to run only at certain specified intervals regulated by the master machine, and do a specific bit of work at those times. The specific work was raising a hammer which struck a cloche, a clocke, a glocken—a bell. That's what made the machine a "clock." No dial, no hands. Just a bell ringing out the passing of the hours.

These devices were sometimes very ornately contrived. In some of them the striking mechanism was in the form of mechanical men which struck the bell with sledges or maces. These were called Jacks, striking-Jacks, Jaquemarts, and perhaps by other names no longer remembered. The use of bells rather than dials to record the passing of time was most likely owing to the influence of the church which, in those far-off days, had its finger in every secular, political, scientific, and religious interest of the nobles, the wise men, and the people. As early as A.D. 605 Pope Sabinianus decreed that bells should be sounded publicly seven times daily. These became the canonical hours. The bells were rung by hand. A clepsydra was probably the timepiece used to tell the bell men when to ring.

The Church was opposed to popular knowledge of science in any form. It was unholy, and dangerous to contemplate the vast arena of possible things. About the only scientific pursuit not wholly frowned upon was the quest to convert lead into gold. Mathematics, the mother of all sciences, was known to but few scholars. The application of steam, as a power, proved practical by Hero of Alexandria as early as the days of the Caesars, was an almost forgotten phenomenon. In the Middle Ages the so-called Christian world was actually a backward world as far as the people were concerned. Today the popular term for this period is the "Dark Ages." That they were not altogether dark, and that little groups of men using the Church as a cloak under which to carry on mechanical, philosophical, and other experiments were at work, is now fairly obvious. Almost all of the inventions, discoveries, and rediscoveries of scientific nature in this period were made by scholar-monks in monasteries.

The Roman clepsydras to which the Christian world fell heir were well-developed timekeeping machines. Some of these were as complex as many modern clocks. The Roman hour was variable in length according to the seasons of the year. They devised clepsydras that automatically recorded the variations in the length of the hours.

The name given a clepsydra and any other timepiece in the Middle Ages was *Horloge*. "Hour-word" would be a fair translation of the term. After the development of the hourglass, or clepsammia (meaning thief of sand), this device was also called a horloge. The sand glass, presumably first made about the year 700, was an imitation of the clepsydra in its simplest form, using sand instead of water. It had one great advantage and one only—it did not freeze up and quit working in cold weather. Its disadvantages were many. Since most sand glasses had to be reversed every hour or less, they required the constant attendance of watchers.

The monk Gerbert, who later became Pope Sylvester II, is credited with making the first mechanical weight-driven timing machine in 990. Other men, including Pacificus in 850, Boetheus in 510, and Pope Sabinianus in 612, are credited with the same invention. According to the superstitions of those days the real inventor was probably the devil. His Satanic Majesty was credited with the creation of anything now considered good.

This present excursion into the background history of clocks should not deal only with the Christian world. While it was muddling along, using the philosophy of the great Master, Christ, as an excuse for power politics, empire building, and man-killing, the so-called pagan world was making progress more peacefully.

The Near East was devising a new, non-Euclidean system of higher mathematics called el-geber. We know it, and use it, as algebra. The Chinese were weaving silks, making timepieces and porcelain, and were printing books from wood blocks. Many of our furniture styles came from the East, Near or Far. So did most of our textiles in both form and pattern, and a great deal of our philosophy.

As has been noted, any mechanism using the fall of a weight to turn wheels requires a device to regulate the escape of the power caused by the pull of gravity on the weight. This regulating is actually a series of interruptions in the fall of the weight. Escapement is the term used to describe this mechanical part. The earliest clocks had a "fan fly" to act as a regulator. Then came the basically sound idea: foliot, verge and crown wheel, or what is commonly called a verge escapement. Crown wheels are short sections of round tubing with one end cut into saw teeth. Pallets, or stoppers, arranged on an upright shaft which turns alternately to the right and the left, permit the crown wheel to move a bit, then stop it, and then permit it to move. In order to swing the shaft carrying the pallets, a bar known as a foliot was fixed to the top of the pallet shaft, with weights hung on its ends. To start the clock, this bar was given a push. It swung right or left, permitting one pallet to disengage the crown wheel, but only until the other pallet engaged a tooth in the crown. Then it had an impulse to swing the other way. Tick-tock! The clock was off on its run, and run it would until the weight reached the end of its pull.

The crown wheel escapement, moving within its verge and so regulating the swinging bar balance, or foliot, accomplished substantially what the ancient Egyptians, Chinese, Greeks, and Romans achieved in their water clocks. The crown escapement made droplets of the reservoir of power stored in the drop of the

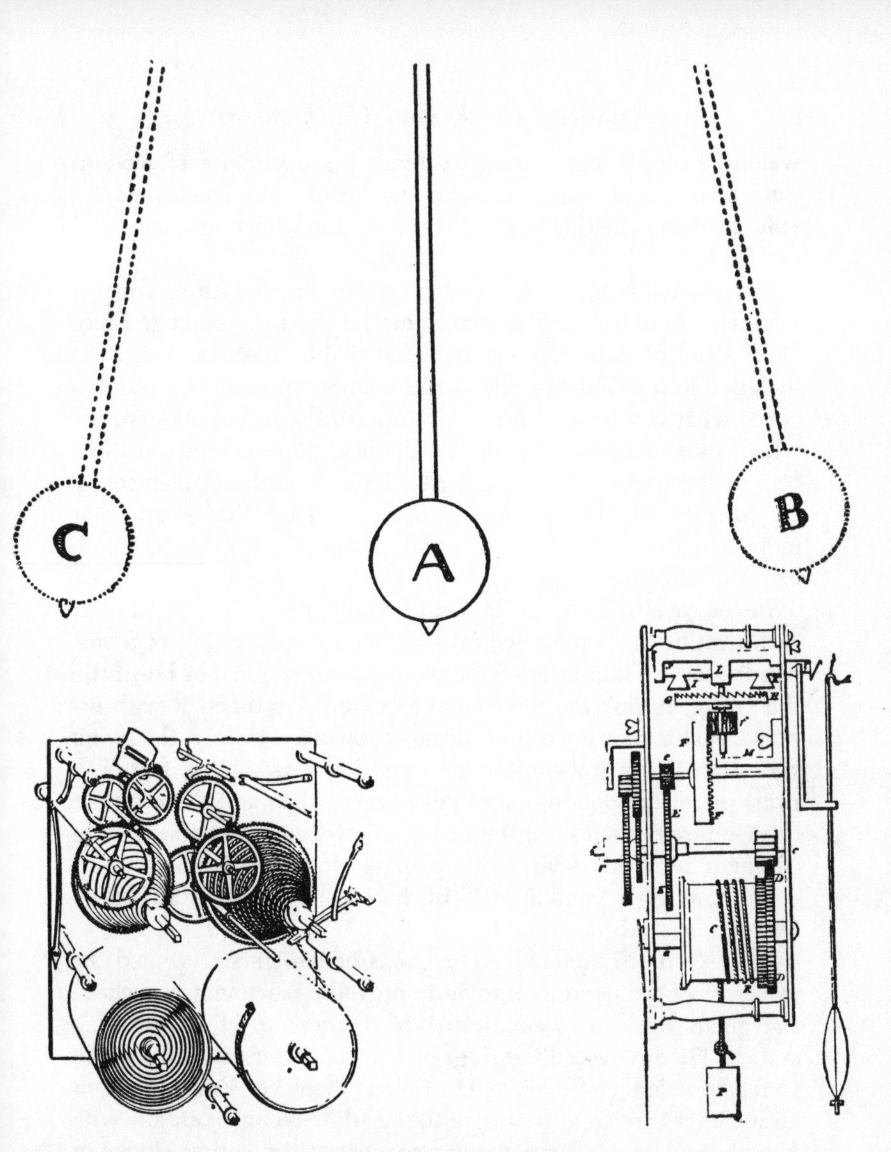


TOP: Pendulum positions explained in text. BOTTOM, LEFT: Early engraving of a clock movement, spring driven, showing the barrels in which coiled springs are housed and the cords connecting the barrels to the conical sections known as fusees. BOTTOM, RIGHT: Early clock movement simplified. Weight (P) pulls on drum (C) geared to the element (c) which is geared to deliver power at (r) where the hands are affixed. If this were the whole of the machine the hands would spin around and the weight drop rapidly. At (E) and (e) are gears transmitting power to (F) and (f) connecting to (G-H) the crown wheel, and (I-K) the pallets which are connected to the crutch (t) that swings the pendulum (A). Thus the power delivered at (r) to the hands is controlled by the escapement and registers minutes and hours; the weight drops slowly. The machine is a timepiece.

weight. From this invention we mark the beginning of modern timekeeping and from this point the history of timekeeping involves higher mathematics, astronomy, calculus, physics, and mechanics.

There are a half-dozen very scholarly volumes waiting for you who wish to delve deeply into the mystery of timekeeping. There are a score of more popular books available, most of which are included in the Bibliography of this volume. In these you can discover what can be said here in a few words; to wit: the crown-wheel escapement did make mechanical timekeeping possible, but not accurate timekeeping. All of the important advances in the science of timekeeping involved making the escapement more accurate. The drop of power had to escape under more efficient and precise control.

In the year 1581, or so it is said, Galileo of Pisa stood in the cathedral of his home town and watched the swinging of a suspended lamp. Galileo noted that no matter how great or how little the swing, it took the same time to swing. He timed it with his pulse. When it swung a short distance, or in a short arc, the swing was slow. When it swung in a long arc, the swing was fast. The principle of the pendulum was discovered then and there by the chance observation of an inquiring mind. Isochronism is a quite common term in today's timekeeping nomenclature. It means equal timing. A pendulum is isochronous because it swings in long or short arcs in equal time.

In 1665 the Netherlander Huyghens or Huijghens, applied the principle of the pendulum to an improved escapement in a clock. Huyghens was a mathematician and astronomer of considerable stature. He discovered the rings of Saturn, and contributed much to the knowledge of science. Dr. Robert Hooke of England seems also to have arrived at the use of the pendulum coincidentally with Huyghens. We can leave the controversy over whether Hooke or Huyghens was "first" to the experts, being sure they will not agree. What is important is the invention of George Graham of London who, in 1690, invented a new and better escapement, commonly called the "dead beat." Graham's escape wheel had teeth very much in the form of the crown wheel, but his pallets were so shaped that they had separate locking and lifting faces. During the times these pallets locked the escape wheel, that wheel remained dead, or motionless. Graham's invention, used in conjunction with the pendulum, made accurate timekeeping possible.

How to make a small clock without weights as motive power engaged the interest of many inventive mechanics in the sixteenth century. Henlein of Nuremberg is generally credited with inventing a timepiece which used a coiled spring as its motive power. Henlein was a locksmith. That means he was familiar with at least one form of complicated and tricky machinery which did things when power, in the form of the manual turning of a key, was applied. It is doubtful if Henlein alone invented the spring-driven clock. There is, however, a written record of the fact that he made such a mechanism. Some of the early spring-driven clocks had striking machinery as well. These were true "clocks." Some had no strike, but dials only. These were called "watches." Why they were not called "looks" or "see-the-time" is another of our philological mysteries. The term "clock" was applied to all timepieces even after the bell became of secondary importance and the dial became the real time-telling factor. The first dials carried but one hand as a time indicator. In this they followed the clepsydra which had single-handed dials long before belling machines were invented.

Henlein and his contemporaries, in using a coiled spring, at once ran into a difficulty not encountered when a weight, whether of water or a solid, was used. The coiled spring lost power as it uncoiled. It was strongest when wound tight and almost powerless when nearly uncoiled. To offset this inherent weakness in the use of a spring, a very ingenious device known as a fusee was developed. A fusee is a cone-shaped pulley, grooved or stepped in a coil—a miniature conical ramp, so to speak. A length of catgut (later a fine metal chain) was wound around the barrel of the uncoiled spring. This was then fixed to the lower or big end of the fusee. When wound, the cord was drawn around the fusee until, when the spring was wound tightly, its connection was with the small end of the fusee. Thus when at full tension the spring pulled against the smaller diameter and when almost run down it pulled against the larger diameter. Henlein did not invent the fusee. Jacob Zech of Prague is credited with inventing it in 1525. Gruet of Geneva made a fine steel chain to take the place of the catgut and other cords used on fusees. His invention paved the way for the making of really small, fine timepieces—pocket watches.

With the advance of science and the gradual discrediting of the devil as the father of all progress, clockmaking by the year 1500 was a fairly safe business. There was no longer much danger of being burned at the stake, stoned, drawn and quartered, hanged, or of being beheaded for making a clock. Consequently, a lot of inventive effort was expended on making clocks that almost preached a sermon. Some were mechanical marvels displaying the history of Christianity as a moving pageant. Peter did his denying, the cock did crow, Pontius Pilate washed his hands, the twelve Apostles moved in procession . . . as manikins within and around a clock. Coryate's *Crudities,* first published in London in 1611, pictures the Strasbourg automaton clock as one of the wonders of Europe.

Years later this same device was used in making clocks that displayed secular instead of religious pleasures and carnal sins rather than cardinal virtues. Kings and merchant princes and, it must be admitted, not a few cardinals and perhaps even some popes, owned clocks that displayed actions anything but religious. But the people did like a little show in addition to the moving of the hands or hand on a dial and the belling of the hours. Hence the clockmakers of the Netherlands, France, and Switzerland devised clocks which showed the phases of the moon, rocking ships, turning waterwheels, turning windmills, anglers casting their lines, sawyers at work, and many other sorts of action. These inventive pieces were part and parcel of the clockmaking tradition carried to the Colonies, and will be mentioned later in this work.

Clockmaking became a craft of considerable importance about the year 1550. Clocks for the homes of the upper middle classes became a possibility. By 1600 there were enough clockmakers at work to indicate the eventual conversion of the clock from a luxury to a staple article of commerce.

The significance of an accurate timepiece as an aid to navigation was generally appreciated in maritime and naval circles. In 1714 the English Parliament offered a grand prize to any clockmaker who would make a timepiece that would measure time accurately enough to determine longitude within thirty miles. John Harrison (1693–1776) developed one that made determination within eighteen miles possible. This was in 1761.

He called his timepiece a chronometer. If determining position by the aid of an accurate timepiece is something of a mystery to any reader, this explanation may resolve the matter: You set out on a voyage with an accurate clock that is set at the time of the place from which you start. That clock on your ship will, if accurate, keep in time with the master clock back home. Ten days later you want to know about how far you have sailed. At precisely noon you "shoot the sun" with an instrument. You know it is noon by the sun. You calculate the variation between sun time and true time from charts and tables and compare that with the "time" back home as recorded by the clock you have with you. Your clock says it's one o'clock. Your sun shooting says it's twelve o'clock. Ergo, you are approximately one thousand miles west of home. The time difference tells you where you are. A poor timepiece might tell you within one hundred miles. Harrison's timepiece cut the margin of error to eighteen miles.

For the purpose of navigating and travel on uncharted lands we divide the surface of the earth into twenty-four segments of a sphere. These segments are like twenty-four sections of peel cut from a round orange. At any place, crosswise, on that segment, it is an hour across. Only at the equator is it also one thousand miles across. The farther north or south we go, the narrower becomes the cross measure of the segment. When we get to the poles, all the segments meet and they measure exactly zero across. Anything on the earth moves with the earth. If we could put a chronometer with a twenty-four-hour dial, and with only an hour hand on it, precisely over the North Pole we could see something very peculiar. The earth moving toward the east, or counterclockwise, would carry the clock case, dial and all, around with it in twenty-four hours. The movement of the clock, however, would drive the hand at the same rate, but clockwise, or westward. The clock would move but the hand would appear to point always in the same direction!

It might be well to state here that all this seeming hocus-pocus is not introduced to confuse the reader but to demonstrate, as elementally as possible, the vast amount of calculation involved in the development of that apparently simple mechanism, the clock. The mechanical work, ingenious as it is, is as nothing compared to the mathematical problems of timekeeping. A pendulum is a simple thing in itself. It is a weight swinging in an arc. But to control that pendulum, to determine what length it must be to make it swing four times in a second, twice in a second, or once in a second, is a mathematical problem of no mean proportions. A one-quarter second pendulum must be 2.4462 inches long. A half-second pendulum must be 9.7848 inches long. A one-second pendulum must be 39.1393 inches. A two-second pendulum must be more than 156 inches long. Depending on the temperature, and what the pendulum rod is made of, it will at times be a minute fraction longer or shorter owing to natural contraction and expansion of the materials used. That expansion or contraction in length will affect timekeeping. Let's suppose the error is one ten thousandth of a second in the beat of a one-second pendulum. That means that in every ten thousand beats a second is lost or gained. In one day the error totals eight and one-half seconds or more—almost a minute a week.

Negligible? Of course! What is a minute to a week? There was a slight error in the Julian calendar established in 46 B.C. The error was in assuming that the year was precisely three hundred and sixty-five and one-quarter days long, and that hence it was logical to add an extra day every four years. This calculation was eleven minutes and fourteen seconds over the actual length of the year. Today they still use the Julian calendar in the Greek and Russian churches. Their Christmas comes thirteen days later than ours. That's how seconds and minutes, on even a yearly basis, add up through the centuries. Pope Gregory, in 1582, revised the calendar. His experts computed the year's length at three hundred and sixty-five days, five hours, forty-nine minutes, and twelve seconds. This arbitrary ruling is exactly twenty-six seconds longer than the solar year. That is why we have an "extra-day" year, or leap year, every fourth year, excepting those fourth years divisible by one hundred. If, however, said fourth year is also divisible by four hundred, the extra day is added. The year 1900 did not earn a leap-year day. The year 2000 will have one. All this because our calendar year is twenty-six seconds longer than the solar year.

Mother England did not correct her calendar in 1582. She waited until the eighteenth century to do it. That is why we run across birth dates of great men recorded as Old Style and why we celebrate the birthdays of Washington and Franklin on days that would have been their actual birthdays had the Gregorian calendar been in effect when they were born. More than one commentator has paid tribute to the Aztecs for having calculated a calendar comparable to the Gregorian long before the Vatican experts came up with their corrections, their deliberate error of twenty-six seconds, and their long-term amortization of that error over centuries of time.

Much has been written about pendulums since Huyghens's treatise first appeared. At that time, and perhaps before that time, Huyghens, of Zulichem, the Netherlands, was known as Mr. Zulichem—a name deriving, of course, from the name of his birthplace. Almost everything written about pendulums has been a little confusing to the layman. The principle of the pendulum is simple; its laws of operation are mathematical. The action of a pendulum is a natural phenomenon, operating within natural law. When applied to a clock, the use of a pendulum to control the escape (the leak) of power poses two problems. The first, of course, is to use the swing of the pendulum to control the escape of power; the second is to keep the pendulum swinging. A free-swinging pendulum, given one starting impulse, will swing until friction finally stops it dead. The swing, depending upon the length of the pendulum, will be in ever-shortening arcs, each swing, however, taking approximately the same interval of time. In our pendulum clocks, the pendulum not only marks the time but, with each oscillation, is given an infinitesimal "push" by the very power source whose escape it is regulating. This is done in several ways, none of which needs concern the layman and all of which are well known to most clock specialists. The books listed in the Bibliography delve into this phase of pendulum action; some in great detail, with charts and drawings to illustrate each step.

What almost none of the books state is the answer to the greatest curiosity of the layman—what is meant by a "one-second" pendulum, or by a pendulum designated as oscillating at any rate, be it ¼, ½, 1, 1¼, 1½, or 2 seconds? These various designations mean that one swing of the pendulum, whether from right to left or left to right, occurs within the time designated. Let's take a one-second pendulum for example. One swing, from either of its limits of swing to the other limit, takes approximately one second. No pendulum clock, no matter how fine and how well controlled as to temperature, humidity, and atmospheric pressure, keeps "perfect" time. The most perfect timepiece we have is the earth's rate of rotation, and even that is not "perfect." We haven't perfection, and we haven't it in pendulum clocks. But the error is slight and we can't measure the variation within the time it takes a pendulum to swing *one way;* we measure it by noting the cumulative error over twenty-four hours, or even a week.

Some laboratory people prefer to measure or consider the measurement of a pendulum, from its position at rest to one side of its swing and back to its position at rest. This movement is the last half of one arc of swing and the first half of another arc of swing. In a one-second pendulum, this swinging should take one second of time. This is the same as considering one complete arc as a full swing. On tall-case clocks with sweep second hands, the measure of seconds on the time track can be noted quite readily. If you open the door of such clocks and watch the pendulum (most such clocks have one-second pendulums) and also observe the sweep second hand, you will note that a second is marked on the dial each time the pendulum swings once, left-right or right-left. A complete "round trip," so to speak, occurs in two seconds.

Some writers aver that the pendulum was not "invented"; they claim it is an evolution from the "foliot, verge, and crown wheel" escapement in which the foliot is a form of pendulum, and from the escape wheel which is also a form of pendulum. Others aver that the bob pendulum isn't a real pendulum but an extension of the arm of a balance wheel. Listen to these fellows often enough and long enough and they will convince you that a clock shouldn't run, can't run, and will not run. Then your own clocks strike the hour and you know clocks can run and do run. We should thank all the patron saints of collecting that clockmakers made clocks for people and made them as machinery for timekeeping, not as mathematical instruments for experts.

The only diagram in respect of pendulums in this book is shown in this chapter. A pendulum bob and part of the shaft are pictured in solid lines at "rest" on dead center. On either side, the pendulum is shown where it would be at both ends of its arc of swing. These are designated as (A) for dead center, (B) for the right-hand arc limit, and (C) for the left-hand arc limit. A swing from A to B, or from A to C, and back to A, takes one second. A swing from B to C, or C to B, takes one second. A swing from B to C or C to B *and back again* takes two seconds when the pendulum is a one-second pendulum. The same principle holds good for the ¼, ½, 1, 1¼, 1½, or any other "timed" pendulum.

To compensate for the effect of temperature, atmospheric pressure, humidity, et cetera, on pendulum action, many devices are used. All of these are employed in an effort to keep the pendulum constantly at the same length. External influences contract or lengthen the pendulum a little. Thus a temperature and barometric change may make a one-second pendulum just longer enough or shorter enough to make it swing 1/10,000th of a second faster or slower. External influences do *not* affect the swing by some mysterious force; they affect the length of the pendulum itself and it, the pendulum, acting according to the laws of nature, becomes a little less, or a little more, than a one-second pendulum. To offset this tendency of any pendulum rod and bob material to change, there are pendulum rods of alternating bars of steel and copper, or any two other metals which expand and contract, respectively, under any given condition of temperature. Also, bobs are sometimes made to serve as containers for mercury which contracts as the temperature falls and expands as the temperature rises. To those who seek more on pendulums and compensations there are good books waiting to tell you the story. Unless mathematics is a hobby of yours, our advice is to avoid them.

"Tick-tock" is a sound masking ages of calculation. "Ding-dong" is a sound covering centuries of mechanical invention. The movement of the hands on the face of a clock—any clock—is a recording of infinity by man's measure stick, time. Time, says the philosopher, is a dimension. Astrophysicists now aver that the universe is in a constant state of change and reiterate, in their own jargon, the words of the prophet who said, "A thousand years is but a day to God, and a day is a thousand years." These gentry tell us, too, that if man could get away from earth at a speed greater than that of light, he could squat somewhere in space and look at the building of the pyramids. That will be very wonderful when man can travel at speeds greater than light.

We who have professed an interest in clocks need not wait for that day of super-speed. We can, here and now, contemplate the clocks made by our early American clockmakers, can enjoy clocks of the type the first colonists brought with them or imported, and can pay tribute to the makers of these clocks. They did not know they were making machines to measure a fourth dimension. They were just making clocks for all and sundry. They contrived to make fairly accurate clocks, and clocks that would run. They managed to make clocks for the people; clocks that served not only as timekeepers but also as decorative objects for the home. These clocks we can enjoy as observers, as fortunate possessors, and as collectors. So a truce to the mysteries and riddles of the universe, to the probable courses of the stars, and to the mathematical formulas of Euclid, Newton, and Einstein.

We can get down to earth with the clocks America and Americans knew from the days when the Jamestown, Plymouth, Dutch and Swedish colonies were planted, down to the Centennial of 1876 and to the Columbian Exposition of 1893. This will be safer ground for most of us. All we need deal with are the things of wheels and weights and springs that go tick-tock and ding-dong—the one item of household furniture of other days that is just as alive today as it was when it was first made.

# CHAPTER

# II

IT IS quite logical to assume that Columbus, Cabot, Hudson, La Salle, and other explorers and discoverers carried some kind of timepieces with them on their voyages. In all likelihood the Spanish governors and the priests and friars who accompanied them also had clocks. The fate of those clocks need not concern us. It is doubtful if any of them survived the years. Furthermore, we can be sure they were clocks of the type then in use in the several countries from which the explorers sailed and the governors came. It was not until determined attempts at permanent settlement began that clocks became a part of our domestic or social history. The clocks of France undoubtedly found their way into the French colonizations in Canada, and perhaps in the Lake Country and the Mississippi Valley. The clocks of Spain, no doubt, were in the settlements of Santa Fe and Saint Augustine. Clocks from Sweden were on the Delaware by 1640 and, similarly, clocks from the Netherlands were in New Amsterdam, and clocks from England were in Virginia and in New England.

*American Clocks and Clockmakers* as a title for this work can and will be criticized as partial or not all-inclusive. Let it be admitted here and now that this book deals only with the clocks first used, and the clocks later produced, in the original colonies and in the Federation that became the United States. We shall touch but lightly upon the clocks of Canada and consider not at all the clocks of Spain as planted in the New World. Because Sweden had quite a company of clockmakers at work by the time of her American colonization effort, we shall consider some early Swedish clocks of the type that must have been used by her colonists. There is no recorded history of early Swedish clockmakers at work in America; no record of a Swedish artisan specializing in this craft in any of the early settlements along the Delaware.

By 1670 it is believed that sons and grandsons of Swedish colonists were making and repairing clocks at the settlements now known as Philadelphia and Wilmington. Also, we may be fairly sure, Dutch clockmakers were at work in the same locales. The Dutch followed the Swedes and disputed with them ownership of the Delaware Valley. Not until William Penn was given the entire western bank of the Delaware did the Swedish-Dutch controversy end. Both peoples stayed on in Penn's colony and were among its first solid and seasoned citizens.

The Dutch at New Amsterdam and up the Hudson Valley apparently had clocks from home in goodly numbers. From the remaining inventories of Dutch citizens it is evident that a clock was part of the furnishings of many burghers' homes. Similarly, in New England, the clocks of old England were known and used, although it must be admitted in far fewer numbers in relation to population than among the Dutch. In Quebec and the Three Rivers country of Canada there were early French clocks. Let us recapitulate: Swedish, Dutch, English, and French clocks were in America, as household items, from the beginnings of our various settlements. Significantly, Sweden, the Netherlands, England, and France were the countries wherein clockmaking was receiving the attention of scientists, astronomers, and mathematicians working hand in hand with cunning and able artisans and artists. So, in saying our early colonists had the best clocks then available, we are not stepping on thin ice or converting conjecture into boastful statement.

Since all of our colonies, sooner or later, fell under English ownership and rule, our major clock tradition is English. In dealing first with the clocks of England as known in the colonies, we need make no apologies to the other colonists and their homelands. What they brought to these shores as contributions to our clock history was duplicated in old England. All of the good ideas of the Swedish, Dutch, and French clockmakers were melded by English clockmakers who, by 1631, had divorced themselves from affiliation with the blacksmith's company and had set up "The Masters, Wardens and Fellowship of the Art and Mystery of Clockmaking of the City of London." Their jurisdiction, apparently, was confined to London and its environs but this company, nonetheless, controlled the clock trade of all England and certified

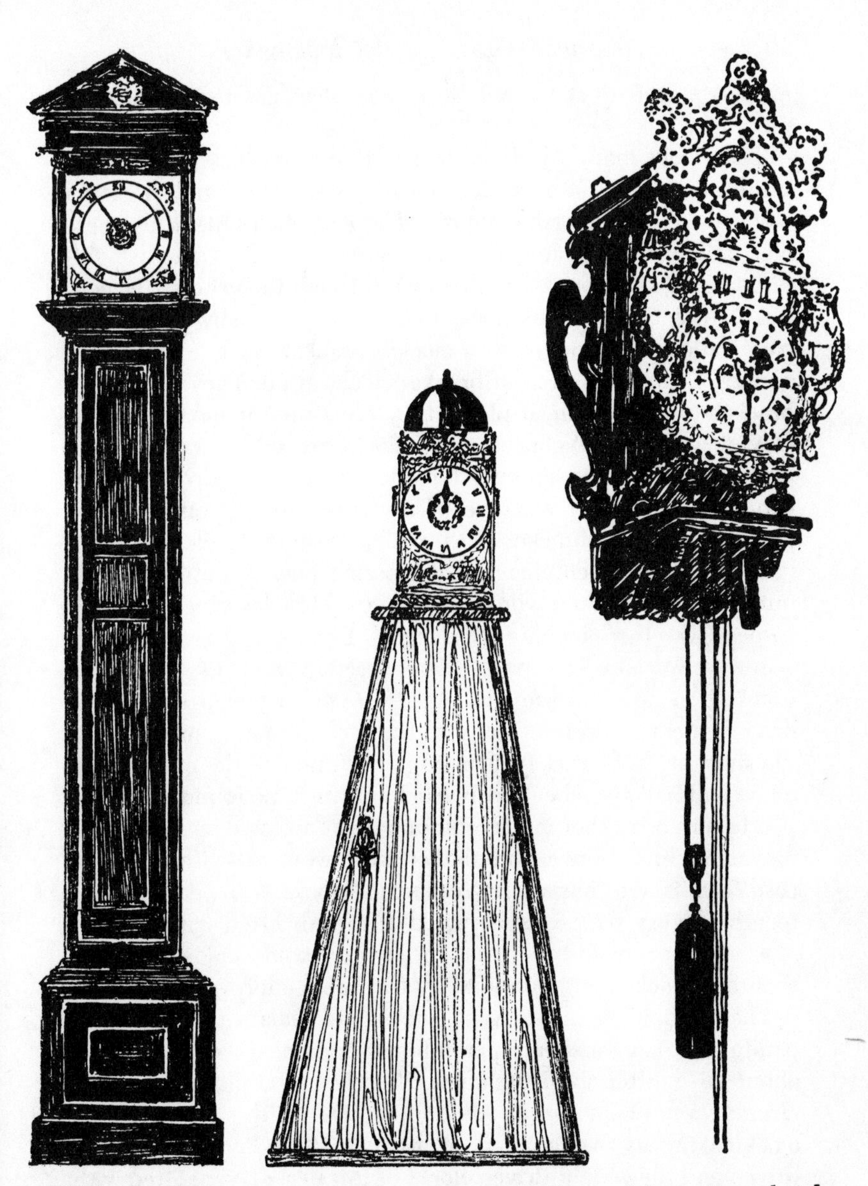

LEFT: Tall-case clock with lift-up hood and bob pendulum. Great height due to drop of weights. Fromanteel-type grandfather clock, made *c.* 1660–65. CENTER: So-called Lighthouse clock; actually a brass bracket clock mounted on a wooden pyramid to cover swing of converted long pendulum and to hide the weights. Clock (in original form) may date from 1660s. Conversion to long pendulum, about 1690, and setting on casing, or cupboard, between 1690 and 1720 or later. RIGHT: Dutch clock on fancy shelf, with side curtains, short pendulum, and long drop of weights. Date is *c.* 1680–1700.

masters to set up shops only after each had created his masterpiece.

The clocks made by these gentry, either as clockmaker-blacksmiths or, after 1631 as clockmakers, were the English clocks enjoyed by our English colonists. The first clocks made by these men fall into two categories: spring-driven clocks and weight-driven clocks. Names for both, down through the years, have confused these two types of clocks in the minds of many people. We have called the spring-driven clocks "bracket clocks" when, as a matter of fact, they are not bracket clocks at all. They require no bracket to hold them in place; they have no appendages in the way of weights and cords. Spring clocks are self-contained timepieces that can be used on a table, on a mantel, atop a piece of cabinet furniture, or wherever else you please. Of course, if you like, you can put a bracket on the wall and stand the clock upon it.

The weight-driven clocks of the period now considered all required a bracket. In a word, they are true bracket clocks. Yet the names given them include "Birdcage," "Lantern," "Sheep's Head," "Cromwell," and "Bedpost." These clocks had to be set on brackets in order to provide a platform from which the weight driving them could fall. Many of these clocks had pendulums of the short or "bob" variety swinging at the rear of the mechanism. Some had balance wheels. Any clocks of this type found with long pendulums are either much later in date or are evidence of a later movement, or reconversion of the old movement, within the old case. This is not unusual. A great many clocks of the early seventeenth century were reconstructed and even fitted with entirely new mechanisms in order that the owners could enjoy the more accurate timekeeping provided by the latest improved devices.

The original spring-driven clocks had balance wheels, not pendulums. Conversion to pendulum type appears to have begun about 1675, after the Dutchman, Huyghens, published his work *Horologium Oscillatorium* describing use of the pendulum in clockmaking as first applied by him in 1657. Both the spring-driven and the weight-driven clocks of this period were fitted with one hand only. Many had striking and alarum bells. Within the chaptering, or numerals on the alarum-type clocks, there is a smaller dial for setting the alarum. Both types of clocks were made of brass with dials that generally project somewhat beyond the body of the brass casing frame. Four brass posts mark the corners of the casing. These are footed, and have finials. Between the posts, sheets of brass (generally on hinges) hide the movement. Fretwork of brass surmounts dial fronts and sides while from the four posts, or pillars, rises an X-frame to support the gong bell. Above this framework there is another finial often called the spire. When fitted with a pendulum, these clocks have the oscillating piece at the back. A few such pendulum clocks had pendulums which swung beyond the sides of the case and so, when swinging, were visible from the front. This exposure of the pendulum was overcome by fitting wings, shaped like cuts from a pie, to the sides of the case.

These are the clocks, believe it or not, that Virginia and New England knew and enjoyed within the first sixty years of colonization. They are today excessively scarce items in original, and even in semi-original, condition. English collectors have cherished these clocks as antiquities since the days of Horace Walpole. A few, remaining as relics in America up to the 1880s, were purchased here and were sent back to England where eager collectors waited for them. We in America, when we became conscious of our antiques, did not take kindly to these, our earliest types of clocks. We wanted Grandfather clocks because we considered that timepiece the final word in antiquity. Today there are thousands of reproductions of the early brass clocks, some made in the nineteenth century and some made in the twentieth century, duplicating the workmanship, the fretwork, dials, names, and all else of early makers. The vast majority of these were not made in an effort to deceive the unwary. They were made by reputable concerns as forthright reproductions for decorative purposes. Some of the firms making them also produced water clocks, sundials, and many other items in imitation of early brasswork.

The size and timekeeping characteristics of these early clocks should be mentioned here. They were small, ranging in height from eight inches to eighteen inches from foot to top of spire, and from three and one half to six inches in dial diameter. Some of these clocks had nests of small chime bells under the main gong. This large gong is sometimes, by the amateur, mistaken for a dome-like cover for the clock. Nearly every one of these early timekeepers is a thirty-hour clock. As timekeepers they were not so accurate as the dollar alarm clocks of our 1920s.

Since there is little chance of the general collector finding even a reconstructed original of one of these early brass clocks in an antiques shop, and even very little chance of one being offered at auction, let us move on to consideration of other early types of clocks. But not without this word of warning: if you do find an early brass clock of the types pictured in this chapter, unless you are a clock specialist inhibit the impulse to buy, no matter what the price, until you can get expert opinion. Replicas of these early brass clocks, as reproduced by experts, have fooled many antiques dealers who, in being fooled, have in turn fooled their customers without for a moment being guilty of deliberate fraud.

In England the general transition from bracket clock with exposed weights to the fully encased tall clock with long pendulum began with the reign of William and Mary. Efforts at making clocks having a longer run than thirty hours—the general running time of bracket and table clocks—resulted in the making of some fully enclosed tall clocks by 1665. These usually had bob pendulums. Ten years later a few such cased clocks with sixty-one-inch pendulums were made by master clockmakers of London.

Clocks of this general type, but without complete casing, were known in New Amsterdam and the Hudson Valley because the Dutch were making them and had begun making them shortly after Huyghens had introduced the pendulum idea in 1657. Early Dutch clocks of brass, basically the same as the English bracket clock but larger in size, embellished with an overhood and side rails and with curtains of fabric hanging from the sides of the hood, offer the first evidence, in America, of the coming of a hooded clock. The earliest of these Dutch clocks had bob pendulums. Later ones had long pendulums. These became known as the "Wag on the Wall"; literally, a tall-case clock without a casing for the weights and pendulums.

The hood became a complete top casing. Fine cabinet woods replaced brass as the favored material for the hood case. Clocks of this type are essentially grandfather clocks minus base and column casing. Hence the statement "Grandfather-clock cases developed from the head down and not from the base upward" is actually

LEFT: Dutch clock, *c.* 1680, bob pendulum, long weight drop, with crested canopy on bracket and with side curtains. TOP, CENTER: True lantern clock, English, *c.* 1660. Spring-driven, with bob pendulum at rear. Such clocks, often called bracket clocks, require no brackets. They can be placed anywhere. TOP, RIGHT: True bracket clock of English make; must be placed on a bracket to provide fall for weights. Bob pendulum at rear. Date *c.* 1660–70. BOTTOM, RIGHT: Dutch table clock. Spring-driven, with balance wheel. Brass case with ornate cast brass feet. Date *c.* 1675, or 1680.

an epitomization of the development of the tall-case clock. The clock was in use before it was cased. The greater accuracy of the tall-case clock was not owing to the casing but to the long one-second or 1¼-second pendulum hidden in that case.

As the transition from bracket clock to fully cased tall clock was under way in England, the clockmakers of America were indulging in the same pursuit. Few if any "native" clockmakers—by which is meant colonial born and trained—were at work, but Dutch, French, and English as well as some Swedish clockmakers had come over to the colonies. While it is doubtful if any French clocks of the period 1670–90 found their way at that time to the British colonies, it is likely that certain of the French-type tall-case clocks were used by the French royal governors of Canada. French tall-case designers were considerably more imaginative than English designers, or even Dutch designers. Perhaps they could afford to be. They had a richer, if less numerous, class of custom. Clocks in seventeenth-century France were not so much for the people as for the nobles. Flemish and Dutch clocks of cheap make seem to have been the clocks of the people of France. The styles of French tall-case clocks, especially those by Paris masters, are almost flamboyant. Clocks somewhat like these were Canada's finest in the years the Dutchman, William of Orange, was King of England and ruler of the British colonies in America.

The early clockmakers of the American colonies were versatile men. They knew blacksmithing, whitesmithing, brassworking, filing, cutting, engraving, patternmaking, casting, machining, planishing, and toolmaking. The individual workman had almost no machinery save that which he constructed himself. All activity, including considerable cyphering and planning, went on in his small shop. He could not, in those days, buy the numerous parts of a clock, put it together, and thereby earn the name clockmaker. From the mid-seventeenth century down to as late as 1750 many a clockmaker made clocks from raw materials.

Boston, Massachusetts, had a town clock in the 1660s. Residents of the town are recorded as having clocks in the 1640s. Some few clocks were owned by Hartford and New Haven colonists in the same decade. These, of course, were balance-wheel or foliot-balance clocks without pendulums. A Boston inventory mentions a "clocke and case" in 1663. This was probably a bob-pendulum,

UPPER LEFT: Swedish-type hang-up clock with winding crank over XII. The date may be between 1680 and 1750. UPPER CENTER: English wall clock of Queen Anne period, *c.* 1710; spring-driven. UPPER RIGHT: Swedish hang-up wall clock, type believed to be in use from 1680 to 1750. LOWER CENTER: English clock of true lantern type, spring-driven, with wide swinging pendulum hidden by the extended wings. Date may be 1675 to 1685. (Swedish-type clocks not drawn from actual examples but from much smaller pictorial presentations by other and not contemporaneous artists.)

or even escape-wheel, clock of brass set in a case somewhat similar to that shown on page 19 made by Fromanteel. Fromanteel was a Dutch clockmaker working in London, and perhaps he is one of the workmen who introduced the Huyghens's pendulum. The New York *Independent*, December 15, 1859, quoted the Hartford, Connecticut, *Times* concerning a Dutch clock by Christian Huyghens made about 1640. The artist, Benjamin Church, found this clock among the possessions of a Dutch family who had lived in Nova Scotia for many generations.

Some brass "table clocks" now owned by American collectors are said to have been imported early in the seventeenth century. These table clocks are rare, even in Europe. They are spring-driven, brass-cased, and stand upon a table face up. Some of the finest examples were made in Amsterdam. It may well be that the Dutch of the Hudson and the Delaware valleys had clocks such as these among their cherished possessions. Early inventories are not always precise as to the kinds of clocks mentioned in them. Many Dutch inventories mention only a clock, or a clock in a specific room or part of the house.

A Dutch magistrate, John Moll, is reputed to have made a clock in the lower Delaware Valley prior to 1680. Richard Taylor of Boston, 1668, was probably a clockmaker for in that year he was placed in charge of the town clock. Giles Dyer was appointed to the post of clock keeper of the Boston town clock in 1673. Among the keepers of this and the North Church clock, Boston's second public clock installed by Dyer in 1680, was William Sumner, a native-born son of the Massachusetts Bay colony. He is termed a blacksmith. Yet he must have had some clockmaking training and, such being the case, would appear to be our first American-trained clockmaker. He removed to Connecticut in 1687 where we wish we could locate him as a clockmaker. Connecticut, as we shall see in a subsequent chapter, was destined to become, and did become, not the cradle but the high school, the college, and the mass-production center of American clockmaking.

William Davis arrived at Boston in 1683. He is listed among the taxables as a clockmaker. Everard Bogardus is mentioned as a clockmaker in New York in 1698. Clockmakers were working at their trades in Philadelphia prior to 1690. Clockmakers from London began advertising in the colonies as soon as we had newspapers. They were at some pains to mention that they could convert old clocks into pendulums. This proves that many old clocks were still owned and in use, but wanting modernization. Other advertisements, after the first Boston newspaper appeared in 1704, indicate that tower, or town clocks, weight-driven tall-cased clocks, and spring-driven mantel or shelf clocks were made by colonial craftsmen.

Early Connecticut clockmakers have been credited with inventing the clock with wooden works. This is almost as much of a canard as the allegation that Connecticut Yankees lathe-turned nutmegs out of spiced wood and sold them for the real thing. Certain European authorities claim that the great Harrison made wooden clocks in his youth, as an apprentice, and that the wooden clock was made in the Netherlands prior to 1690. It is said that clocks made wholly of boxwood, an exceptionally fine-grained hard wood, were made in Sweden at Dalarna, Gäfle, Hedemora, and Jönköping. There is also a somewhat hazy record, akin to legend, that the all-wood houses of the Swedes on the Delaware, the finest homes enjoyed by colonists anywhere on these shores, were furnished with all-wood clocks.

Dr. Irving Whitall Lyon, the first diligent researcher in the field of American antiques (*Colonial Furniture in New England,* 1891), states that the inventory of Thomas Coytemore of Charlestown, Massachusetts, 1645, mentions a clock, and that John Cotton's, 1652, mentions a clock and case. A random sampling of thirty-four other early inventories discloses mention of clocks with alarums, clocks with lines (weight-driven), and clocks "with appurtenances," which may have meant lines and weights, bracket, pendulum, or case. Dr. Lyon also mentions a clock brought over from Amsterdam in the year 1663. In 1707 James Batterson advertised that "he is a clockmaker lately arrived at Boston from London, by way of Pensilvania." He promised to turn old clocks into pendulums. Certain account books kept in the seventeenth century contain items of fee payment to clockmakers. One such account, kept at Sudbury, Massachusetts, by Peter Noyes, records paying Mr. Smith, "ye clockmaker," in 1649. The earliest record of a clock owned by a New England colonist is dated 1638.

Perhaps the biggest joke of all in the history of American clocks and clockmaking has to do with an all-wood clock embellished with a portrait medallion of Christopher Columbus and the date Anno 1492. In 1945 Dr. Willis Milham of Williams College, author of *Time and Timekeepers,* published a monograph on this clock. Dr. Milham cites a number of newspaper stories which assign to this clock the appellation of our earliest timepiece. This clock with a foliot balance, weight-driven, was made to sell as a souvenir at the Columbian Exposition, Chicago, 1893. The Bostwick & Burgess Company of Norwalk, Ohio, made between ten and twenty thousand of them. The clocks were packed in wooden boxes and sold originally at $5.00 each. In 1894 Columbus clocks were given away as door prizes at theatrical performances of Rice's *1492,* a play of that day. The price of the Columbus clock finally dropped to $1.00. The dimensions of the Columbus clock are as follows: Face board thirteen inches high, dial diameter, five and one-half inches. The clock has but one hand; the dial numerals are Arabic. Dr. Milham calls this clock inaccurate, temperamental, and hygrometric.

# CHAPTER III

PRIOR to 1700 most of the clockmakers of the Colonies were working in three chief cities: Boston, New York, and Philadelphia. Some few may have been at work at the Charleston, Carolina, settlement, at Newport and Providence, Rhode Island, and at Hartford, New Haven, and other spots in the Connecticut Colony. Hartford was a Dutch trading post in 1633. One of the chief new industries of the Netherlands was clockmaking. It is not illogical to assume that clocks were articles of trade and that in the Connecticut Valley post were artisans who knew clockmaking. Wherever outside our three major cities there were clockmakers at work, we can be sure they worked under the same difficulties—if not greater difficulties—faced by their brethren in the big towns. On occasion we find an early clock, not necessarily made before 1700, that speaks eloquently of the handicaps met and overcome by the maker. Some colonial clock movements were laboriously constructed by cutting and filing the parts from castings melted from old brass kettles. Some dials show evidence of having been made from large pewter dishes, and there are clock hands apparently filed from pieces of sheet iron or hammered from the shanks of pewter, brass, and iron spoons.

Surmounting seemingly unsurmountable obstacles was a quite common occurrence in colonial days, and it was not peculiar to the clockmakers. The common challenge to the exercise of ingenuity posed for all artisans the necessity of solving all production problems in order to compete in the struggle for existence. This, more than anything else, developed the sense of self-reliance, the feeling of separateness, and the idea of independence that finally became the all-pervading state of mind of the majority of the colonists.

The transition from brass bracket clock with exposed weights and cords or chains to the fully encased tall clock became general during the reign of William and Mary in Old England, 1688–1702. A few examples showing complete casing were made from the 1660s onward, but when the great Lord of Orange and his consort ruled England, brass bracket clockmaking came almost to a standstill, and tall clockmaking became the order of the day. Naturally the furniture style known as William and Mary is found reflected in the tall cases of these clocks. This style, popularized in England by virtue of the nationality of the ruling house, was well known in the Dutch settlements in America. New York, the Delaware Valley, sections of the Connecticut Valley, and western New Jersey knew this style before it was named William and Mary and before it became a prevailing furniture style in England.

It is a moot question as to whether the first tall-case clocks made in America were after the Dutch pattern or the English pattern. The history of clockmaking would seem to indicate that the English were the first clockmakers completely to encase a clock movement in a tall cabinet, about 1650. Yet the clockmakers of Amsterdam by 1660 had developed hood-cased clocks which look for all the world like the tops of tall-cased clocks as made in the Colonies as late as 1750. We must be guided in our opinion by the clocks which have survived the years and, of course, we have examples which, made in America between 1680 and 1770, are almost of a pattern with the early English-made tall-case clocks constructed, incidentally, by the Dutchman Fromanteel, who was working in London *c.* 1660. Which is to say that our early tall-case clocks show an admixture of Dutch and English influence regardless of the nationality of the colonial makers.

No matter from whence our early clockmakers drew their ideas and traditions, they started an industry that was to grow and grow and grow and finally, after almost two centuries of time, become one of the important industries of these United States. Perhaps not a single one of the early clockmakers had even an inkling of what they were starting and to what lengths the American clock industry would go. Yet they were a group of craftsmen whose product was to be desired by more people per thousand here in the Colonies than in any other land. Our colonists may not have had much hard money or ready cash, but they had com-

TOP, LEFT: Hang-up clock by Richard Manning of Ipswich, Mass., *c.* 1760. Movement is cased in hard pine, weights and pendulum exposed. TOP CENTER: American mantel clock of mid-eighteenth century. This style of casing used on mantel clocks from Queen Anne period down to 1800. TOP, RIGHT: Hooded hang-up clock of exceptionally fine quality. Movement is brass, of Dutch make. Case may be American. Date may be from 1690 to 1725. BOTTOM, RIGHT: Section of early clock dial showing the arrangement of time track to provide for time telling with one hand. See text for further data on this type of dial.

modities of their own production with which to trade. We were developing a new kind of economy and establishing, in miniature, the sort of non-official "mints" for the creation and distribution of common wealth that have made this, in total wealth and in wealth per capita, the richest nation on earth. We enjoy a standard of living that includes staples, possessions, and endowments that are nothing short of luxuries in other lands.

In this chapter major attention will be given to the tall-case clocks made in the Colonies between 1680 and 1770. This ninety-year period is not the golden age of American clockmaking nor is it the era of greatest production. But it is the era in which clock-making was taught to many apprentices by masters from England, the Netherlands, Switzerland, the Palatinate, France, and Sweden, and the era in which our colonization pattern was consolidated. It is the age of preparation for things to come; the period during which every community capable of supporting a clockmaker had its clockmaker. We expanded our colonies by an almost continuous setting up of villages and towns, each of which became a trading and production center for a new rural-agricultural section. And, no matter what emotional feelings may be held in respect of other nationalities who attempted colonizations, the fact remains that not until all of the colonies were under English dominion did colonization spread, expand, and prosper. Take Pennsylvania, for example. The Swedes and the Dutch, after forty years, had made no settlements off the Delaware and Schuylkill valleys and very few hardy groups from their settlements had ventured far inland. Within fifty years after William Penn took over the colony there were settlements beyond the Susquehanna River, and soon thereafter there were clockmakers serving the settlers. If, in this chapter, more frequent reference is made to Pennsylvania clockmakers than to those of other colonies, it is because Penn's colony drew to it more nationalities and beckoned with waving hand to the clockmakers of other lands. In Penn's colony Swedish, Swiss, French, Dutch, and English clockmakers pooled their knowledge. This was not the case in New York, Boston, Albany, Charleston, and other places, save by overseas control. The same melding that went on in Pennsylvania in respect of clockmaking was going on in London and in Amsterdam. From these melting points ideas, and workmen with the ideas, moved on to the various colonies.

LEFT: Tall-case clock of San Domingo mahogany by William Lee of Charleston, S.C., *c.* 1717. CENTER: Simply cased tall clock by David Rittenhouse, Philadelphia, *c.* 1760. RIGHT: A "mural" or wall clock, often also designated as a half-clock, displaying all the characteristics of a tall-case clock but with waist terminating in a bracket rather than in a chest wirh feet or base. The date of this clock may be from 1740 to 1765.

But in Pennsylvania the pooling of knowledge was happening right on the spot.

Colonial tall-case clocks made between 1680 and 1770 have one characteristic in common that is almost a sure badge of age. The dials are of metal, usually brass. Of these dials there are many varieties, major and minor, that engage the interest of collectors and connoisseurs. Most of them have silvered chapter rings upon which the time tracks and numerals are engraved. Many have molded or cast cornerpieces, called spandrels, displaying floral, animalistic, cherubim, and other designs. The centers of these dials are ring turned, hammered, matted, punched, and stippled. The engraving, if crude in some, is superb in others. During this period of working it is doubtful if any clocks were made with painted dials. The unpainted metal dial was traditional and the clockmakers stuck to tradition, even if they had to flatten out a pewter dish and from it contrive a clock dial.

Since the dials of the clocks now considered are adjudged by experts as a more reliable guide to age than the cases, an excursion into the world of these clock dials is in order. Numerals are almost invariably Roman. The bottoms of the numerals point toward the center of the dial. The Roman IIII is used instead of IV. Up to about 1720 the dial plates are square. After that date the arched top dial appears. On the arch—also called the tympanum—appear bosses on which the name of the maker is sometimes engraved or there is a small supplemental dial on which the "strike-silent" hand of striking movement clocks is placed. When neither name nor other feature is in the arch, it may be embellished with a cartouche, a fretwork piece, or some other decoration, applied, embossed, or engraved. About 1745 a new feature was introduced in this space—it was used to carry a moon phase indicator. In some clocks there are no actual moons but only a slot through which a numbered disk may be seen. More often, however, the feature did include a disk on which the moon was engraved and which, from behind a hemisphere to the left, was revealed as new moon, in its waxing quarters; as full moon, and in its waning quarters, as it sank from view behind another hemisphere to the right. The disk usually had two moons engraved upon it and made one revolution in two lunar months.

The dials of clocks which served only as timepieces have but one winding hole. Striking clocks had two winding holes. Chiming clocks have three. When there is no winding hole in the dial, the clock had to be wound by opening the case door and pulling on the cords which drew the weight upward. Some dials have a tiny orifice under the center through which a rotating disk revealed the day of the month. Others have this, and, in addition, an extra small dial above the hands on which a second indicating hand revolved. A few dials made especially for complicated clocks have auxiliary or subsidiary dials in the corners instead of spandrels or cornerpieces. Perhaps the finest complicated clock made in the period now under discussion was made by David Rittenhouse of Philadelphia. It is a huge clock, but cased superbly by a master cabinetmaker of the Philadelphia School. In fact, the case may well have been made by Benjamin Randolph. This clock, from a photograph by the Pennsylvania Museum, is pictured in Chapter X. It stands nine feet high and is two feet wide. On the dial arch or tympanum is a planetarium. The corner dials record star and constellation movements, daylight hours from season to season, and the decimal divisions of the day. Slots at the sides of the dial regulate the striking and the chiming mechanisms. Moon phases are indicated through the slot over the hands. The small orifice under the hands reveals the day of the month. The two-octave chime of this clock plays four tunes, selectively. A clock such as this masterpiece by Rittenhouse would demand considerable, if not the constant, attention of an expert clockmaker in order to keep it in running order. It is now owned by the Drexel Institute of Philadelphia and, at last report, was not running.

Another feature of the dials of the clocks of this period has to do with the narrow time tracks which appear beyond the numerals and sometimes, also, inside the numerals. The outer time tracks are usually divided into sixty spaces, sometimes marked by fives in Arabic numerals. On some dials the division of the outer time track is not in sixty spaces but in forty-eight. On many dials which bear the inner and outer track, when the outer track has sixty spaces, the inner track has forty-eight. On occasion an expert, looking at an old clock, will exclaim, "This clock originally had but one hand," or, "This dial was made for a one-hand clock!" We may regard the man in amazement. He has X-ray eyes, or something. He can apparently see right into the movement! But he can't. He just looks at the time track, the only time track, or the outer time track of the dial. If it is divided into forty-eight instead of sixty spaces, it was made for time telling by one hand.

Note the illustration of a section of a dial with a forty-eight-division time track. There are four spaces between XII and I and four spaces between I and II. In each space there are two dots. Lay a matchstick hand-wise pointing to XII. That is twelve o'clock. Point the matchstick to the dot in the first space beyond XII. The time is five minutes past twelve. Each dot represents a five-minute interval. Each radial line represents a quarter hour. Each of the fleurs-de-lis represent a half hour. When the hand of the clock points to the dot immediately before the radial line in the track over I, it is 12:55, or five minutes until one. When such is the outer or only time track on a dial, that dial was made for one-hand time telling.

Now we come to the inner time track. Usually, if it is there at all, it is divided into forty-eight spaces even when the outer dial is divided into sixty spaces and obviously made for two-hand time-keeping. Why would they persist in the use of the forty-eight divisions on this time track, and why this time track at all if there is an outer sixty-division time track on the dial? A most sensible question. Believe it or not, the answer is also sensible. During the transition period which marked the shift from one-hand clocks to two-hand clocks there were more people schooled in telling time by one hand than by two. They were catered to by having a time track by which they could tell time by the hour hand alone! Clock and dial making being a business with a myriad of traditions, they continued to put an inner time track with forty-eight divisions on clock dials long after all clocks were made with two major time-telling hands!

The spidery, daddy longlegs, or sweep second hand does not appear on our early grandfather or tall-case clocks. Some early clocks have a small second hand ticking around an auxiliary dial, usually above the main hands and on rare occasions in the arch. Also, but rarely, there is an opening in the dial through which can be seen the movement of a disk affixed to the pendulum. These devices served very much the purpose of the later sweep second hand: they were telltales to indicate at a glance that the clock was running.

Throughout this and other chapters of this book only occasional mention will be made of specific clockmakers. The matter is introduced here in order to explain what may seem deliberate ignorance of the names of the men who made our early clocks. They are not being ignored. The names of the now known makers of American clocks, from 1680 to 1876, are listed in Chapter XI. That list is admittedly incomplete. We may never have a complete list of all American clockmakers. Even within the somewhat narrow field of specialized interest in clocks as antiques we run across new names of old clockmakers almost daily. Some of these must be accepted, literally, at face value. A name is reported as appearing on the dial of a clock. There may be also a place name on the dial. The approximate date of the clock must be judged from its case, dial, and movement characteristics. After days of research it is discovered the name is that of a clock dealer. Did he make the clock? Chances are he did not. Is he to be listed as a clockmaker? Remember, somewhere, somebody may have a clock with this man's name on the dial and wants to know who he was and where and if he made it. What to do? List the man as a clockmaker with the notation "probably a dealer." That is what we have done in our listings. Further details regarding the lists, the many patient researchers who have contributed in some way to making up that list, and other pertinent data about it will be found in Chapter XI.

In this chapter and in all other chapters of this book many line drawings of clocks are reproduced. These are captioned. Where the picture is that of a clock by a known maker, the name, sometimes with approximate dates of working, and present ownership of the clock, if known, are given. In some cases, and especially where the clocks are the product of a clock manufacturer, only the name of the maker and model or style information will be given. After all, this is a primary book about clocks. It is the clock that most of us collect. The names of the makers are purely coincidental information. To some antiques collectors, the case of a tall clock is more important than the movement. This, perhaps, is as it should be when we consider the clock as an item of furniture rather than as a machine for telling time.

The furniture "styles" reflected in the cases of our early tall clocks pose considerable of a problem in classification. Perhaps our problem is not so great as was the problem of the clockmaker who had to have his clock cased. The tall-cased clock called for a wedding of two major crafts, clockmaking and cabinetmaking. When the clockmaker had to double in brass, as the saying goes, and make his own cases, some wonderfully naïve and fearful cabinetwork resulted. Clockmakers making their own cases made them simple. Not infrequently they made them in a style popular fifty years earlier than the clock. We know of certain clocks made between 1740 and 1750 housed in cases redolent of styles up to one hundred years earlier than the movements. The following general classification offers safe ground for initial appraisal of style and date only if we permit of sufficient elasticity to cover the inevitable exceptions that are bound to crop up.

1680–1700 Flat-topped cases of simple cabinetwork, some with paneled doors, some with hoods, or heads having twist-turned and twist-carved pillars, and with "chests" or bottoms standing squarely on the floor. Paneled or plain doors. This style, generally, is "William and Mary."

1700–10 Flat-topped cases capped with elevations in the form of shaped coffers or caskets called "bell-tops," twist carved and turned pillars, with chests resting squarely on the floor or with bun feet. Paneled doors. Redolent of the William and Mary style.

1710–25 Arched tops, conforming somewhat to the arch of the dial; rounded tops, generally finished off with a molding, light or heavy. Turned and carved side pillars on hoods. Bun or ball feet. A few with ogee feet. Paneled doors, some with arched tops, sometimes carved with a shell or sunburst. William and Mary converted to "Queen Anne" or early Georgian styling.

1725–50 Arched and "broken-arch" tops, some embellished with fretwork similar to that found on tops of Queen Anne and early Georgian mirrors. Brass and turned-wood finials. Turned pillars on hoods. Ogee or "s-curved" feet. Paneled doors with carvings and sometimes with carving over the face of the hood section above the dials.

1750–70 Scroll tops, fine carving on hood fronts, turned pillars, carved and molded finials, shell carvings and block fronting on doors, and many superior elements of Georgian and Chippendale styling. Cases made at

LEFT: Tall clock by Isaac Pearson of Burlington, N.J., *c.* 1760. (Courtesy of Arthur Sussel.) ABOVE, LEFT: Clock by Isaiah Lukens of Philadelphia, looking like a French clock of *c.* 1750 but made about 1800. (Philadelphia Athenaeum.) ABOVE, CENTER: One-hand clock by Isaac Jackson, New Garden, Pa., *c.* 1750. (Chester County Historical Society.) ABOVE, RIGHT: Simply cased tall clock, *c.* 1740, by Thomas Jackson of Boston, Portsmouth, and other points, including Preston, Conn. (Baltimore Museum of Art.)

Philadelphia, Newport, and in the suburban village of Lampeter, near Lancaster, Pennsylvania, in this period approximate the best that London and Paris cabinetmakers were producing. Bachman, the casemaker near Lancaster, was a Swiss-trained cabinetmaker working in the French style. He did not make cases in the form they were made in France. He followed the English or American tall-case styles but worked in the French tradition. Chippendale borrowed many of his designs from the same source. The Georgian ball-and-claw foot, the ogee, and others, including the French foot, appear on these clocks.

Few early American clocks are known in cases of marquetry inlay, a variety of the Dutch style we call William and Mary. Some are known in oyster walnut veneer, and fewer still in japanned cases (really Chinese lacquer) decorated in gold *chinoiserie.* Walnut is the favored case wood until well after 1750. Mahogany began coming into favor after 1750. Pine was used from 1680 through to 1770 by some casemakers.

Within the years 1740–70 some American clockmakers tried their hands at making chiming clocks. Making a clock that will chime out a specific tune at specific times is a task only for a master workman. To describe the mechanism is to go into technicalities and terms that are not only scientific but tiresome. Let it suffice to say they used gong-shaped bells and so nested them in series that eight or even sixteen bells were housed in an unbelievably small space within the movement. The hammers were actuated by a trip drum having pins and looking something like the drum of a music box. When more than one tune was included in the repertory of the clockwork, a shift in the position of the drum brought the pins of the desired tune in position to play. An example of the mechanism used is pictured. If you own an early chiming clock you have both an asset and a liability. You have a very valuable antique which, to enjoy to the full, may require the attention of a good clockmaker about as often as your piano needs tuning.

Clocks of the 1680–1770 period, dial types, and other details are pictured in this chapter, and in Chapter X. Most of the American makers of the period are included in the clockmakers' list of

LEFT: Tall clock by Martin Shreiner, Lancaster, Pa., in Bachman case, from I. Sack. CENTER: Broken pediment tall-case clock, *c.* 1750–60. RIGHT: A "short" tall-case commonly called grandmother. Pine case; painted black. From Arthur Sussel.

Chapter XI. In the Glossary, Chapter XII, will be found certain terms, technical and colloquial, appertaining to these early and other clocks. These need not be a part of this present discussion. What should be told here, however, has to do with the materials used by our early clockmakers in general and where they got that material. They either made parts themselves by casting, cutting, and filing, or imported parts from London and Amsterdam, and perhaps even some from France and Sweden. We had no brass mills in the Colonies. Brass had to be imported. It was not until after 1720 that brass wheel blanks, plates, blank dials, and other needed parts became an article of import for and by our clockmakers.

Few colonial clockmakers after 1720 insisted upon making a clock from scratch, so to speak, if they could get wheel blanks and parts. Even this aid to production did not eliminate the tedious work of cutting the teeth in the wheels, turning the pinions to size, and laying out, centering, and otherwise creating the complete movement. According to Penrose R. Hoopes, one of the foremost authorities on early American industry, many of our early clockmakers had to cast the brass blanks for their plates and wheels, melting down brass at their own little furnaces and pouring it into sanded flasks from molds of their own making.

Thus far in this chapter we have paid attention only to tall-case clocks made between 1680 and 1770. During these same years some mantel and some shelf clocks were made. Certain of these are so remarkably well constructed and cased as to leave one to wonder if the entire clock may not have been imported, with even the name of the American clockmaker put on the dial by the actual English, Dutch, or French maker. That some of these clocks bearing names of American colonial clockmakers were imported, and in precisely this fashion, cannot at this time be denied as a possibility. There are advertisements, dating from 1704 and occurring with greater frequency down through the 1720s, to the 1770s, which indicate that Boston, Charleston, Philadelphia, New York, Annapolis, and other big-town clockmakers had salesrooms as well as clock shops and that they had imported as well as domestic clocks of their own make on sale.

At Chambersburg, Pennsylvania, perhaps in the 1760s, Charles Young, Clockmaker, produced the masterpiece shown in Chap-

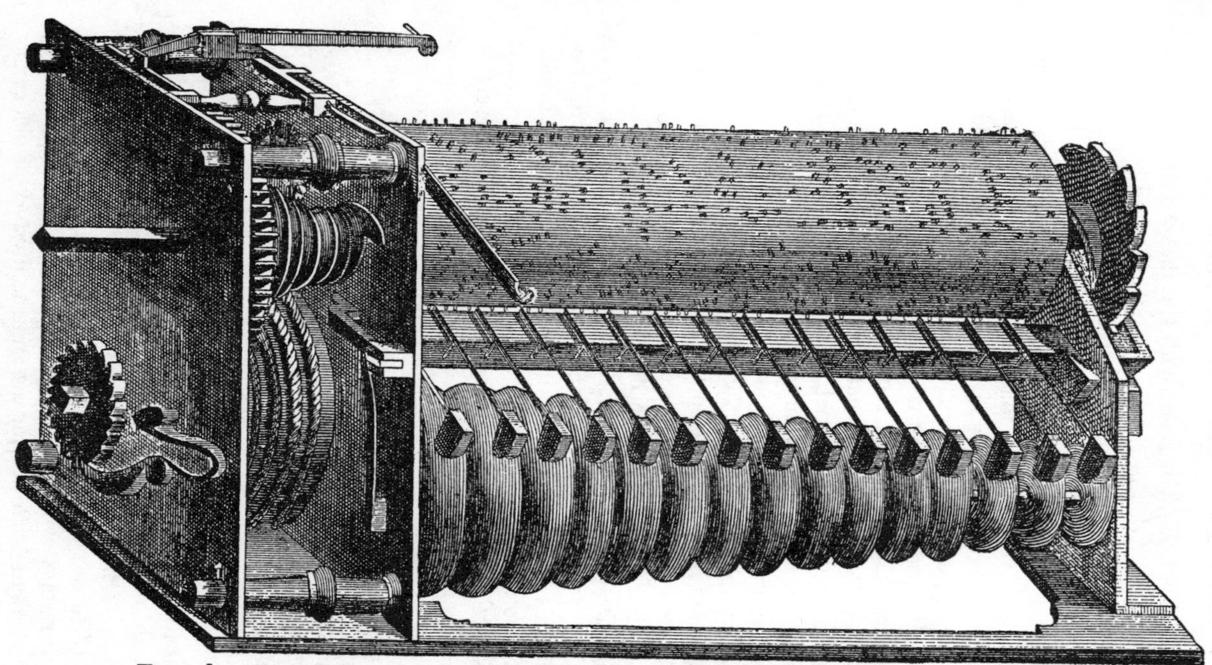

Tune drum, controlling mechanism, hammers, and bells of a musical clock. Such mechanisms were weight driven, and functioned as a separate entity when put into action by the master, or time-telling, clockwork. This is the type of chime nesting and striking machinery mentioned in the text as used in eighteenth-century clocks. The picture is from an eighteenth-century encyclopedia.

ter X. The dial is brass, engraved with the maker's name. Hours and minutes and the day of the month are indicated on this dial. It is a spring-driven, bob-pendulum clock with strike. The case of mahogany is unusual in that it has a small drawer in the base. In spite of its beauty and rarity this is a mystery clock. Was it actually made by Charles Young? Who made the fine mahogany case and for whom was the clock made? These are pertinent questions. All evidence extant points to the conclusion that Young did make the clock. It was owned for many decades by a family living near Chambersburg. This being so, the clock is evidence of another kind. We need to revise somewhat our ideas about the kinds of clocks our clockmakers were capable of making, even when working in pioneer districts almost on the colonial frontiers.

At the Ephrata Cloisters in Lancaster County, Pennsylvania, there is a tower clock made in 1735 by Christopher Witt, of Germantown, Pennsylvania. This clock was once thought to be the first tower clock made in America. It was not. Tower clocks were produced in the Colonies before 1700. What is interesting, however, is this: Dr. Christopher Witt, from Wiltshire, England, about 1703 joined a mystical sect at Germantown, Pennsylvania, and became one of its chief directors. Until his death in 1765 he taught medicine, mysticism, theosophy, and heavens alone knows what other arts, and yet found time to make clocks and teach clockmaking. A clock by Witt is pictured in Chapter X. It has a brass dial with day-of-the-month slot and second dial of small size turning in the little dial under the numeral XII. It is a striking clock. The date may be as early as 1725 or as late as 1760.

Witt, because of his medical knowledge, his craftsmanship, and his affiliations, may be considered as having been quite a card. He was. It is now believed he was the son—or the grandson—of a Dutch clockmaker who had settled in England in the 1660s. In America he became the power behind the throne of the mystic movement that resulted in many fantastic religious ideas and expressions. He is partly responsible for the Beissel-directed Cloisters at Ephrata in Lancaster County, Pennsylvania, and for the activities of Sower or Sauer, the publisher of Germantown who printed many mystical and religious books in German and English. Witt also taught Sower the art and the mystery of clockmaking. A number of tall-case clocks by Sower are now in private and public collections.

As a clockmaker with other abilities, however, Witt does not stand out as unique. Our clockmakers between 1680 and 1770 were engravers, blacksmiths, and also makers of brass buttons, mathematical and surgical instruments, fire engines, and guns. Some made thermometers and barometers; others made smoke jacks, turnspits, "waywisers," parts for spinning wheels and looms, wool cards, cradle rockers, and a host of other things. They were, literally, men of parts. Also, they fathered the inventiveness that became almost a common quality of mind among our colonial artisans.

Thus runs the story of our early clockmakers and the clocks they made. If this excursion has whetted your appetite for more information and greater details, delve deeply into the books mentioned in the Bibliography of this work. In them you will find most of what you seek. If, after reading them, you want still more information, there is only one thing for you to do: You must dedicate yourself to American clock research. That will be a lifetime avocation.

# CHAPTER IIII

THE majority of grandfather or tall-case clocks made in our country were made between 1770 and 1840. During this period the styles of Chippendale, Adam, Hepplewhite, Sheraton, and the Directoire are reflected in the cases. Reflection is the right term—usually the styles are mixed. A case strictly in a period style is far from common. During this period also the tympanum, or the arched area over the dial, is found carrying not only the moon phase, dating from around 1745, but a variety of other movement indicators actuated by the pendulum's swing.

Prior to this period the movements of tall-case clocks were made of cast brass parts, cut and fitted by the clockmaker and often cast by him at his own furnace. He melted down the brass, cast it, hammered it, turned and filed it. After 1770 this work continued, but in lesser degree. Brass founders, who began setting up shops about 1760, soon took a part of the work burden off the clockmaker. American bellfounders, many of whom graduated from clockmaking into this trade, made cast blanks for clockmakers. More important, however, is the development of cheap grandfather-clock movements made up of wooden wheels and parts, which occurred in the last quarter of the eighteenth century. It is said that wooden wheel clocks were made by Connecticut and Massachusetts clockmakers as early as the 1720s. But not until after 1780 did this idea come to the forefront. After the Revolution a great many clockmakers bought their cast brass clock parts and worked only at turning, gear cutting, filing, and assembly. Perhaps they did not know it, but they were starting the "division of labor" noted later by Alexander Hamilton, and which led, inevitably, to mass production.

By the year 1800 the low-priced wooden clock movement, de-

LEFT: Tall clock by Martin Shreiner, Lancaster, Pa., *c.* 1790. Case is of beautifully figured cherry. CENTER: Tall clock by C. & D. Forrer, Lampeter Square, Lancaster, Pa., *c.* 1765, in Virginia walnut case. RIGHT: "Grand-tour" clock—a souvenir of high quality, of marble and bronze; Viennese or Parisian make. The Shreiner clock is seventy-eight inches high, the Forrer is eighty-five inches high, the grand tour, a wall clock, is fifty-two inches high.

signed for quick production and assembly with little trouble, became something of a boon to clockmakers. The wooden movement cut the price of a grandfather clock to an unbelievably low figure and quadrupled the prospective market. Farmers and workmen who could not afford a cased brass clock could get an uncased wooden tall clock movement for as little as fifteen dollars. Then, when the owner could afford to have a case made, a local cabinetmaker was patronized. This habit may explain why certain clocks, bearing on the dials the names of makers working prior to 1800, are found in cases obviously made after 1820. Many of today's cased grandfather clocks may have run for a while as uncased clocks.

There is something of a tradition in the antiques trade that clocks with brass dials are of pre-Revolutionary construction. Brass dials are supposed to have gone out of fashion, or were unprocurable or something, especially during the Revolution. This tradition is rooted in quite solid fact, but the tradition itself is a distortion. Clockmaking came almost to a standstill during the Revolution. The special knowledge of clockmakers, certain of whom knew gunsmithing and other essential wartime crafts, was turned to wartime pursuits. Also, many clockmakers served their country in the Army. Some of them became captains and majors of infantry and artillery.

The fancy brass dial with silvered time track and cast and molded spandrels or cornerpieces did go out of fashion around 1770. In its place came the brass dial with engraved numerals but without applied ornaments and without a raised ring for the time track. Ornamentation, name of maker, and other details were engraved or etched on the flat brass plate. Such dials were in use up to 1800 though the white enameled and painted dial began to come into general favor and use by 1790. Painted wooden dials are also noted in use by 1790.

In the 1790s another cheap dial was introduced. This was printed on paper and could be glued to a sheet of iron or a wooden panel. The dial painted on wood and the paper dial glued on wood were used only on the cheapest clocks and especially on the clocks with wooden movements, sold cased or uncased to all and sundry.

Enameled dials were purchased by the clockmakers from manu-

Hayden & Freeman,

WATCH and CLOCK MAKERS, No. 47, Water-ſtreet, near the Fly-market, and adjoining Mr. Andrew Van Tuyl's Store,

BEG leave to inform their Friends and the Public in general, that they carry on the buſineſs of Watch and Clock making; Gold and Silver work, GILDING and ENGRAVING done in the neateſt manner, and on the loweſt terms. Caſh will be given for old Gold and Silver. June 23. tf

**CLOCKS.**

THE subscriber manufactures, and keeps constantly on hand, CLOCKS, of different descriptions, of the best materials and workmanship, which he offers for sale by the Box, as low as can be purchased elsewhere. Pedlars, and others, wishing to purchase, are requested to give him a call.

WILLIAM BEACH.

Hartford, Mill-street, October 6. 1834. 10w37

Clock Manufactory.

*No. 83, Cornhill, (late Market-street.)*

JOHN SAWIN respectfully informs his friends and the public, that his Manufactory is now in full operation for making all kinds of Clocks and Timepieces, such as Church, Gallery, Bank, Insurance Office, Counting Room, Alarm and Parlour Timepieces; eight day striking Clocks, Watch Makers Regulators, Factory Watch, Clocks with alarms attached to them, to alarm at any and every given period.

J. S. Has made such improvements in his machinery for making Town Clocks, that he can furnish them much less than his former prices, say from $300 to $600 each.

Also—A complete assortment of Timepiece Stock, and Trimmings, always on hand.

**JOHN SAWIN.**

**CLOCK MAKER,**

*NO. 66 COURT STREET, BOSTON.*

WOULD inform the citizens of Chelsea, that he keeps a sett of tools at his house, at the *Corner of Fourth and Chestnut Sts. Chelsea,* for the purpose of repairing Clocks, and Time Pieces, of every description.

☞ Orders left at either of the above places, or with the Tollman at the Ferry, will be promptly attended to, the work faithfully done, and charges moderate.

**BENJ. WITMAN,**

CLOCK AND WATCH-MAKER,

HAS juſt opened his Shop in Callowhill-ſtreet, North from the Court-Houſe, and oppoſite the public offices, in the Borough of Reading, and County of Berkſ, where he repairs

*Clocks and Watches,*

In the beſt and neateſt manner. He has alſo, an aſſortment of

New warranted WATCHES,
Watch CHAINS,
SEALS and KEYS,

Which he will ſell and diſpoſe of at a very reaſonable price.

☞ All Perſons inclining to favour him with their commands in his branch of buſineſs, will be punctually attended to.

July 21ſt. 1796.

RICE AND BARRY,

WATCH and CLOCK-MAKERS,

At the North-Weſt Corner of MARKET and CALVERT-STREETS, Baltimore,

MAKE and Repair WATCHES and CLOCKS on the ſhorteſt Notice; alſo GOLD and SILVER WORK.

DEVICES work'd in Hair, and ENGRAVING neatly Performed.

All Orders thankfully received, carefully attended to, and executed on reaſonable Terms.

☞ Old GOLD and SILVER received in Payment, or a generous Price allowed in Caſh.

*** An Apprentice wanted.

*IMPROVED MANTEL*

**CLOCKS,**

Manufactured and sold.

WHOLESALE AND RETAIL.

by

**L. WATSON,**

SEVENTH, BETWEEN MAIN AND SYCAMORE STREETS.

☞ Warranted superior to any brought from the Eastern state.

Clockmakers' advertising: Hayden & Freeman, 1788; William Beach, 1834; John Sawin, 1829 and 1850; Benj. Witman, 1796; Rice & Barry, 1785; L. Watson (Cincinnati), 1829.

facturers and jobbers. These were imported items. Sometimes the clockmakers painted names and places of working on the dials, sometimes they did not. There is a false dial or dial plate of cast iron set behind many of these enameled dials. Such plates often bear the mark of an English foundry, giving rise to the assumption that the entire clock may have been an import. The assumption is unwarranted. Enameled dials and dial plates only were purchased by the clockmaker, not the movements, although he probably also purchased blank wheels and plates from which to make his clock movements.

The details of clockmaking down through the years constitute a history filled with items of complex nature. We must either deal with that history generally, or make a study of the work of every clockmaker of record. Some clockmakers imported dials direct. Others bought them from wholesalers or fellow clockmakers. Some bought cast parts from other clockmakers, from jobbers, hardware dealers, had founders make them, or imported them. Each clockmaker, depending on where he worked and when, used the sources of supply available to him. The making of a clock, especially after 1785, pointed inevitably to the days of specialization when wheel blanks would be made by founders, when dials and parts would be made by others as blanks, partly finished or completely finished, and when, ultimately, all these various parts, ready for assembly, would be made into clocks in a clock factory.

However, in 1785 the clock factory was still a thing of the future. The current situation in which clockmakers found themselves was something else again. We were an independent nation. We were all out for home industry. Expansion, consolidation, politics, and fortune-hunting were in the air. New sections of the country were in process of settlement. Mechanical ideas and production ideas were popping into the heads of all artisans and workmen. The furniture style known as Hepplewhite engaged the interest of important cabinetmakers and was in high favor with our top-drawer people.

Working at other crafts and trades, in many cases more lucrative during the war, gave many clockmakers cause to consider whether or not they should return to their craft. One could make money faster by casting brass than by cutting and filing it into clock parts. A brass foundry could make many things besides

LEFT AND CENTER: Sheraton-style tall-case clocks, one from Massachusetts and one from Pennsylvania. Both *c.* 1800. RIGHT: Two late tall-clock case designs featured by *Godey's Lady's Book,* 1850s.

clock-part blanks. Pins, nails, tacks, buttons, and other things of metal wanted making. Production to lower prices and increase the size of markets was recognized as an economic principle even if it was not stated in so many words.

Some years ago the late Dr. D. W. Hering, when Curator of the Arthur Collection of clocks and watches, collated the then known lists of clockmakers who worked in the various colonies and states up to 1825. Pennsylvania led the parade with one hundred and ninety-four clockmakers. Other states followed in this order: Massachusetts, one hundred and fifty-one; New York, one hundred and twenty-two; Connecticut, one hundred and nineteen; Rhode Island, forty-one; Maryland, forty; New Hampshire, twenty-three; Delaware, fourteen; Maine, twelve.

At this writing many more names are in the list of known clockmakers. The proportion in each colony or state remains almost the same. Carolina, Virginia, Georgia, and Ohio had clockmakers at work within this period. These states are not mentioned in the first compilation because the names of the makers were not then known.

This comment is not injected merely as an item of passing interest. Dr. Hering's compilation helped to establish who was making what and where and when, and even why. Massachusetts clockmakers first supplied the demands of their own state, shipped some clocks to Virginia and coastal ports, and some to Maine, New Hampshire, and Vermont. Connecticut clockmakers were shipping clocks into Vermont, to southern ports, and selling many clocks in New York and New Jersey. New York clockmakers were centered in New York City and up the Hudson Valley to Albany. But in Pennsylvania, where most of the clockmakers were working, the demand was almost entirely from within the state. Only Philadelphia's superlatively fine clocks, in casing at least, seem to have been items of trade with southern cities. Some clockmakers in the so-called southern tier of Pennsylvania counties—Delaware, Chester, Lancaster, York, and Adams—made clocks that were traded into Maryland. Certain of the Chester, Lancaster, and York County clockmakers eventually moved into Maryland, some setting up shops in Baltimore and Hagerstown. This moving from place to place is noted not only in Pennsylvania. In Massachusetts and Connecticut the same thing occurred. In these two

Three very odd fellows. LEFT: Lyre-case tall clock; Pennsylvania, *c.* 1800. CENTER: Pilaster clock. Designed to look like a pilaster against a wall. This clock is of English make, of Adam period (*c.* 1765–70). RIGHT: Tall clock made from an eight-day brass mantel clock movement; Pennsylvania, *c.* 1810–20. Similar cases are known housing Terry thirty-hour wooden tall-clock movements of the early 1800s. These "odd" clocks are exemplary of what the collector can expect to find. Many odd cases were made by local cabinetmakers to house hang-up clock movements bought without cases during the years 1796–1810. Often the casing job was done a decade after purchase of movement.

New England states clockmakers could contemplate a move in terms of a one-day journey by wagon. In Pennsylvania, as it was then colloquially put, "the miles was the same distance but the places was fu'ther apart." Down East places were closer together.

But a truce to technics, clockmakers, and how the clocks were made. It may be more fun considering the clocks themselves, the grandfather clocks made by the thousands during this 1770–1840 period and a few that spilled over the date line up to 1850. In this period also those delightful little tall-case clocks now called "grandmother" were made, and these too, in all their glory, are a part of this story.

Which means that attention must now be paid to clock cases; to the cabinetmaking part of the story. In the antiques business there is a name for chairs and cabinet pieces which show an admixture of two styles. They are called "transition pieces." They are the exception rather than the rule. In our clock cases, a case strictly in a period or a master designer's style is the exception. Transition and mixed-style pieces are the rule.

Chippendale scroll-top hoods on Hepplewhite-style bodies are not uncommon. Sheraton hoods on Hepplewhite bodies are known in considerable numbers. Clock doors in the style of Queen Anne and even William and Mary are found on Chippendale and Hepplewhite-style cases. Even as late as 1800 there were cases made which, in style, belong with the clock cases of the seventeenth century. Cabinet woods include pine, yellow pine, cherry, walnut, and mahogany. Pear and other fruit woods have also been used. Some cases are made of poplar, veneered or painted. After 1790–1800 the dials are usually painted or enameled. The former cast-metal spandrels or cornerpieces are, in this period, painted on. Roses and other floral decoration, angels' heads, masonic emblems, birds, beasts, fish, dolphins, and geometrical designs in all the colors of the rainbow are found painted on clock dial corners and in the tympanum or arch.

Clock dialing became a separate trade. Artists who later achieved some measure of fame as portrait and landscape painters are known to have painted dials for clockmakers. Fire-engine and carriage decorators painted dials as a side line. Others, versed in the art of decoration, set up shops for dial production.

After 1770 clockmakers began adding the sweep second hand

LEFT: Tall clock by Riley Whiting of Winchester, Conn., preserved with the original bill and written guarantee to the purchaser, Daniel Lounsbury, by Algernon Whiting. Owned by Miss Nellie Lounsbury. CENTER: Mural or wall clock of the period 1740–60. RIGHT, TOP: Clock advertised and illustrated by Hayden & Freeman, in N.Y. *Daily Advertiser*, July 2, 1788. This may be an import, or it may have been created by the clockmakers offering it for sale. RIGHT, BOTTOM: Watch paper issued by Hayden & Freeman to advertise their services as clock and watch makers, 1780s. New York.

to their movements. From 1785 almost every important clock had this feature. In taking advantage of the tastes and desires of an ever-widening market for their product, other features, mentioned earlier in this chapter, were added to the clocks. These features were actually telltales, indicating that the clock was in motion. The pendulum, or an extension of it, imparted motion to cutout and painted rocking ships, a device borrowed from Dutch clockmakers who had added this feature to their clocks early in the eighteenth century, if not before. The same mechanical motion was given to other cutout and painted metal manikins. Sawyers at work, a fisherman continually casting his rod, children on a teeter or seesaw, heads with cutout eyes behind which a bob imparted continuous blinking, winking, or rolling from side to side—all these added to the entertainment given by the clocks, in addition to striking the hours and half hours and telling the time.

Many noted cabinetmakers fashioned cases for the clocks of this period. The famed Goddards and Townsends of Newport, the masters of Boston and Philadelphia, Chapin of Connecticut, and Savery and Gostelow of Philadelphia made clock cases, as did the masters of Salem and Duncan Phyfe of New York. Near Lancaster, Pennsylvania, the Bachmans, father, son, and grandson, continued to make cases from 1770 to 1825 in a style that is often mistaken for Philadelphia Chippendale of the early 1770s. They made these cases for at least four, and perhaps six, Lancaster County clockmakers. At times they traded two finished cases for one complete clock movement, and then made a case for the traded movement. This clock was sometimes sold with the name Bachman on the dial, and sometimes without a name.

There is evidence that many other clock and cabinetmakers traded cases for movements, in New York State, Massachusetts, and Connecticut. It was most likely a general practice not confined to any particular region. It probably accounts in part for the existence of many well-cased clocks that do not bear the maker's or any other name on the dial.

Today, with the antiques business and the collecting of clocks being fairly active pursuits, it is possible to find clocks of Connecticut makers in the stock of Illinois or Pacific Coast dealers. We are apt to attribute the transportation of clocks from place to place, miles and days apart, to the avid desire of collectors, and

LEFT: One of Chauncey Jerome's casing jobs; movement by Ives, or Jeromes & Darrow. Painted pine case made in one piece, not sections. This type clock, dating from *c.* 1818–28, was often, in 1920s and 1930s, called a grandmother. RIGHT: Shelf clock, four feet two inches high, by Joshua Wilder; *c.* 1790–1800. This clock might, with propriety, be called a grandmother type.

to the dealers' desire to have clocks for sale. It should not be forgotten that grandfather clocks were more respected as relics and as antiques by families falling heir to them than any other items of household inheritance. Even when they did not bring even fair prices at sales of household furniture—and there are men and women living today who remember seeing grandfather clocks sold at ten, twenty, and thirty dollars—the clocks were seldom sold. Almost always there was a relative who wanted the old clock, and sometimes that relative lived a thousand miles away.

One of the really great names in Connecticut clockmaking, Eli Terry, started his career in 1792 as a maker of brass, eight-day-movement tall clocks, and later was a maker and vendor of low-priced wooden movements for tall-case or grandfather clocks. Terry's story belongs largely in Chapter VI, but his grandfather-clock story belongs here.

Terry was born in 1772. He was apprenticed to Daniel Burnap of East Windsor, Connecticut, and perhaps served some time with Timothy Cheney of East Hartford. In 1792 he went into business for himself as a clock and watchmaker and repairman at East Windsor, but soon thereafter moved to Plymouth. His first grandfather-clock dials were made and engraved for him by his former master, Burnap.

In 1800 Terry conceived the idea of mass producing grandfather-clock movements of wood with the aid of water-power machinery. By 1808 he started a run of four thousand wooden clock movements on order. In short, he had not only a factory but a big factory for the production of grandfather-clock movements. These were thirty-hour movements. They were sold by peddlers, by traders, and by retail stores. They had to be shipped overland as any prolonged exposure to dampness, as was the case when shipped by water, caused the wooden works to swell and fail to run. Terry grandfather clocks were often sold to customers without cases at twenty-five dollars. The customer then, or later, had his case made by a local cabinetmaker. Eli Terry continued to produce wooden-movement grandfather clocks until about 1810. From thence onward he had other and bigger ideas, albeit they were concerned with a smaller clock.

Enos Doolittle, nephew of Isaac Doolittle, clockmaker of New Haven, was born in 1751. He served his apprenticeship with his

LEFT: Shelf clock of New England make, no maker designated, but *c.* 1800–10. Case is forty-six inches tall. (Collection of late J. B. Kerfoot.) CENTER AND RIGHT: Two cases designed for and perhaps produced by or under the direction of Dr. Titus Merriman of Bristol, Conn., *c.* 1810. These delightful cases are eleven inches wide and thirty-one inches high. A number of them, unused, were said to have been found in the old Merriman House at Bristol some years ago. The two pictured have unidentified movements in them.

uncle Isaac and in 1772 advertised himself as in business at Hartford. He entered into brass founding as a side line, perhaps to provide plate and wheel blanks for his own and other clockmaking shops. In his foundry he also produced andirons, door knockers, candlesticks, door handles, china hooks, mortars, and bells.

In 1778 a Connecticut clockmaker was offering a dollar a pound for broken glass beakers or the sides of large flint-glass vials. He offered half a dollar a pound for thin crown glass free from blemishes. This was Simeon Jocelin, who had a process of making watch glasses. He cut thin glass to shape, laid it on small metal forms, and heated it to the point where the glass spread out to the contour of the form. This yielded him watch glasses, or crystals, worth at least ten dollars a pound. In 1930 another Connecticut man had the same idea in respect of glasses for alarm clocks. He had a series of iron molds made with a slight "dish" in them. He cut rounds of glass from ordinary commercial panes, laid them on the forms, heated them to the flexing point, and lo, the glass collapsed into the dish and became what is known as bezeled glass. This kind of glass on an alarm clock adds to the appearance of the clock and to its retail sales value. It is said that quite a sizable business in this line was developed during the depression years. It is mentioned here to point to the resourcefulness of our early clockmakers and not to the men of this age of whom we expect resourcefulness, even though bitter experience has proved to many of us that our confidence is sometimes misplaced.

In 1801 Sibley & Marble advertised a clock manufactory at New Haven that would turn out eight-day house clocks with moon or plain, elegant faces.

In 1810 Eli Terry sold his factory for the production of grandfather clocks to Seth Thomas and Silas Hoadley.

In 1813 Seth Thomas purchased a factory at Plymouth Hollow (now Thomaston, Connecticut) from Heman Clark, where he made not only grandfather clocks but experimented also with making the smaller tall-case clock now known as a "grandmother." It is not recorded how many of these small tall-case clocks Thomas made. They are quite scarce, both as Seth Thomas clocks and as clocks by any maker.

Which is to say that the grandmother clock is at least ten, and more likely twenty, times as scarce as the grandfather-type tall-

LEFT: Case-on-case clock of New England type, *c.* 1810–20. The extra case at bottom, with its painted tablet, provides for the long fall of the weights. (I. Sack.) CENTER: New England shelf clock, *c.* 1795–1810. Such clocks were usually placed on a bracket shelf and fastened to the wall at the top. RIGHT: Believed to be one of Chauncey Jerome's hurriedly cased eight-day wooden-movement clocks. No name on dial and no marking in case which is of pine painted black and varnished. This clock is wound by opening the door and pulling on the cords. The headpiece of this clock is a modified pillar and scroll. Date may be 1820 to 1830.

case clock. Perhaps every example of what is now termed a grandmother clock that has come down to us was once a very special "bespoke," or made-to-order, clock. It is not necessary here to discuss movement variations, pendulum swing, and other interior details of the grandmother clock. "Grandmother" as a term for the small tall-case clock is an American invention which English collectors have adopted as a part of their own clock nomenclature. American grandmother clocks range in height from three feet to five feet four inches. There does not seem to be a specific height from the floor beyond which a tall-case clock becomes a grandfather. These small-size tall-case clocks, while made from 1770, seem to have been made mostly after 1800. Maybe houses were becoming smaller or perhaps the finer ones were originally made for the withdrawing rooms of the ladies. One thing, however, is sure. Because of their scarcity, many spurious grandmother clocks have been created. Old cases have been cut down, new cases have been made and antiqued, to house any small movement. An original tall clock with a small original dial is an almost irresistible temptation to the antiques clock faker. A choice grandmother clock, as the term is used now, is actually a grandfather clock made to smaller scale. Examples which display a short waist, big base and hood, have a squat appearance. They are dumpy, not beautiful, as a grandmother should be. The loveliest of known examples are in either Hepplewhite, Sheraton, Directoire, or late Chippendale cases.

This could, and perhaps should, be the last word about grandmother clocks, but it isn't. For while today the term means a genuine small-size grandfather clock, its first meaning was descriptive of, and certainly also embraced, *shelf clocks* made somewhat in the form of tall-case clocks. At the Cooperstown Museum of the New York Historical Association there is a small shelf clock in a style that can only by courtesy be called Sheraton, that was once—and rightly—called a grandmother clock. Its case is in only vague imitation of a tall-case clock.

There are records of "casing jobs" of Connecticut eight-day clock movements requiring a case four feet high, and involving the use of hundreds of movements. This sounds like the mass creation of grandmother clocks—mantel or shelf clocks in the form of miniature tall-case clocks. Some of these casing projects were

LEFT: New York State grandmother or shelf clock, forty-one inches high; case is of cherry; one-day movement. No maker's name but date is approximately 1830. CENTER: Is it a grandmother or was it made as a shelf clock? The date is *c.* 1820–30. Found in New Hampshire. Time and strike movement without name. RIGHT: Solid black, painted pine case, with a movement by Joshua Wilder of Hingham, Mass. This type clock is (or was) often called a grandmother. It was made and sold as a shelf clock. Case is forty and one half inches high and twelve and one half inches wide. Shreve, Crump & Low Co.

also performed in Massachusetts. Mention is made of these ventures elsewhere in this volume.

There is little chance of our changing our present-day nomenclature to find a new word for what we today designate as a true grandmother clock. But the fact remains, and anyone who wants to verify this can do so by studying certain advertisements in the early issues of *Antiquarian, Antiques, American Collector,* and *Hobbies* magazines, that the term "grandmother," in the 1920s and even the early 1930s, was often applied to any small clock, mantel or shelf type, that was in imitation of a tall-case clock, and to some examples that look very much like the Willard "case-on-case" clocks of the early nineteenth century. Now the so-called "knowing ones" laugh at the term "grandmother clock" applied to anything but a dainty undersize grandfather clock.

# CHAPTER

# V

IN THE Connecticut *Courant* for December 3, 1764, Benjamin Willard, "last-maker" from Boston, advertised that he had set up shop in East Hartford at the house of Benjamin Cheney, whereat shoemakers and others wanting shoe lasts, singly or in pairs, would be supplied on reasonable terms. Willard, then just twenty-one years old, lodging at the house of Benjamin Cheney, one of the important clockmakers of Connecticut, learned enough about the craft to instruct his younger brother Simon upon his return to his native Massachusetts. Simon Willard became one of the nation's famous clockmakers largely because of his alleged invention of the banjo clock which he patented in 1802. In designating Simon Willard as the "alleged" inventor of the banjo clock, one of the chief clocks to be dealt with in this chapter, it should not be assumed that the term "alleged" is injected as a weasel word. Simon Willard apparently did not invent the banjo shape and form of clock case. He did design and patent the remarkably accurate timepiece which he put in a banjo-shaped case. The Essex Institute, Salem, Massachusetts, owns a banjo clock that was made in London, England, not later than 1775. Of course it has been "assumed" that the case for this movement was made after Willard's clock became popular. This banjo has a twenty-four-hour dial on which the numerals I to XII are repeated. The figure XII is both at the normal twelve position and also at the normal VI position.

The banjo-type clock is number three in our tick-tock parade. Excepting only grandfather-type clocks and Terry-type mantel clocks, the banjo, a wall clock, is the most popular specific type of clock sought by general antiques collectors. This popularity is not a modern phenomenon. The banjo achieved great popularity within a few years of its first production by Willard. In spite of the term "patented" the design was pirated by many clockmakers, and copied by many others, perhaps with the sanction and consent of Willard himself.

Before focusing attention on banjo-type clocks exclusively, however, the other clocks made by Simon Willard and his fellow New England clockmakers should be studied. Most of them made some grandfather clocks. Also many of them made wall clocks and mantel clocks that are now even more rare than banjo clocks. They are objects of high interest among the elite of the company of clock collectors.

Willard wall and mantel clocks fall into two broad categories from which, at first glance, the clocks seem far removed. The categories would be wall clocks of the "Parliament" type and the bracket type; also shelf clocks. Which is to say these fine clocks, as made by Simon Willard and numerous other Willards, in company with a dozen or so ex-Willard apprentices and many other copiers, were designed to be hung directly on the wall as the so-called Parliament type; to be set upon a shelf, mantel, or atop a chest of drawers or other elevated cabinet piece; or wall clocks having the appearance of two-part timepieces, the lower part of which is finished off with a bracketlike element that is a part of the case. Most of Willard's fine clocks are "timepieces" only; that is, they have no striking mechanism.

The term "Parliament" for the wall-clock type mentioned is said to be a relic of the days when the English Parliament, in putting a tax on clocks, discouraged private purchase and made the corner public house the neighborhood rendezvous for the time of day. A good wall clock made for public houses took the general form of the Parliament example pictured. The entire story of the naming of this type of clock is perhaps a fiction. The large English public-house clock of this general form was made for some years before Parliament passed the Clock Tax in 1797. A more likely story would be that when first made these wall clocks looked important enough to be in the House of Parliament. At any rate the Willard adaptation of the general style of clock known as Parliament is a smaller wall clock. The English prototype is known in sizes ranging from four to five feet high. The New England variety measures from twenty-eight to forty inches high. There is an example more than six feet tall, owned by the Dedham, Massachusetts, Historical Society, pictured in Chapter X. This clock has also been

LEFT: Experimental banjo casing of a timepiece by Simon Willard, about 1790–1800. Once owned by the late J. B. Kerfoot. The dial is brass; the "neck" quite long. CENTER: The standard-type Willard banjo with brass side brackets and brass eagle which was probably substituted for an acorn finial about 1815. Case is mahogany, without gilding. Glass tablets are simple, though colorful, and without attempt at scenic decoration. RIGHT: Large banjo-type wall clock in all-wood case. No maker's name on movement or dial. All these are eight-day clocks.

called a "mural clock." Mural is just an aristocratic word meaning "wall."

Examples of the New England shelf and standing clocks as made by the Willards and others are pictured here in line drawings and also in Chapter X. So also are typical examples of the hanging clocks that fall within the category of bracket-type wall clocks. All of these are American clocks of rich and rare status. Never common, although always considered highly desirable, they served a unique purpose when made. They established desire for clocks something like them but less expensive; they created a distinct "I want" in many people's minds.

It was a Connecticut clockmaker, Eli Terry, who sensed this "I want" was inherent in all people and not only in people in whom it had been generated by seeing a fine new clock. Terry made a beautiful clock available at a low price. Simon Willard's banjo clock is also a beautiful clock, but it was not a cheap clock. It was, even then, a clock for people whose purses were at least partially well filled. A clock, if you please, that belonged with other appurtenances of quality, if not of luxury.

The banjo clock, as made by Simon Willard about 1800, was made by an ever-increasing number of New England, New York, Philadelphia, and Baltimore clockmakers. The era of popularity, in terms of production, was at least half a century. In the final decade of that span some banjo clocks were made in sizes comparable to the earlier English Parliament clock, up to six and even seven feet high. In the late 1840s and through the 1850s these and smaller banjo-type clocks were used by railroads as station timekeepers. The more important the station the larger was the banjo clock hanging on its wall.

In regaining popularity as an antique comparable to its original aristocratic status, the banjo clock has become a greatly desired, fine timepiece among a far more numerous company of customers able to afford ownership. For this reason, any banjo clock must now be examined meticulously. Far, far too many of those now in circulation, and now resting on walls as "genuine antiques" are outright reconstructions, restorations, and even fakes. Buying a banjo, whether the buyer knew it or not, has been a challenge for more than twenty years. Never common, in fact almost always in the category of scarce, the demand for these clocks literally en-

LEFT: The so-called "Eddystone" lighthouse clock. Simon Willard made clocks of this type, probably to order only. They are excellent timekeepers, running under a dustproof glass bell; *c.* 1788–1800. CENTER: Lyre clock by Sawin & Dyar, Boston. Date may be *c.* 1815–20. (Shreve, Crump & Low Co.) RIGHT: Willard lighthouse clock of unusually fine quality. Date is perhaps in the 1790s. (James F. Graham & Sons.) The two lighthouse clocks here pictured are substantially same size in spite of the variance suggested by the pictures.

couraged all kinds of skulduggery and sleight of hand. Today only the most reliable dealers can be counted upon to know and, in knowing, reveal to a prospective customer, the precise state and condition of any banjo clocks they have for sale. Most dealers can be fooled by a cleverly reconstructed banjo as easily as can their customers. Many of the partly or wholly faked examples were sold first to dealers who were convinced they were buying the real thing. Not infrequently they bought from homes and from private owners with whom the faked clocks had been planted.

Banjo clocks by Willard, by his numerous one-time apprentices, and by other New England makers, have been studied so well by experts in the gentle art of faking that only fine clockmakers, skilled cabinetmakers, and artisans have been employed in the work of reconstruction and re-creation. New or old cases have been used to case old movements found without cases. No original banjo, even though the case was a complete wreck and the movement a shambles, has been destroyed. Painstaking restoration has gone on in clock shops and in studios in Boston, New York, Philadelphia, and Baltimore. New painted glass panels, using all of the old artist's techniques; sidepieces and top ornaments of brass; and movements perhaps having only original escapement or time train, have come together in cases which may have had but two sticks and a back piece from an original case. The resulting clock has been sold as genuine. When the vogue for banjo clocks displaying painted glass panels of naval victories of the War of 1812 became general, an amazing number of banjo clocks with this feature came to light. The panels in many cases were new. When they replaced original old panels of less interest, the old panels were carefully preserved for insertion in other restored examples.

There is, of course, nothing criminal or even reprehensible in restoring, renovating, and refurbishing an old clock of any kind. Clockmakers have been engaged in this work since the establishment of the craft. Our early clockmakers made a business of reconverting old timepieces into more modern instruments. They rebuilt, recased, and sometimes made entirely new clocks from old ones. The only questionable part of the business lies in selling a reconstruction or restoration as a genuine original. It is possible to buy in the open market new clock dials painted with the Willard name, panels painted "S. Willard, Patent," Willard-type banjo

LEFT: Willard-type mantel clock with arched top, *c.* 1800–10. CENTER: Willard-type mantel clock with the "half-kidney" door; *c.* 1795–1805. RIGHT: Willard-type "half clock" or case-on-case clock; actually a mantel clock, *c.* 1800–20. Only one of these clocks is marked with the name of Willard as maker (CENTER). Cases are mahogany. The case-on-case clock is painted cream and gold.

movements, and many other parts for completing a Willard banjo case.

An open invitation to a quite simple act of faking, that of changing a dial, resulted from the fact that a goodly number of fine banjo clocks were originally marketed without a maker's name on them anywhere. Willard's own apprentices, Elnathan Taber, William Lemist, and William Cummens, are believed to have made banjo clocks which the master sold with his name on them. These men also made clocks under their own names and, presumably, under some patent-licensing arrangement with Simon Willard. Aaron and other Willards, Sawin, Sawin and Dyar, and Lemuel Curtis made banjo clocks of fine quality, and presumably also without incurring the enmity of Willard. But whether or not these several makers who put their names on their clocks had an arrangement with Willard by which they could make his "patented" timepiece was, to other makers, a big question. They, too, wanted to make the clock. They solved their doubts by making and selling the clocks without their names on them—and perhaps salved their consciences in this way. Some are almost replicas of Willard's own production. All that is needed to make such clocks a Willard is either a Willard dial or a painted glass panel with the magic line "S. Willard, Patent."

The late Edgar G. Miller, Jr., in the clock section of his great work *American Antique Furniture,* mentions a broad-scale remarking of unmarked banjo clocks by a reputable firm which, convinced that the movements were all the work of a specific clockmaker, had that clockmaker's name painted on all of the dials in the old manner.

Banjo clocks, by various makers whose names are recorded as clockmakers in Chapter XI, and by makers whose names are still unrecorded because they did not identify themselves on their clocks, fall within one of the following categories. Typical clocks from each category are pictured either in this chapter or in Chapter X.

(1) Round head with brass bezel, acorn, or ball finial or with urn, eagle, or other type finials; case of wood with front framing plain, grooved, or of decorative molding; meeting at corner blocks having rosettes or turned decoration; sidepieces of pierced brass; slender necks, sloping down to a rectangular box which has either a flat bottom or

TOP, LEFT TO RIGHT: Rich banjo clocks: The first of standard Willard type; the second a lyre, by Curtis; the third a round-bottom banjo by Lemuel Curtis; the fourth a true lyre-form clock. All date within period 1800–20. BOTTOM: Poor relations. First pair by Riggs of Philadelphia, *c.* 1845–50. Third and fourth, two banjo-form clocks by the Howard Watch & Clock Co., of Boston, 1866. Howard and Riggs banjo movements are every bit as accurate as those of Willard. The major difference is in the casings.

which is finished off with a molded bracket. Some gilding on the cases, sometimes painted a creamy white and sometimes in a natural hardwood. Glass panels painted in geometric and sometimes floral forms, in gold and colors, on a creamy white or light buff background, or with the lower panel scenic, allegorical, or of naval interest. Simon Willard identified his clocks of this general type with a signature in the lower glass panel, not on the dial. Dials have one winding hole, Roman numerals, and time track outside the numerals. Weight-driven, eight-day clocks, with brass movement and pendulum. There is always a peephole in the lower panel to permit view of the pendulum swing. These are timepieces only, not striking clocks.

(2) Sub-variety of No. 1, known as the "presentation" type, with many case refinements, some entirely gilded.

(3) Sub-variety of No. 1, with striking feature, at times the bell mounted above and outside the round head. These dials show two winding holes. Necks of these clocks are thicker to accommodate the extra striking mechanism weight.

(4) Sub-variety of No. 1, made as a mantel clock not as a wall clock, with or without striking feature.

(5) Sub-variety of No. 1, with square heads, square dial plates, and a painted glass with spandrels having an open circle to expose the numerals, hands, and time track.

(6) Sub-variety of No. 1, having a square head set point up and called "diamond head."

(7) Round head, thicker neck, and round instead of rectangular bottom, with a bracketlike appendage under the case. Balls decorate the periphery of the face and the round bottom section. Eagles and other birds used as finials. Fretted sidepieces of brass, shaped in elongated S-curves. Painted glass panels in the necks are decorative, panels in the circular bottoms are allegorical, scenic, and marine or naval.

(8) True lyre-form clocks, fronts carved, with lyre strings continuing up the neck to the head. Bracket at bottom of lyre. No underbox; pendulum swings in lower section of lyre. Under lyre there is a bracket of molding, with an acorn or some other form of pendant.

(9) Variant of the lyre form, having a rectangular bottom with glass panel and with bracket under the bottom of base box.

TOP LEFT: S. Willard banjo with bracket. CENTER: Lemuel Curtis lyre clock with round bottom. RIGHT: S. Willard "presentation" banjo. BOTTOM LEFT: Willard House-of-Parliament type wall clock. RIGHT: Forestville acorn clock. All these types of American clocks, dating from *c.* 1800 down to 1850, are now much sought after by collectors.

(10) Round head, slender neck, rectangular bottom with slightly bulging or curving sides, sidepieces of brass or of carved wood. Molding around front of case plain, beveled, or rounded. Simple glass panels of geometric pattern in black and gold.

It would seem that cast brass eagles, doves, and other birds were used as finials on banjo clocks made after the War of 1812. Hence the restoration of clocks made after this probable date permits the use of such embellishments. It is also possible that clocks made between 1800 and, say, 1815, were later fitted with eagles at the request of the owners. "Let it alone" may have been a clockmaker's admonition to his purchasers, but not always was it heeded.

The American citizens of the early nineteenth century were anything but static in mind and action. They had a constant desire to keep up with the times, if not with the Joneses. It is not unreasonable to assume they did as they damn pleased with any of their possessions if what they pleased seemed to them an improvement. Since some of them, envying the inlay on certain Hepplewhite-style cabinetwork, or the carving on Sheraton- and Directoire-styled furniture, between 1785 and 1810 had inlay and carving added to Queen Anne and early Georgian pieces, we need not wonder at anything they did to any clocks they owned. Almost daily antiques dealers find pieces of the sort that cause them to say, with appropriate expletives, "Why didn't the so and so let it alone!" One can almost forgive the lily-gilding fakers who make three genuine antiques out of two wrecks and a bundle of sticks. They may be indulging in modern faking but they are also working in the tradition of many early owners who wanted to improve what they had and thus feel their possessions were up to date.

# CHAPTER VI

CHAPTERWISE and otherwise in this volume we come to the point of time to consider the man who put clockmaking in America on a mass-production basis. That man is Eli Terry. His story is a saga of the sort Horatio Alger, Jr., liked to write. In fact, the life history of Eli Terry would be an admirable story for some group of American manufacturers to publish in order to demonstrate the meaning of "thinking to produce"—of free enterprise and liberty of action in business. Eli Terry's story is that of an apprentice boy with an idea, a master with the same idea preparing for action, and then the action.

Few people would be interested in the story of Eli Terry if his story were told the way American business so often tells its own story—with figures, balance sheets, and ponderously recited fiscal policies. The so-called common man doesn't react favorably to any kind of corporate statements. Other people's troubles are not his troubles and other people's profits are, if anything, an invitation to envy or ire.

When Eli Terry started on his career there were many clockmakers wanting to get out of the clock business because its days of opportunity for money-making seemed to have waned. But Terry and perhaps half-a-dozen others looked over the acres of diamonds lying in their own front yard and looked no farther. They discovered that but one family in ten in all the United States had a clock. They reasoned out why this was so. They came to realize that the desire to own a clock was common to all families, but price stood in the way of ownership. How to reduce the price of clocks engaged the interest of Eli Terry. The simple solution stared at him from his own bench. Increase production! Make more clocks at one time!

Eli Terry was born at East Windsor, Connecticut, April 13,

1772. He was apprenticed to Daniel Burnap and may have had some instruction from Timothy Cheney. By 1792 Terry had set himself up as a clockmaker in East Windsor. He made wood- and brass-movement tall-case clocks with brass dials. In September 1793 he removed to Plymouth, Connecticut. In 1797 he was granted a patent on a somewhat unusual clock—a timepiece showing apparent and mean time on the same dial by means of two minute hands operating from the same center. This, of course, showed the difference between the two kinds of time (mentioned in the Glossary) at any time of the day. Terry advertised these clocks in 1800. They are now rarities much sought after by specialists of the clock-collecting fraternity. "All this is quite true," said a clock specialist who read this manuscript, "but you should tell the whole story. We haven't found a single surviving example of this Terry clock!"

About 1806 Eli Terry began his first experiment in the making of a low-priced, wooden thirty-hour clock movement for tall-case clocks. He hired two master workmen of his own ilk. They were Seth Thomas and Silas Hoadley. What these two men learned from Terry, plus their own initiative, was within a few years to leave its mark on American industry. There is a tradition to the effect that in 1807 Terry sold his shop to Heman Clark and opened up a new shop for his mass-production plan.

Chauncey Jerome, in his *History of the American Clock Business*, published in 1860, tells how one day in the year 1800 Terry was out peddling cheap wooden-movement clocks. He came to a farmhouse and bargained with the farmer for two saddlebags full of salt pork in payment for a clock. "At that time," says Jerome, "Terry was a poor man. Twenty-five years later he was worth two hundred thousand dollars, all of which he made in the clock business."

With Thomas and Hoadley working with him on clock movements, and with his own peddling of finished movements throughout the countryside, Terry proved his premise that clocks could be made cheaply and sold to many people. By 1805 he is believed to have considered making clocks in batches of twenty-five or more. By 1807 he was starting them in lots of five hundred! In 1808 he contracted with the Reverend Edward Porter and his brother, Levi Porter, to make four thousand clocks. The Porters guaranteed to take the clocks and attend to the sale of them. They were to profit as wholesalers and retailers. Terry at once laid down one thousand clocks and completed them within a year. In 1809 he laid down three thousand clocks and completed them. Many of these wooden clocks, now nobly cased, are considered choice antiques. Terry began to get rich making them but, when they were made, they were the lowest-priced clocks ever made on the face of the earth. Clocks for the people. Clocks for anybody and everybody.

The great idea which Eli Terry had hoarded within his own mind now demanded time for fruition. He sold his water-powered wooden-movement clock factory to Thomas and Hoadley and removed to Plymouth Hollow, Connecticut, where, in a small experimental shop, he worked out his master idea—a thirty-hour shelf clock with wooden movement and strike, in a case, to retail complete for fifteen dollars! Just how many experimental models this craftsman with the mind of an industrial genius made before he finally marketed his now-famous "pillar-and-scroll" shelf or mantel clock may never be known. One of his very early experimental models is pictured. It looks for all the world like the shaved head of a grandfather clock of the period of 1812. By 1814 Terry had developed the movement and case design he thought could be made and marketed in great numbers at the unheard-of low price he had established, fifteen dollars. He patented this clock in 1816. The patent papers for it designate the case as "boxlike" without ornament, twenty inches high, fourteen inches wide, and four inches deep. This patent marks the idea that changed clockmaking from shop craftsmanship to factory production in the United States. It didn't happen all at once, but the bell for mass production of clocks had pealed its call.

The final Terry pillar-and-scroll-top clock had pillars twenty-one inches high, taper-turned from a base diameter of three quarters of an inch to a top diameter of three eighths of an inch. Over the pillars the case had a handsome cap, or cutout scroll panel. The dial was eleven inches square with round time track, two winding holes, and nice decoration. Under the dial, in the clock door, was a painted glass panel seven by eleven inches.

This was called a "tablet." The case was twenty inches high, fourteen inches wide, and three inches deep. Terry's 1816 patent papers reveal the pillar-and-scroll case was yet to come.

Originally the plate of the movement was of openwork—four strips or straps of wood held the entire movement together. The whole movement—pendulum, weights, and bell—was visible from the front. Terry's patent covered both brass and wooden movements. He reaped his reward, and scores of other clockmakers turned manufacturer to reap their rewards, on the wooden shelf-clock idea.

Only a few of the openwork-face Terry clocks are now known. It would seem that experiment in movement design continued until the dial completely covered all of the movement and the glass tablet in the door covered all else but a glimpse of the pendulum swing. The final case design, the pillar and scroll, did not suffer much change under Terry's direction. It shouldn't have. Even though no less than two hundred all slightly different variants of this case design were eventually made by other clock manufacturers, none of them is an improvement on the basic pillar-and-scroll design. The pillar-and-scroll top design is not exclusive in the same sense that the banjo design is exclusive. The banjo design was varied only in the form of round bottom instead of rectangular, as a lyre-form, and with square instead of round heads. The pillar-and-scroll design was varied in so many ways that we shrink from any attempt at describing them. Only a complete exposition of the catalogue pages of early Connecticut clock manufacturers will serve to display the pillar-and-scroll top variants that were made. That many of them should never have been made is neither an original nor a profound statement. Most likely the early variants were deliberate attempts to escape from paying a license fee. Later variants were attempts to avoid suits of law over the pirating of designs in precise detail, or to avoid infringement of other patent claims.

The popular success of Terry's pillar-and-scroll clock started something in Connecticut that was akin to the gold rush of 1849. There was gold in clockmaking if one did it on the Terry principle. Factory sites were staked out in gristmills, warehouses, foundries, churches, meeting halls, and other likely working spaces. Mill sites with the advantage of water power became

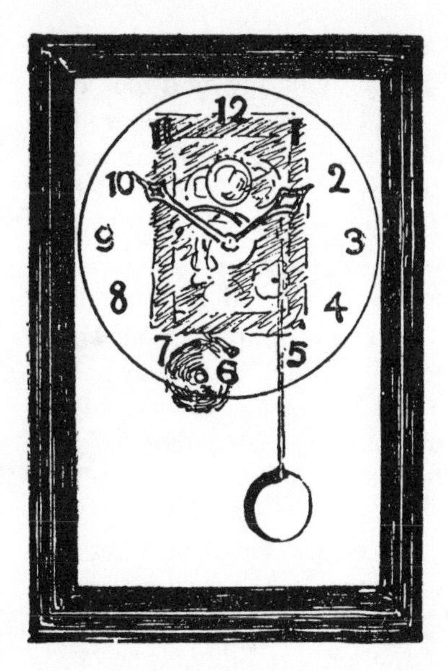

UPPER LEFT: One of Eli Terry's experimental models for his shelf clock; probably the one he used as the base of his description in his patent application. The date is *c.* 1814. UPPER RIGHT: An early Terry pillar-and-scroll casing of a trial model but put in production. This is the type Terry many clock specialists seek; escapement is exposed and pendulum swings over the dial. The date is late 1816. LOWER LEFT: Heman Clark eight-day brass movement with pillar-and-scroll case, made *c.* 1810–11 and certainly not later than 1813 when Clark sold his factory to Seth Thomas. All of these clocks made at Plymouth, Conn. See text for further data on Clark's pillar-and-scroll. Also Chapter X for exterior and interior view of the Clark clock and other Terry clocks.

valuable property. Woodworking machinery of any kind took on new significance. Trades and deals, involving production existing only in the minds of potential clock manufacturers, were a part of the day's gossip. Connecticut was hot. Terry licensed Seth Thomas to make his first "patented" clock; other makers did not bother about legal license. They made imitations. It is believed that the Seth Thomas license was "granted" in advance of the issue of Terry's patent, perhaps about the time of application. The license, apparently, did not cover making the final pillar-and-scroll clock.

The Eli Terry firm eventually included his own sons Eli, Jr., Henry, and Silas Burnham. His clock label, pasted in the backboard of cases, reads: "Patent Clocks Invented by Eli Terry. Made and Sold at Plymouth, Connecticut, by E. Terry & Sons." These were printed labels; that is, printed from type. His earlier labels for this clock, and the labels used by Seth Thomas identifying his clock as made under the Terry patent, are either lithographed or engraved. The first Terry clocks had one large sheet of glass in the door. The dial was painted on the inner side of the glass. These were among the experimental models made before the pillar-and-scroll-top case as we know it today was used.

A few Terry clocks of the early Pillar-and-scroll period have the escape wheel exposed through an orifice in the dial. Others have the pendulum suspended from the front of the dial. All of these are minor or major variants of the basic design, and very few examples have survived as complete clocks. As variants they intrigue the interest of clock specialists. The general collector wants the final Terry model—the most beautiful Terry-type pillar-and-scroll clock generally available. Eli Terry's brother, Samuel, harking to the call of clock money, went to Plymouth and opened a shop to do custom work for Eli and other clockmakers in 1818. By that time a third son of Eli, Henry Terry, was in the firm. By 1824 Eli and his brother Samuel had formed a three-year partnership agreement and the firm became Eli and Samuel Terry. The sons were not in this venture. Two of the sons, Eli, Jr., and Silas B., both entered the clock business on their own. Henry carried on the old business of E. Terry and Sons. Eli, Jr., in 1825 or 1826, built a new factory at a point two miles east of Plymouth Center, which place, eventually, became Terryville, Connecticut. Silas B.

also had a factory here. This entire section of Connecticut might well be termed Terryville or, better still, Pillar-and-Scroll County.

Between the years 1827 and 1833 Eli Terry gradually withdrew from active clock manufacture. He continued, however, to make fine brass regulator clocks, steeple, tower, and similar clocks, and to improve clock mechanisms. Samuel Terry also retired from active manufacturing in 1834. His sons, Ralph and John B., carried on the father's business but made only eight-day brass clocks.

To many readers this will be enough Terry family history. To others it will but whet the appetite for the whole story. That certain of his contemporaries were envious of Terry is fairly obvious. It is axiomatic that we hate none so much as those we envy or have injured. Most of Terry's haters were well aware of the fact that they had infringed on his patent, had stolen his ideas, and were waxing rich by their acts. It is believed that Terry's suit for infringement against Seth Thomas, his first licensee, was a friendly one to establish a court precedent and scare off other infringers. But again we cannot be quite sure. "We had plenty of pirates in Connecticut who never went to sea" is a boast the Nutmeg State can make without blushing.

In 1870 Henry Terry, a son of Eli, issued a monograph entitled *American Clockmaking, Its Early History.* The title is misleading. Actually the monograph is more a condensation than an enlargement of his review of Dr. Alcott's *History of Clockmaking.* Henry Terry's review appeared Friday, June 10, 1853, in the Waterbury *American.* Since this story, both in the monograph and as it appears in the Waterbury *American,* is an epitomization of the Terry story by a Terry, and because both newspaper story and monograph are scarce clock collectors' items worthy of more general circulation, we herewith present, verbatim, the story as it first appeared in 1853. That some experts do not agree completely with this story is quite true. The recitation of facts by Henry Terry does not square with the facts found by certain well-qualified researchers. The present-day researcher is, however, at one great disadvantage: many of the local and town records of Connecticut have been destroyed or lost and many of the partnerships of Connecticut clockmakers were not officially recorded. They were private papers or verbal agreements.

WATERBURY AMERICAN

E. B. Cooke & Co., Publishers Terms to Clubs—One Dollar per Year in Advance

VOL. IX——NO. 28 WHOLE NO. 444

*A Family Newspaper——Independent of Party or Sect.*

*WATERBURY, CT., FRIDAY, JUNE 10, 1853.*

For the Waterbury American

A REVIEW OF DR. ALCOTT'S HISTORY OF CLOCK-MAKING.

By a Clock-Maker.

*Plymouth, Ct. June 1, 1853*

*To William Alcott, M.D.:*

DEAR SIR:

A communication of yours, first published in the Boston Traveler or Journal, under the caption, "A History of Yankee Clock-making," needs enlargement, if not correction. It is very far from being a full history of clock-making in New England, and quite defective in many particulars, as to the commencement and progress of the business in the several places and by the persons you have mentioned. You will therefore allow me to review your article, correct the errors into which you have inadvertently fallen, and at the same time give a more full and particular history of clock-making in New England (especially Connecticut) than you have done, and through the medium of a newspaper published nearer the places where the actors in this drama had their residence, than the journals which were first made the organs of your communication. Let it be understood, however, that no criticism or censure of your article is intended. Neither is the idea indulged of imparting more interest to the account, farther than the additional matter is calculated to awaken.

The first item to which I will call attention, relates to the time when the adventurer, you so favorably noticed, commenced the business of clock-making in Plymouth. Although you may have known little or nothing of him prior to the year 1807 or 8, still he had been in the business; had had apprentices, several workmen, and a factory with a water power, previous to the time mentioned by you, when the gristmill was converted into a factory for making clocks. This man (Eli Terry) commenced business in clock-making and watch repairing in Plymouth (then Northbury)

ABOVE, LEFT: Pennsylvania pillar-and-scroll of unique type, apparently developed by Jacob Custer of Norristown, about 1825–30. Case is mahogany. UPPER RIGHT: Another Pennsylvania pillar-and-scroll clock by Jacob Custer of Norristown, *c.* 1825–30. These are exceptionally fine eight-day, brass-movement clocks, with time and strike. LOWER LEFT: A fine pillar-and-scroll with a Boardman & Wells thirty-hour wooden movement. The tablet shows a view of Mount Vernon, the seat of General Washington. Both Custer clocks from C. E. Landis, Newburgh, N.Y.

A.D. 1793. He came from East Windsor, Conn., to this place sixty years ago, and had before that time been engaged in making clocks, and had been instructed in the art, as it was then known and practiced in East Windsor by Daniel Burnap, and in East Hartford by a Mr. Cheeney. Some of the best American Clocks were made by this Mr. Burnap. A few of them are to be found now, said to be seventy years old and more, and are not a whit inferior in workmanship to the best English clocks that have been imported from that time to this day, and far superior to many of the present day, with a more costly exterior. At that time (A.D. 1793) when Mr. Terry commenced business in Plymouth, Timothy Barnes of Litchfield, So. Farms, James Harrison of Waterbury (not "Lemuel Harrison"), and Gideon Roberts of Bristol, were known as clock-makers. Wooden clocks, calculated for a long pendulum and case, were sold at this time for £4, or $13 33/100 dollars. When the clock was made with a brass dial, and a dial for seconds and the moon's age, the price was $25.

The price of brass clocks was from £10 to £15, or $33 33/100ths dollars to $50. This was the price without a case. The case might be procured at a price varying from $5 to $30, according to the quality and materials of which it was made; so that the entire cost of a wooden clock with the case was from $18 to $48, and for brass clocks, $38 to $80. He made clocks both of wood and brass in the then ordinary way, having a hand engine for cutting the teeth or cogs of the wheels and pinions, and using a foot lathe for doing the turning. It is probable he used a knife, as well as many other tools then in use, in doing some part of the work, but that the different parts of the clock "were cut with the penknife" is a tale of many years' growth, having no foundation, and ought not to be stereotyped as part of the history of clock-making in this country. So limited was the demand for clocks at this time, and so inadequate his means for making them, that after finishing three or four he was obliged to go out with them on horseback, and put them up, where they had been previously engaged or sold. His usual way was to put one forward of the saddle on which he rode, one behind, and one on each side in his portmanteau. During this day of small things, however, there was an attempt at something more. As early as the year 1797 he procured a patent for what he then supposed to be an important improvement in clocks. This patent was for a new construction of an equation clock, shewing the difference between the mean and apparent time. The patent is now in the possession of the writer, as executor of his estate. It was obtained during the early part of John Adams's administration, and bears his autograph signature, together with that of Timothy Pickering, then Secretary of State, and Charles Lee, Attorney General. This invention proved to be a useful one to him, in no way save the discipline he acquired by it; for the secret in money-making at that time, as well as the present day, was not in manufacturing so expensive clocks as this kind must necessarily have been. The greater demand was, and still is, for a less costly article.

The business was prosecuted by him in this old way until about the year 1802 or 3, when, finding he could sell his clocks without being an itinerant himself, he made provision for manufacturing them more extensively. He erected a small building on a small stream, where he had the benefit of water power and additional machinery in doing some portion of the work. At this time he made arrangements for manufacturing clocks by the thousand. It was regarded by some at the time as so extravagant an undertaking as to subject him to considerable ridicule. A conceited wag of the town offered to become the purchaser of the last one of the thousand, thinking he would never be able to finish that number. The clocks, however, were soon finished, and the waggish gentleman learned that he was not only deficient in judgment, but poorly endowed with wit.

We come now to the era when the gristmill was converted into a factory for making clocks, and to the statistics with which you commence your account of the business. At this place A.D. 1807–8, this man whom you characterize as the "taciturn adventurer and pioneer" made still more extensive arrangements for the business. He had obtained a contract with the Rev. Edward Porter, a Congregational minister and ex-pastor of the Congregational Church and Society of Waterbury, and Levi Porter, his partner, for making four thousand clocks. It took a considerable part of the first year to fit up the machinery, most of the second year to finish the first thousand clocks, and the third to complete the remaining three thousand. The success attending this enterprise was such as to give a new impulse to clock manufacturing as a money-making business, and was so successfully brought to a close that the idea of retiring from business was entertained, although he was still a young man. He accordingly sold the Factory, machinery, and other property there, to Messrs. Seth Thomas and Silas Hoadley, who had been employed during the three years in making these clocks, and then removed to his former residence, in the central part of the town. The business had at this time been commenced in Winsted by Riley Whiting, and had been revived in Bristol, Waterbury, and elsewhere. Asa Hopkins, a man residing in the Parish of Northfield, town of Litchfield, had erected a factory on the Naugatuck River,—This Mr. Hopkins was a man of considerable mechanical skill, and a successful manufacturer of clocks. He obtained a patent about the year 1813 or 1814, on a machine for cutting the cogs or teeth of the wheels. This invention or improvement was for the use and introduction of three arbors or mandrels, by means of which one row of teeth on a number of wheels were finished by one operation; a machine still in use, although superseded at the time, by the construction of an engine by Mr. Terry, with only one mandrel, which was used for many years afterward, and has not been abandoned to this day. Messrs. Thomas and Hoadley prosecuted the business as partners, for three years or more, when they dissolved, Mr. Hoadley retaining the factory and other property. Heman Clark, who had been an apprentice to Mr. Terry, built a factory about the year 1811, in the place now known as Plymouth Hollow, where he pursued the business two or more years. Mr. Thomas purchased this factory Dec., 1813, where he again embarked in this calling, and where he has been eminently successful in making clocks, and is at this time at an advanced age in life, extensively engaged in this and other business. Mr. Hoadley has done less business, but has been successful, and more so, than many who subsequently engaged in this occupation.

In A.D. 1814 the short or shelf clock was devised, made and introduced by Mr. Terry, who had then removed to a site on the Naugatuck River, where he commenced the making of these clocks; Mr. Thomas being then engaged in making the common or old-fashioned clocks, and also, to some extent, the new shelf or mantel clock. A patent was procured for this improvement in clocks by Mr. Terry, A.D. 1816. For a few years from this time, the old or long clocks were made by Mr. Thomas and others, but gradually the demand declined, as the demand increased for the others. The patent was a source of no little trouble, strife, and litigation. Patents were not unfrequently granted at that time, with very imperfect specifications, the inventors not being aware of the importance of an exact definition of their claim, independent of a general description. An inventor, however meritorious, could be easily defeated in his rights. A patentee in those days needed a more thorough acquaintance with the laws relating to patents, than with anything pertaining to the art or improvement which might be the subject of his patent. So far as the writer has any means of judging, the remark holds true to this day. The less meritorious are as likely to derive pecuniary benefit from a monopoly of this kind, as the inventor most worthy and deserving. That day of strife, however, has gone by. The writer was familiar with all the difficulties and conflicting claims of the contending parties, and knows full well that the improvements made by Mr. Terry, at this time and subsequently, marked distinctly a new era in clockmaking, and laid the foundation for a lucrative business, by which many have gained their thousands, however willing or unwilling they may be to acknowledge it. Some of the important improvements which should have been secured by this patent are in use to this day, and cannot be dispensed with in the making of low-priced clocks, nor indeed with any convenient mantel clock. The mode or method of escapement universally adopted at this time in all common shelf clocks was his plan or invention. The construction of the clock so as to allow the carrying of the weights each side of the movement or wheels of the clock, to the top of the case, bringing the pendulum, crown-wheel and verge in front, the dial-wheels between the plates, making the pendulum accessible by removing the dial only, were his arrangement and invention. These things cannot now be dispensed with, even in the clocks driven by a spring, as the motive power, much less in those carried by weights. Millions of them have been made during the last ten years, the precise model of the one (in these particulars) now in the possession of one of his family, and made by him, 1814. No clock either in this or any foreign country was ever made previous to this time with the weights carried each side the movement the whole length of the case; the dial wheels inside the plates, the pendulum, crown-wheel, verge, or pallet together in fiont of the other wheels. This mode of escapement is one of great value still, and will probably never be abandoned, so long as low-priced clocks are needed.

It is true timepieces of a small size were imported many years before. It is also true that timepieces were made in Boston (Willard's timepieces) and are made to this day with one weight back of the movement, and moving below it; but this and the imported smaller size were mere timepieces, that is, destitute of the parts striking the hour, and had none of the three peculiarities above mentioned, so universally adopted at this time.

Chauncey Jerome commenced his career in clockmaking at a later period, gaining his first knowledge of the business under the tuition and encouragement of Mr. Terry. He commenced some part of the clock business in Plymouth, as early as the year 1821. He afterwards removed to Bristol, where he embarked in making clocks, introducing clock-cases of different sizes, and clocks adapted to the new forms of cases made. At a still later period, and according to the recollection of the writer, not far from the year 1837, he introduced, or did much towards the introduction of the most common form of the brass clock now in vogue. The pinion leaves or cogs are made of round wire. This is a cheap way of making pinions, never before practiced, whatever may be said as to the quality and durability of the clock so made. The present form of the brass count-wheel, so divided as to allow the stop dog to drop between the teeth, and being driven by a pin in the fly-wheel, Mr. Jerome claims as his improvement, for which he obtained letters patent. The success attending the prosecution of his business after his removal to New Haven, a few years since and his reverses of fortune, need not be rehearsed.

In justice, however, it should here be stated that some anterior to, and others soon after the period Mr. Jerome commenced business in Bristol, embarked this occupation, to wit: Mark Leavenworth, of Waterbury; Samuel Terry, afterwards removed to Bristol, and Eli Terry, Jr., of Plymouth; Chauncey Boardman Ives, Brewster, and others in Bristol filling the market with a great variety of clocks of an exterior in every conceivable form, until some of those who had immediately succeeded Mr. Terry were ready to abandon the business, and did so on account of the very reduced price of clocks, and the interminable credit it was then customary to give their customers. The writer was one of this number, who had until then very little acquaintance with any other business, having been a witness to all the improvements in clocks, and the machinery for making the same, from the time the shelf clock was first introduced, in the year 1814, to the period, or the year 1836.

"Mr. Terry and his sons continued in the business till the death of the father, which happened only a few years since." This statement needs qualification. Mr. Terry had no connection with his sons in business after the year 1833. He did not make clocks by the hundred, nor even by the dozen, for many years before his death, and still he never abandoned the work shop. He was during many years engaged in making now and then a church clock, a few watch-regulators, and the like. The church clocks were made in three independent parts, or nearly so, the connection between each being such as not to be injuriously affected by the other. The timekeeping part was of the ordinary size, and moved by a separate weight. The striking part was moved by one large weight, and the dial-wheels by another, while that of the timekeeping part weighed only three or four pounds. The dial-wheels, hands or pointers, moved only once in a minute. Church clocks constructed in this way, were thus rendered as perfect timekeepers, and as little affected by wind or storm, as any houseclock or watch-regulator could be. These clocks were made with compensation pendulum rods, of his own design, and the escapement after a model of his own. During these years of comparative leisure, his time was mostly spent in making this description of clocks, chiefly in reference to accuracy as timekeepers, making a variety of regulators with new forms of escapements and compensation rods. No year elapsed up to the time of his last sickness without some new design in clock work, specimens of which are now abundant. These things he did, to the neglect, many times, of taking suitable care of what property he had before accumulated. "Though not so wealthy as some of those who followed the track he marked out," as you have observed; still he distributed to his family, and gave away to different objects during the latter part of his life, not less than one hundred thousand dollars, retaining at the same time an amount of available property sufficient to afford him an annual income of three thousand dollars. This he regarded as sufficient for all his temporal wants. When commencing business in early life, he never once indulged the thought of accumulating one-tenth the amount. He died, not "a few years since," but the last of Feb., 1852. His oldest son died twelve years ago, leaving an estate of some sixty-five or seventy thousand dollars. History however, and not biography, is more especially the object of this review.

It is unnecessary to add much in regard to clockmaking, as it is prosecuted at this time. It is scarcely to be credited that half a million of shelf-clocks are now annually made in Connecticut, and places not far distant. We have reason, however, to believe, that this estimate is not an exaggeration.

The improvements in machinery, and the skill attained in manufacturing, gradually reduced the price of clocks. Thus it is that a brass clock which formerly cost from $38 to $80 is superceded by a more neat and convenient shelf clock, and afforded and sold at the very low prices of $5, $3, and $2. Some may suppose these clocks to be a poorer article, and not so durable. This may be true of many of the clocks now manufactured, still it is equally true, that a clock as good and durable can now be made and sold at a profit, at these low prices. What is true, also, of the entire clock, is well illustrated by the reduction in price, of several of the separate parts of the clock, as now made. Such parts as at one time cost ten, twenty, and even fifty cents, to each clock, are now manufactured for one fourth the amount, and in some instances for less than a tithe of what they formerly cost. Spring clocks are made more extensively than they were a few years since. The springs for one clock, that cost, only six or seven years ago, seventy-five cents or more, are now made and sold for eight and seven cents. It is proper to add here, that this description of springs cannot be imported, nor is the secret of manufacturing them known in foreign countries.

These facts show the folly of any slight experimenting to ascertain what can or what cannot be manufactured in this country. President Wayland in his *Elements of Political Economy* virtually denies the right of a government to impose discriminating and prohibitory duties, but, says he, "a government can do much . . . by experimental manufactures, which might show, from time to time, what branches of manufacture could profitably be intro-

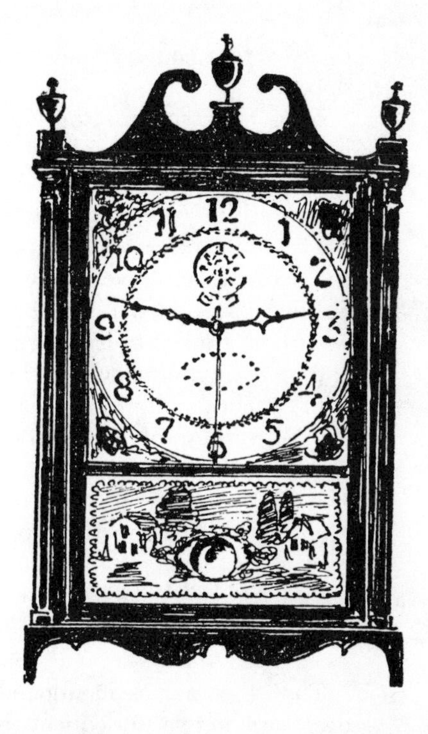

ABOVE: Another study in Terry contrasts: left, an experimental model of *c.* 1813–14, perhaps Terry's first effort to case his thirty-hour wood-movement shelf clock. RIGHT: Terry movement of 1816 in pillar-and-scroll case. Escapement is exposed and pendulum rod swings over the dial. BELOW, LEFT: Rare type pillar-and-scroll on base, housing an eight-day movement of late eighteenth century. This clock at times has been dated as early as 1750. From its characteristics of styling and cabinetmaking, it would most likely fall, at the very earliest, *c.* 1810–20. Both clocks pictured by courtesy of Paul G. Darrot of Seth Thomas Company. The drawing of the first experimental Terry is by courtesy of C. W. Lyon, Inc.

duced into a country, and how they might be successfully conducted."

Now, then, suppose the United States Government had, sixty years ago, set up an "experimental" workshop, and undertaken the business of manufacturing a few clocks in Philadelphia, and afterwards in Washington for the purpose of ascertaining whether the "manufacture could be profitably introduced into this country." How many government-paid operatives, with some distinguished governmental nabob to superintend them, think you, it would have taken to have kept pace with Connecticut enterprise and ingenuity in manufacturing clocks?

In conclusion, it should be stated, that these statistics are given for the purpose of preservation. The writer is aware that other branches of American industry, are equally deserving attention—that the improvement attained in other pursuits has been as great, the skill as apparent, the progress as rapid, and the results still more surprising.

Yours, truly,
HENRY TERRY

The other names mentioned in Henry Terry's piece will be dealt with in two subsequent chapters. Nothing need be said here in respect of these clockmakers. Other near-geniuses were to come out of the Connecticut clock industry; other evolutionists and designers were to add their contributions to mass production. Terry started it. Terry proved it was practical, feasible, and profitable. The proof to him was a two-hundred-thousand-dollar profit from serving the people well. He is still serving a lot of us; serving all collectors who own pillar-and-scroll-top clocks of the Terry type, all lucky owners of such clocks by inheritance, and all antiques dealers. Pictured in this chapter are line drawings of the various Terry pillar and scroll mantel or shelf clocks mentioned in the text. In Chapter X other examples are displayed. Terry left to Connecticut a clock industry. The clocks are the heritage he has left to the collectors of antiques—to the clock collectors of his native land.

Now, having said a lot of very nice things about Eli Terry, and having repeated his story as told by Henry Terry, we are disposed to do something quite dangerous for an author. Figuratively speaking we want to go 'way out on a limb with a saw and saw off the limb behind us. We hold to the opinion that Eli Terry did *not design, or perfect the design, of the pillar-and-scroll case.* We believe that the pillar-and-scroll case was first designed by, or for, Heman Clark, who was working at Plymouth, Connecticut, in 1807 and 1811 to 1813, and that even that clock case was from an earlier pillar-and-scroll design. There are recorded transactions between Heman Clark and Eli Terry when Terry lived in Plymouth. Heman Clark has been one of the "mystery" men of Connecticut clockmaking. None of the diligent researchers have unearthed much about him. But on rare occasion a clock by him, and bearing his label, comes to light. On April 23, 1947, at the Parke Bernet Galleries, in New York City, the following item was sold: "Mahogany Pillar & Scroll eight-day clock with Eglomise Panel, H. Clark, Plymouth, Conn., circa 1810; interior with maker's label." This clock, thirty-two and one half inches high and seventeen and one half inches wide, is considerably larger than Terry's first, or so-called original, twenty-inch high, fourteen-inch wide pillar-and-scroll. But it is in perfect proportions, with brass urn finials. It will be remembered that Henry Terry said in his memorial: "In 1814 the short or shelf clock was devised, made, and introduced by Mr. Terry who had then removed to a site on the Naugatuck River where he commenced the making of these clocks; Mr. Thomas being then engaged in making the common, or old-fashioned clocks and also, to some extent, the *new* shelf or mantel clock. A patent was procured for this improvement in clocks by Mr. Terry, A.D. 1816."

When, according to Henry Terry, Eli Terry sold his "hang-up" clock factory and business to Thomas and Hoadley, Terry "removed to his residence in the central part of town." In a word, he toyed with the idea of retirement. "Heman Clark," says Henry Terry, "who had been an apprentice to Mr. Terry, built a factory about the year 1811 in the place now known as Plymouth Hollow, where he pursued the business two or more years." When Thomas and Hoadley dissolved their partnership in the old Terry plant, Hoadley kept that plant *and Seth Thomas purchased the Heman Clark factory in 1813.* This establishes Heman Clark most emphatically as being "in" the clock business between 1811 and 1813. During that time, unless he re-entered the business again, he must have made whatever clocks we now have bearing his name. We have no record of his re-entry into the clock business as an individual, but we do have several exquisite pillar-and-scroll-cased eight-day brass movement clocks with his label in them, as the maker, at Plymouth, Connecticut.

Unless we wish to look at these data as the yokel looked at the giraffe and said, "There ain't no such animal," we must at least pose something of a reasonable doubt, if not about Eli Terry, at least about our attributing to him the design and creation of the pillar-and-scroll case.

We are not now concerned with Terry's clock-movement design; his thirty-hour wooden movement that would sell cased for $15, or his resolve to do with mantel clocks what he had proved could be done with low-priced hang-up or tall-case clock movements. We are dealing with artistic case design and considering whether Terry did design, could have designed, or should be credited with designing the pillar-and-scroll case. For some years my every instinct in respect of this case has been just this: if Terry did design it, it was a flash of artistic genius coming from a man who showed no other such flash of case-designing genius either before or after this creation. In fact, some of his experimental cases are atrocious, crude, and even hill-billy in design. We have had "reasonable" doubts. We have believed he had help, either direct or by example, in designing his case.

We have suspected Heman Clark as being the first man to produce a clock in a pillar-and-scroll case. Yet we are just as loath to attribute the design of the case to Clark as we are loath to attribute it to Terry. This might be called muddying up the pool of clarified expert opinion. But it isn't. Independent opinion as to the real source of the pillar-and-scroll case has been lacking. In its place we have had tradition—habitual acceptance of Terry as the father of the design because so and so, or somebody, said so many years ago. By the same method of traditional belief, we have accepted Chauncey Jerome's statements that he "invented" the bronzed looking-glass clock and the low-priced brass movement clock when, upon research, we discover that other men had the same ideas, and made the clocks, before Jerome "invented" them.

The limb is almost sawed through. Here is pictured a Heman Clark pillar-and-scroll clock of about 1811–13 with eight-day brass movement. This clock was made before Eli Terry had patented his low-cost thirty-hour mantel clock movement of wood, and almost seven years before he had that movement in a finished pillar-and-scroll case. Bang! The limb has snapped. Please turn to page 173, Chapter X!

In thus breaking with long-established Terry tradition, we strip not a fragment of fame from Eli Terry, the clockmaker who put clock-movement making on a mass-production basis, whether he was the first man "to think of it" or not. Further research on the history of Heman Clark and Terry may reveal that in his pillar-and-scroll Terry must bow to Heman Clark.

There is another thing we must accept in considering this Terry pillar-and-scroll situation. After his patent was granted in 1816, Eli Terry hired Chauncey Jerome—the man whose entire history is one of borrowing ideas from others, and the resourceful use of those ideas for his own profit—to work in and supervise his case shop. This pleased Jerome no end. He was finally where he had always wanted to be—"in" the clock business. Jerome, in charge of casing and casemaking for Terry most likely did—and our suspicion of this is tantamount to conviction—make the new case in direct imitation of Heman Clark's eight-day shelf clocks of the 1811–13 period. By this very device he could make the low-priced Terry thirty-hour, mass-produced wooden movement clock look like something rich and rare. Jerome confesses that he made some cases himself, traded them with Terry for movements (two cases for one movement), and then cased the movements, which he sold as complete clocks wholesale at $12 each. His first sale of twelve of these for $144 started Chauncey Jerome on his path to clockmaking glory and ultimate bitter failure. But was it, after all, fortuitous failure that came to Jerome? His entire industrial fabric was well built and on the rock of hard money, but his philosophy of business was not so constructed. He finally had his comeuppance. The business he built has lived on but his own fortune evaporated.

Serious collectors who have studied the Terry patent of 1816 know it states the case was boxlike, without ornament. Terry was patenting a clock-movement idea, not a completely cased clock. This is evidence also that his pillar-and-scroll casing idea came after the patenting of the movement. Most of us, or many of us, have accepted the magic term "patented" as applying to the entire ensemble. But perhaps this sort of delving is of little interest to the general antiques collector who is concerned only with clocks in terms of beauty, and as appurtenances for the furnishing of a room. Clock collectors, however, are a different species. Some of our clock collectors are as much interested in variants of escapement, pendulum suspension, and wheel-train assembly as furniture specialists are interested in the variants of leg carving and splat carving on Georgian and Chippendale chairs.

# CHAPTER VII

IN 1769 a company of pioneers from Connecticut moved westward into Wyoming Valley, Pennsylvania, to take up land then believed to belong to Connecticut as part of its western claims. In that company was a certain Gideon Roberts who, returning to Bristol in 1770, set up a clockmaking shop and began to ponder ways and means of making more clocks in less time. Unfortunately for Gideon Roberts, his country was at war by the time he had the idea which he felt would do the trick. He joined the Army as a private and, after some service, was promoted to sergeant and finally made an ensign. When mustered out he returned to Bristol and took up his clockmaking work where he had left off. This man, contemporaneously designated as a good mechanic, made a significant contribution to the clockmaking industry of Bristol: he began making three and four clocks at a time. When these were finished he would peddle them across the country and sometimes in "York" State.

In 1813, when Roberts was sixty-four years old, he wrote to his sons concerning his experience as a clock salesman in the South, and of his planning to start production of one thousand clocks at his Bristol shop. Gideon Roberts died that same year. He never saw his one thousand "hang-up" or tall-case clock movements finished. They were wooden movements, made by the parts-assembly method, with laurel-wood pinions, cherry-wood wheels, and oak plates. Some of the dials were of printed paper glued upon wood panels. Low-cost clocks, mass produced at Bristol, competing with the clocks of Eli Terry and Seth Thomas and Silas Hoadley.

At the library of Yale University there is a manuscript and photographic history of clockmaking in Bristol, Connecticut, that is the Bristol blue book. It was compiled for Edward and Dudley S. Ingraham, of the E. Ingraham Company, by Carleton Buell and

ABOVE, LEFT: Ives "wagon-spring" clock in double steeple case. CENTER: Mirror clock in ornately carved double or "case on case." Not identified on dial or by clock paper in case, but probably *c.* 1830. The lower tablet is a mirror. RIGHT: A beautifully cased mirror panel clock with carved pineapple finials. Ives or Jerome movement. Probably made in late 1820s or early 1830s. BELOW, LEFT: Hang-on-the-wall mirror-cased clock by Benjamin Morrill of Boscawen, N.H. Date is *c.* 1833–35. The case is very shallow.

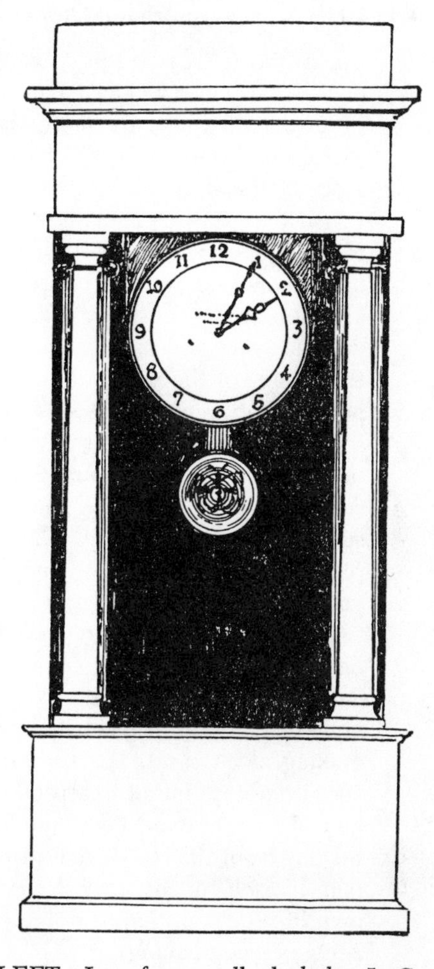

UPPER LEFT: Lyre-form wall clock by J. C. Brown, Bristol, Conn. Time only; painted glass panel in lower section. Another example of this clock is pictured in Chapter X. UPPER RIGHT: Clock by Luman Watson of Cincinnati, Ohio, *c.* 1815–20. In the French style, this case is of wood and ivory. LEFT: Ingeniously designed clock by George Marsh & Co., Bristol and Walcottville, Conn., *c.* 1830. The weights fall within the pillars, which are hollow. (Mitchell Inn Collection.) E. and G. Bartholomew made clocks similar to the Marsh example but not so resourcefully designed.

Lockwood Barr. In addition to the volumes of typescript history dealing with every clockmaker of record working in Bristol from 1790 to 1865 there are more than five hundred photographs of Bristol-made clocks. It is to be hoped that someday this extensive piece of research will be published.

It may never be decided, even with the aid of further extension of the great research work of Buell and Barr, whether Eli Terry or Gideon Roberts first conceived of clockmaking by the parts-assembly method. At any rate it has been asserted that inventors do not invent and that designers do not design. They only reflect the desires of the people. There is some mysterious wireless connection between the subconscious desires of the people and the sensitive minds of inventors and designers. When a man invents or designs something, no matter what, in the way of a device or a service, he is only creating the concrete, objective answer to a vast subjective popular desire. This is true of steamboats, radios, airplanes, postage stamps, washing machines, cameras, or what have you—and of clocks.

At Bristol, between the years 1822 and 1845, Chauncey Jerome became the outstanding figure in Connecticut clockmaking. He entered the clock business from the outside, so to speak. He was not a clockmaker or mechanic, but a cabinetmaker with a flair for making clock cases. His success story reveals him as a man of considerable cunning, executive ability, and an organizer, planner, and super-salesman. These qualities made him a success in clockmaking from 1828 to 1855. Fortunately we need not go beyond the man himself for his story. He was resourceful enough to pen his own life story and, in so doing, write also a little history of Connecticut clockmaking.

Chauncey Jerome was born in Canaan, Litchfield County, Connecticut, June 10, 1793. His father was a blacksmith and nailmaker. In 1797 the family moved to Plymouth, where the father set up a four-man shop for the production of wrought nails, forged by hand from iron rods. In 1802, when only nine years old, Chauncey went to work in the nail shop. His father died in 1804. At the age of eleven the young lad went to work on a farm. At the age of fourteen he was doing a man's work. When fifteen he was apprenticed to a carpenter to serve until he was twenty-one. In the year 1811 he made a bargain with his master. He got a four-

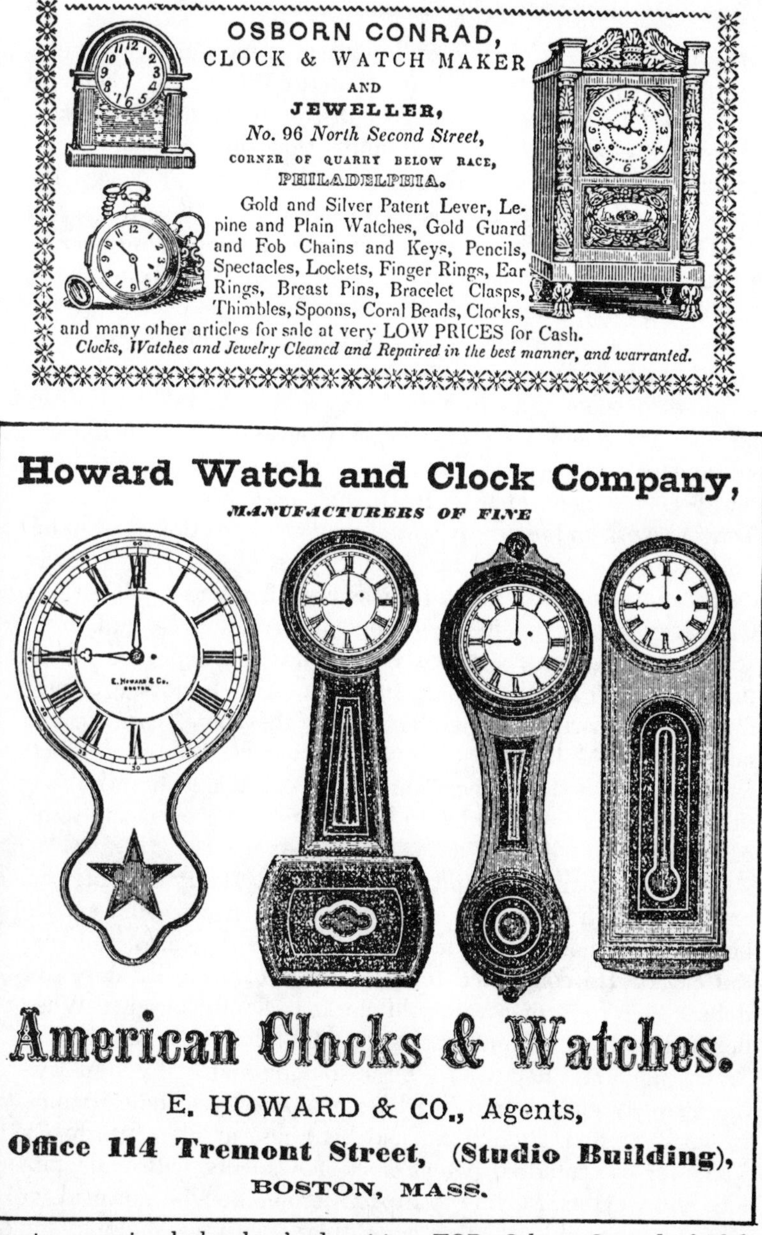


'wenty years in clockmakers' advertising. TOP: Osborn Conrad of Philadelphia, 1845. BOTTOM: Howard Watch & Clock Co., Boston, 1865.

month leave during the winter, in exchange for which he agreed to buy his own clothes. Jerome went to Waterbury where he worked for Lewis Stebbins, singing master and clock dial maker, at making clock dials. Jerome admits that this was very satisfactory work, as he had always wanted to work at clocks. He proposed to his master that he be given a chance to work for Mr. Eli Terry of Plymouth, who was then making two hundred clocks a year. His guardian said "so many clocks are now being made that the country will soon be filled with them."

At Waterbury, Jerome steeped himself in clockmaking and met all the clockmakers. In 1812 he made a deal with Messrs. Hotchkiss and Pierpont to go to New Jersey and make tall-clock cases for the Terry and Roberts wooden movements they had been selling. In 1813 he joined the Army, serving for a short time in that year and again in 1814. In 1816 he made a bargain with Eli Terry to work on the new patented shelf clock. At this point in his history Jerome states that he made the first of Mr. Terry's newly designed cases. This, of course, was the pillar-and-scroll. At last Chauncey Jerome was in the business he wanted to be in. Late in 1816 he worked on the new-style case for the improved patent timepiece, that is now considered the finest shelf clock ever produced. In reporting Jerome as making the "new" case for the newly patented Eli Terry thirty-hour, wooden-movement shelf clock, the historian of the Connecticut clock industry who first said it gives us another clue to the origin of the pillar-and-scroll case design.

Jerome, apparently, while in charge of the Terry case factory, entered into the clock business for himself in a small way. He bought movements, dials, and tablets, made the cases, and sold the clocks. He contracted to make up twelve clocks at twelve dollars each for a man who sold clocks in South Carolina. When he received his one hundred and forty-four dollars in cash, he was "encouraged and happy." He began buying mahogany logs, sawing his own veneers, and hired his one-time boss, the carpenter, to work for him. In 1821 he sold his house at Plymouth to Eli Terry for one hundred patent clock movements, with dials, tablets, and weights. Moving to Bristol, Jerome bought and paid for a house, barn, and seventeen acres of land with two hundred and fourteen Terry pillar-and-scroll clocks, all of which Jerome cased.

TOP ROW: Chauncey Jerome thirty-three-inch-high clocks as follows: Gilt top and column, eight-day, roller pinion; thirty-hour O-G; cornice-top eight-day. All these are weight-driven clocks, made in the late 1830s to 1850s. BOTTOM ROW: Chauncey Jerome clocks as follows: Eight-day O-G in mahogany-and-zebra-wood case, thirty-three inches high; twenty-five-inch-high alarm clock in pillared case; Gothic design, thirty-three inches high. Same dates as top row. All pictures from Jerome catalogues.

In 1822 he built a case shop at Bristol. His own words are: "This was the commencement of making cases by machinery in that town which has since been so renowned for its clock productions."

Meantime, Eli Terry, Seth Thomas and Silas Hoadley had no movements for sale. Jerome made a contract with Chauncey Boardman for two hundred hang-up style clocks with certain alterations in the movement that permitted its casing in a cabinet about four feet high. Since no other commentator seems to have examined this transaction, it behooves us to reread it. This sounds like the making of two hundred small, cheap, tall-case clocks of the type once, and even occasionally now, called grandmother. Hang-up clocks were tall-case movements. Four feet is a delightful grandmother clock height. The cases were of pine, richly stained and varnished. They were sold to "farmers." Who has one today? In 1824 Jerome carried a similar lot of two hundred clock movements to East Randolph, Massachusetts, making the cases on the spot in a shop owned by John Adams.

By 1824 Chauncey Jerome had formed a partnership with his brother Noble and Elijah Darrow for the manufacture of clocks. The firm was called Jeromes & Darrow. They produced a variant of the Terry pillar-and-scroll with a case about six to eight inches higher. In 1825 Jerome claimed to have "invented" the bronzed looking-glass clock. Since the term "bronzed looking-glass clock" has been misunderstood by many, it might be well to state here just what was meant by it. A low-priced case, using one pillar, split, to make two, applied to either side of a boxlike case, painted, gilt bronzed wholly or in stenciled design, and fitted with a cheap mirror glass instead of a hand-painted glass tablet. There is no record of the term ever meaning a mirror with bronze rather than the usual silvery coating, or that the cases were made of bronze metal.

According to Jerome, his bronzed looking-glass clock seems to have revived a somewhat lagging Connecticut clock business. This new clock did appeal to the Southern market. Examples sold in New Orleans for as much as a hundred and fifteen dollars each. Seth Thomas is reported as saying in a fit of jealousy that he would not make the new clock invented by Jerome and would stick to his pillar-and-scroll. But Thomas did make the looking-glass clock, eventually abandoning the pillar-and-scroll altogether.

TOP ROW: Jerome fifteen-inch-high clocks as follows; Victoria, eight-day spring; Reversed O-G (the door bulges outward because of the reverse use of O-G molding); rough and ready, a thirty-hour clock; Prince Albert, a thirty-hour striking clock, *c.* 1848–52. CENTER ROW: columned spring clock, twenty inches high; Octagon wall clock, ten-inch dial; pointed Gothic, nineteen inches high, with alarm; *c.* 1840 to 1852. LEFT: Navy eight-day timepiece, spring driven, in papier-maché case, nine-inch dial. All pictures from Chauncey Jerome catalogues.

Samuel Terry, a brother of Eli, came to Bristol and began making the Jerome-style clock. Jerome was getting rich. In 1831 a new church, built at Bristol, was said to have been paid for by the looking-glass clock. Samuel Terry donated the tower clock in that church.

Chauncey and Lawson Ives, 1831, began the production of an eight-day brass clock at Bristol. By 1836, when they closed up the business, they had made one hundred thousand dollars. The Ives family, closely related to the Roberts family of Bristol, included the following brothers, all of whom were clockmakers or interested in clock production: Ira (1775–1848), Amasa (1771–1817), Philo (1780–1822), Joseph (1782–1862), Shaylor (1785–1840), and Chauncey (1787–1857). The Ives firm closed just before the panic of 1837. That panic dealt a terrific blow to Connecticut clockmaking. Everything that had ever been the matter with wooden clock movements came out into the open. They were no better than wooden nutmegs and wooden cucumber seeds. They couldn't be shipped by water. The works swelled in damp weather. They were a delusion and a snare in a beautiful case. Evidently the depression of 1837 had the same effect on the people as did the panic of 1930. Blame everything and everybody. Jerome began to think of another business.

At Richmond, Virginia—according to his own book—our hero put one of his clocks on a table near a lamp and went to bed. He couldn't sleep. There was an idea cooking in his head. Actually, he was "tuning in," as inventors do, on the unuttered desires of the people. Take your choice of this cosmic view, or take the hard-boiled, mechanistic stand that he just got—or unconsciously stole—an idea. That night Chauncey Jerome, in the midst of the depression, got an idea for the clock he felt the public wanted—a one-day brass clock. A smaller clock. A cheaper clock. Before he got to sleep he could actually see the fortune that was in the idea. What he didn't see was that in his idea was the germ of another future great business for Connecticut, the making of rolled brass.

As Jerome continued on his Southern trip he became so enthusiastic that he began to tell people that his new clocks would run the wooden clocks out of existence. They laughed. Within a year they were buying Jerome's brass clocks like hot cakes. So many people in Connecticut wanted to get into the brass clock

Hitherto-unpublished display of original wood-cuts made for a Chauncey Jerome catalogue of 1848 or 1850. From the collection of Edward Ingraham, Bristol, Conn.

business that Jerome had to protect himself from investors wanting to get in with him. In 1841 he made thirty-five thousand dollars' clear profit. In 1842 he shipped a lot of his brass clocks to England. At first the British authorities thought Jerome was setting too low an entry value on them. They took over entire shipments at his valuation. He shipped more at the same value. Again the British Government bought the clocks at declared face value. Only when Jerome continued to ship clocks did they come to realize that the man meant business and that a really cheap and good clock was entering the land whose boast it was "we make clocks for the world."

When Chauncey Jerome set up his shop in Bristol he was following a trend: clockmaking as an industry was migrating from Plymouth to Bristol. By 1844 he had two brass clock movement factories in operation and moved on to New Haven to establish a case factory at that city. In 1845 one of his Bristol factories burned down, destroying between fifty and seventy-five thousand brass movements. In 1846 he removed his entire operation from Bristol to New Haven.

Chauncey Jerome tangled with less scrupulous men—or more bold appropriators than himself—and learned the bitterness of failure and financial ruin. His Jerome Manufacturing Company at New Haven absorbed the firm of Terry & Barnum. The name Terry in this firm came from Theodore, the son of Samuel Terry. The Barnum was the famed Phineas T. His firm, according to Jerome, was taken over the jumps unmercifully in the deal; Terry & Barnum was insolvent when the merger took place. Ruin for Jerome followed this failure. The clock company was saved. It was taken over by the New Haven Clock Company and has remained in business, one of the famous five that have survived.

Among the Bristol clockmaking firms established during the rise of Chauncey Jerome there were several with sufficient vitality to enable them to overcome all the vicissitudes of depression, competition, and change in philosophy of clockmaking. Penrose Hoopes states in his *Connecticut Clockmakers of the 18th Century* that of all the clockmakers and concerns that started in the first half of the nineteenth century only five survive to this day. Of the five, two are in Bristol: The E. Ingraham Company and the Sessions Clock Company. In addition, there is the Wallace

TOP ROW: Jerome's eighteen-inch double O-G thirty-hour. Lafayette model, eight-day; strike; with pearl-inlaid case. Union model, introduced about 1848, eight-day; strike. The "Barnum," fifteen inches high, made in zebra, walnut, mahogany, and rosewood. BOTTOM, LEFT: Looking-glass clock of large size (forty-inch); a form of "resist" decoration on the mirror panel. CENTER: The Kossuth pearl-inlaid papier-maché case, *c.* 1848–52. RIGHT: Cornice top and pillar; eight-day; twenty-four inches high. MIDDLE OF PAGE: Eight-day octagon wall clock; time and strike; twelve-inch dial. All pictures from Chauncey Jerome catalogues.

Barnes Company, now making springs, but which was once a Bristol clock factory.

The genealogy of Bristol clockmakers is far too lengthy to include in this volume. Many of the details, of course, are of interest only to seasoned clock collectors and to specialists. It is believed that all, or the vast majority, of the individuals and firms are listed in Chapter XI; certainly all now known to have made clocks will be found in the list. Yet the following are deserving of special mention here because of some peculiarity of circumstance, or because of great production: Chauncey Boardman, Elijah Darrow, Titus Merriman, Ephraim Downs, Levi Lewis, Thomas Barnes, Jr., John Birge, George and Eli Bartholomew, Elisha Brewster, J. C. Brown, Elisha N. Welsh, Irenus Atkins, Elisha Manross, the Ives Brothers, and the Ingrahams.

Irenus Atkins, a Baptist minister, started a clock factory at Bristol in 1830. Finding no factory site available he converted a church into a factory. Twelve different partnerships and concerns grew out of that factory.

Thomas Barnes, Jr., distiller, trader, and clockmaker, started a factory in Bristol in 1819. Ten partnerships and companies grew out of that venture.

Chauncey Boardman and Butler Dunbar started a factory in 1811. Dunbar withdrew in 1812. Thereafter Boardman, in various partnerships, including the firm of Boardman & Wells, continued in business until 1850.

Elisha Brewster, who sold many clocks in the South, started a factory at Bristol in 1833. This finally became Brewster & Ingraham.

In 1828 Elias Ingraham settled in Bristol. Like Chauncey Jerome, he was a cabinet and casemaker. He founded the present E. Ingraham Company in 1831. Various of the Ives brothers, from 1800 to 1862, were identified with ten different companies in which the name Ives appears.

This, trimmed of all superlatives and streamlined to meet the desires of the general collector for clock data, is the story of Bristol clocks and of Chauncey Jerome who, carrying the torch lit by Eli Terry and Gideon Roberts, made one of the great contributions to Connecticut clockmaking—the one-day brass clock that revolutionized the clock industry. Jerome substituted rolled brass

TOP ROW, LEFT AND RIGHT: Papier-maché clocks of Paris design; thirty-hour, spring and strike. TOP CENTER: Jenny Lind eight-day; striking. All measure fifteen to sixteen inches high. BOTTOM, LEFT: Eight-day, O-G case thirty-nine inches tall, with starred mirror panel. BOTTOM, RIGHT: Clock of bronze, named the Webster, fourteen inches high; eight-day spring movement. All clocks date from *c.* 1845 to 1852. All pictures from Jerome catalogues.

for cast brass parts. He proved that thin wheels would mesh as readily as thick wheels, and could be stamped and worked far more easily. His clock demanded sheet brass of various gauges in great quantities. Thus his clockmaking fathered the rolled brass industry of his native state.

Incidental illustrations in this chapter are drawn almost exclusively from the original catalogues of Chauncey Jerome, the Ingraham Clock Company, and other Bristol makers. Thus we can see the clocks, in pictures, precisely as they were presented to the great American market when the clocks were new merchandise and none thought of them as future antiques. In the next chapter the rest of the annals of Connecticut clocks will be considered; there will be reviewed the history of Seth Thomas, Silas Hoadley, and others, or as much of that history as is needed to complete the quick-fact romance of the most amazing clock story ever told.

# CHAPTER VIII

THERE is a tradition, perhaps based upon either hearsay or say-so, that before Eli Terry sold his Plymouth clock factory to his workmen, Seth Thomas and Silas Hoadley, in 1810, he established a partnership with them that did business under the name of Terry, Thomas & Hoadley from 1809 to 1810. No clock bearing all three of these names was discovered in the research project on clocks from which this book derives. Yet if there be any who like to think this firm of tradition was a firm in fact, there is no reason whatsoever for not holding to the opinion. Many partnerships in Connecticut clockmaking were conducted on verbal agreement or understanding. Some lasted a day or two; others lasted a week, a month, or a year. In spite of the fact that the partnership of Thomas and Hoadley is mentioned by several commentators of the period, even this business is classified by some experts as "traditional" rather than a firm in fact. That Eli Terry sold his mass-production wooden hang-up clock factory at Plymouth to Thomas and Hoadley is not proved by an extant bill of sale. Mention of the transaction is a matter of printed commentary. Proof of the partnership hinges on clocks which bear the name Thomas & Hoadley.

There is, however, no question about this: after 1813 Seth Thomas was not in partnership with Silas Hoadley. In 1813 Seth Thomas bought the factory of Heman Clark in the section of Plymouth called the Hollow. Silas Hoadley continued to operate the old Eli Terry shop. In starting on his own, in his newly purchased factory, Seth Thomas founded a clock business that has continued since that day, even though Seth Thomas is now owned by a holding company known as General Time Instruments Corporation, which also owns the Western Clock Company of La Salle, Illinois, and which, in 1930, absorbed the Hamilton-Sangamo Electric

TOP LEFT: Candlestand clock, popular *c.* 1865–74. TOP RIGHT: Candlestand clock by Seth Thomas Sons & Co., 1876. BOTTOM LEFT: Mantel clock by Seth Thomas, 1876. BOTTOM RIGHT: Clock made by the Amana Sect at Buffalo, N.Y., *c.* 1850. This is a wall clock. Viewed upside down it looks like the hood of an early type tall-case clock. (Collection of Henry Weil, Buffalo, N.Y.)

From the Seth Thomas catalogue of 1885, showing persistence of early models and styles. Note also the prices!

Clock Company. One of the old Seth Thomas factories, a long, low clapboard building fitted with water-power machinery, once turned by the waters of the tiny Naugatuck River, is still standing. One end of this may be the original Heman Clark factory. Plymouth Hollow is now Thomaston, Connecticut, a town that has "lived" on clocks since Seth Thomas started his very own first factory or, more accurately, since Eli Terry picked on Plymouth as the site of his first multiple-production shop.

Silas Hoadley continued to operate the old Terry shop under his own name until 1849. In 1812 Eli Terry set up the experimental shop from which, by 1814, were coming his first experimental, low-priced wooden shelf clocks. At New Haven, in 1801, Sibley and Marble announced a clockmaking partnership. This firm made steeple or tower clocks priced at from two hundred dollars to one thousand dollars; eight-day house clocks (tall-case) with moon and plain, elegantly enameled faces; and clock and watchmakers' engines. An "engine" for clock and watchmakers was not a motor, or power source, but a machine for cutting gears or teeth in wheels. The Sibley & Marble firm lasted only until 1807, when Sibley died.

In 1808, at Hartford, Heydorn and Imlay formed a partnership which continued until 1811. Their shop, or manufactory, then contained the most complete tools known to a clock shop on this continent. Heydorn and Imlay went their several ways, perhaps to make clocks elsewhere in the country. At any rate they did not remain in Connecticut. Hart and Brewer started a clock manufactory at Middletown in 1800 which was dissolved in 1803. Hart removed to Norwich, formed a partnership with Alvan Willcox, and conducted a business there from about 1805 to 1816. Then Hart moved to Ohio, where he probably did some clockmaking.

It might be well to mention here that the Ohio country, known as "Western Reserve" was, even in the early nineteenth century, considered a part of Connecticut. Very early in the history of the Connecticut colony, claims were staked out which gave the colony, presumably, jurisdiction over a slice of land which, skipping New Jersey, extended through what was later Pennsylvania and Ohio. Early maps showing the Connecticut claims extend the colony in a strip about as wide as its present north-south boundary, far to the westward. In migrating to Wyoming Valley, Pennsylvania,

TOP ROW: Clocks from the Seth Thomas catalogue of 1876. BOTTOM ROW, LEFT: Seth Thomas model still sold in 1876. CENTER: Seth Thomas clock of 1864 made for the Canadian market by putting a tablet in the door depicting the British coat of arms. RIGHT: Sharp Gothic by Seth Thomas, 1885.

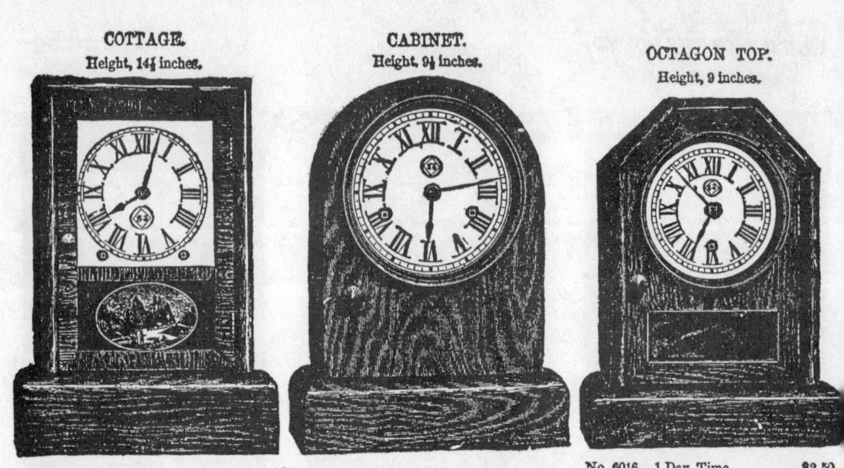


| | | Strike. | Alarm. |
|---|---|---|---|
| No. 6012. | 1 Day, Spring... | $3 75 | $4 25 |
| No. 6013. | 8 Day, Spring... | 5 25 | 5 75 |

No. 6014. 8 Day, Time, $3 35 Alarm, $3 85
No. 6015. 1 Day, Strike, 3 35 " 3 85

No. 6016. 1 Day, Time............$2 50
No. 6916. 1 Day, Time, Alarm.... 3 00

**ROSEWOOD—Column.** **O. G.** **ROSEWOOD. Shell Column.**

30 Hour or Small 8 Day. Strike. Weight. Hight, 25 inches.

30 Hour. Strike. Weight. Hight, 25 inches.

30 Hour or Small 8 Day. Strik Weight. Hight, 25 inches.

TOP ROW: Three clocks from the Seth Thomas catalogue of 1885. BOTTOM ROW: Three clocks from the Seth Thomas catalogue of 1876. These same three clocks appear in the first catalogue issued by Seth Thomas. How many of each type were made from the 1850s through to 1876 is anybody's guess. Production must have reached well over 100,000 for each model in the period of time covered by this catalogue span.

and to the Western Reserve in Ohio, Connecticut clockmakers and others had reason to feel that they were just moving to another part of their state.

One interesting example of the extension of Connecticut clockmaking to Ohio has to do with the migration of George Marsh of Farmington, Bristol, and Walcottville. The last Connecticut record our researchers could find having to do with George Marsh is dated 1831. About 1833 there was a clock factory established at Dayton, Ohio, named Marsh, Williams & Company, and later Marsh, Williams & Hayden. It was a water-power factory, operating on one of the sluiceways of the Miami canal or hydraulic. This factory, set up on the Connecticut plan, made up to twenty-five hundred clocks a year! Its proprietors claimed for it the distinction of being the only clock factory in the West. "George Marsh from Farmington, Connecticut, an immigrant," is the way they designated the man who ran that factory for fifteen years. In 1846 he removed to Van Wert, Ohio, where his son, Hayden Marsh, became quite wealthy and left funds for the establishment of the Marsh Foundation. A Marsh & Williams clock made at Dayton is pictured in Chapter X.

Eli Terry, Jr., succeeded in 1827 to his father's clock factory in the section of Plymouth now known as Terryville. He seems to have conducted that business very capably although he had few of his father's gifts. He was respected enough to have that section of Plymouth, now called Terryville, named in his honor.

Joseph Ives, one of the famous Ives brothers, is credited with pioneering in the production of low-priced brass clocks. In 1818 Ives invented a clock with iron plates and brass wheels. This movement was large, requiring a case at least five feet tall. Again the pertinent question crops up: Were some of these movements cased in short "tall" cases deserving of the designation grandmother clocks? Ives, also, in 1822 was granted a patent on the "looking-glass clock case." No doubt this is the clock idea later claimed by Chauncey Jerome as his own invention.

The more one studies the life and works of Joseph Ives the greater is the conviction that in this man resided the real genius of Connecticut clockmaking and mass production. According to facts revealed in the researches of Lockwood Barr and others in connection with clockmaking at Bristol, Connecticut, Ives was

TOP, LEFT: Ingraham's Grecian model of 1869. CENTER: Seth Thomas Gothic, 1880; RIGHT: E. N. Welch O-G. LOWER, LEFT: Welch, Spring & Co. Grecian, 1860s. CENTER AND RIGHT: Three Seth Thomas clocks of the 1880s and a Gothic by New Haven Clock Co., 1880–90. All pictures from catalogues of the makers. Edward Ingraham Collection.

Woodcut proofs of illustrations made for the Seth Thomas catalogues of the 1860s. The clock at lower left was made until *c.* 1892. The other models seem to have been dropped in the late 1880s.

making thirty-hour and eight-day tall clock movements of wood with roller pinions from 1800 to 1812. In 1818 or 1819 he designed a brass movement with steel plates, long pendulum, and twelve pound weights. Before 1825 he had solved the hitherto "English secret" of rolling brass.

In 1825 Ives removed to Brooklyn, where he began production of his eight-day wagon-spring movement clock. In this venture Ives's inventive genius did not come to his aid as a businessman. He went into debt to such an extent that, like Goodyear, the genius of rubber, he was imprisoned for debt. A group of Bristol men, headed by John Birge, settled Ives's debts to the amount of $10,-000. He was immediately released from debtors' prison and assigned to these Bristol men certain rights, patents, and other assets of his inventive resources. Again free to attempt clock production, he fell into his former errors. He was no businessman. He went bankrupt again in 1842.

These data on Joseph Ives, the man, should be sufficient for this volume. We have seen how Jerome purloined Ives's looking-glass clock idea and his brass movement clock idea. It is a great pity that a basically sound financier did not take Ives under his wing, endow him with sufficient income to overcome his natural desire to make money in clock manufacturing, and thus permit the talent of the man to unfold. Had this happened, we might well rank Joseph Ives in clockmaking as a genius on a parity with Steinmetz and Tesla in electrical science.

Chauncey and Lawson C. Ives was one of the firms formed to make Ives's eight-day clock movement of rolled brass parts, under license from the inventor. This clock had the "roller pinion" which, at the risk of being somewhat technical, should be described here. The pinion of a clock is made up of two discs joined by a series of rods to form a piece looking like a small lantern or bird cage. In most pinions the rods are fixed. In Ives's pinion the rods "rolled" in their seating in each of the ends. According to Lockwood Barr, some of these rollers were of wood over brass or steel pins. Thus the Ives's roller pinion was a sort of roller bearing. It was later abandoned as too expensive for use in low-cost clocks. Atkins, Whiting & Company, 1850, and the Atkins Clock Company, 1856, all made clocks under the Ives's roller pinion and other patents.

John Birge, 1785–1862, began his active business life as a car-

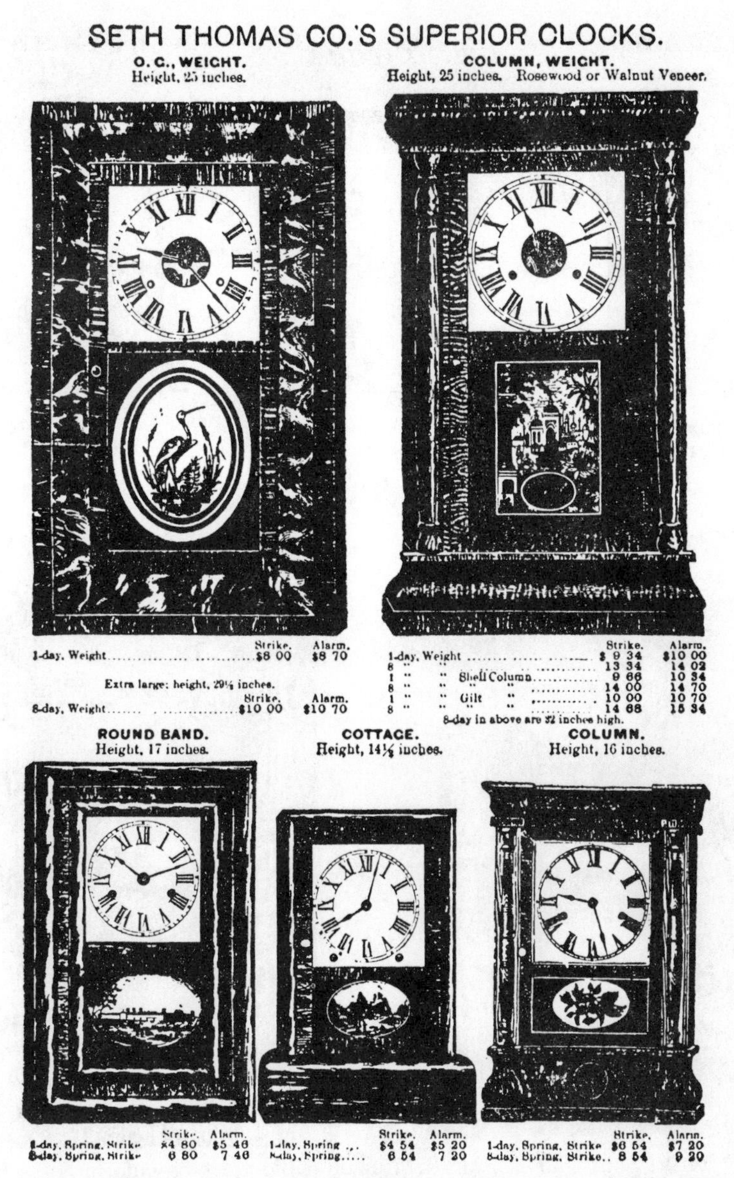

SETH THOMAS CO.'S SUPERIOR CLOCKS.

**O. C., WEIGHT.**
Height, 25 inches.

| | Strike. | Alarm. |
|---|---|---|
| 1-day, Weight | $8 00 | $8 70 |

Extra large; height, 29¼ inches.

| | Strike. | Alarm. |
|---|---|---|
| 8-day, Weight | $10 00 | $10 70 |

**COLUMN, WEIGHT.**
Height, 25 inches. Rosewood or Walnut Veneer.

| | Strike. | Alarm. |
|---|---|---|
| 1-day, Weight | $ 9 34 | $10 00 |
| 8 " " | 13 34 | 14 02 |
| 1 " " Shell Column | 9 66 | 10 34 |
| 8 " " " " | 14 00 | 14 70 |
| 1 " " Gilt " | 10 00 | 10 70 |
| 8 " " " " | 14 68 | 15 34 |

8-day in above are 32 inches high.

**ROUND BAND.**
Height, 17 inches.

| | Strike. | Alarm. |
|---|---|---|
| 1-day, Spring, Strike | $4 80 | $5 46 |
| 8-day, Spring, Strike | 6 80 | 7 46 |

**COTTAGE.**
Height, 14⅛ inches.

| | Strike. | Alarm. |
|---|---|---|
| 1-day, Spring | $4 54 | $5 20 |
| 8-day, Spring | 6 54 | 7 20 |

**COLUMN.**
Height, 16 inches.

| | Strike. | Alarm. |
|---|---|---|
| 1-day, Spring, Strike | $6 54 | $7 20 |
| 8-day, Spring, Strike | 8 54 | 9 20 |

Page of Seth Thomas clocks from the catalogue of B. W. Studly, San Rafael, Cal., 1887.

CHICAGO.

8 Day. Strike. Spring.
Hight, 17 inches.

ST. LOUIS.

8 Day or 30 Hour. Strike. Spring.
Hight, 15½ inches.

CINCINNATI

8 Day. Strike. Spring.
Hight, 16 inches.

TOP ROW: Seth Thomas, in 1876, made a bid for city-wide business by naming certain clocks for American communities. BOTTOM, LEFT: Parlor calendar clock introduced about 1859; RIGHT: A modified pillar, without scroll, still in the catalogue of 1886.

penter and wagon builder, but after 1830 became a factor in Bristol clockmaking. Birge headed the syndicate of Bristol men who paid Joseph Ives's debts and in 1834 formed the firm of Ives & Birge. Birge was the principal partner in a number of firms including Birge, Case & Company, 1834; Birge, Gilbert & Company, 1835–36; Birge & Gilbert, 1837; Birge, Mallory & Company, 1838–43; Birge & Fuller, 1844–47; John Birge & Company, 1848; and Birge, Peck & Company, 1849–58.

Solomon Spring, whose name in early catalogues caused some misunderstanding in the clock business, had a clock company of his own in 1858—the former Birge, Peck & Company factory. In certain early catalogues clocks are designated as "spring," yet bearing the confusing subtitles: "thirty-hour weight" and "eight-day weight." Not until the designation "spring" was known to refer to the maker and not to the motive power used in the clocks did this occasional confusion disappear. In 1869 Spring merged with Elisha N. Welch as Welch, Spring & Company. Welch's father was a maker of clock weights which were traded to clockmakers for finished clocks which, in turn, were then peddled by the weight maker. Clocks and clock parts of any kind, as we have seen, constituted "money" in Connecticut. Finally, the E. N. Welch Manufacturing Company succeeded Welch, Spring & Company, and, in turn, became the Sessions Clock Company of Bristol, Connecticut.

"By their works let us know them" has been the axiom of all wise observers since biblical days. The phrase is altogether fitting when applied to clockmakers although to a seasoned collector and to the specialist the term "works" for a clock movement brings forth a shudder. Nonetheless it is the works or the movement of a clock that makes it a timekeeper and not merely a thing of beauty. The clockmakers of Connecticut were primarily concerned with two phases of activity: making clock movements that would keep time and putting the movements in cases that would sell the clocks against competition. Price, terms, discounts, and deals of all sorts were collateral business details. Selling the clocks on their appearance at the lowest possible prices, with guaranteed timekeeping quality in the movement, was the major task.

In accomplishing these objectives by every means at their command, the clockmakers of Connecticut put out so many clocks in

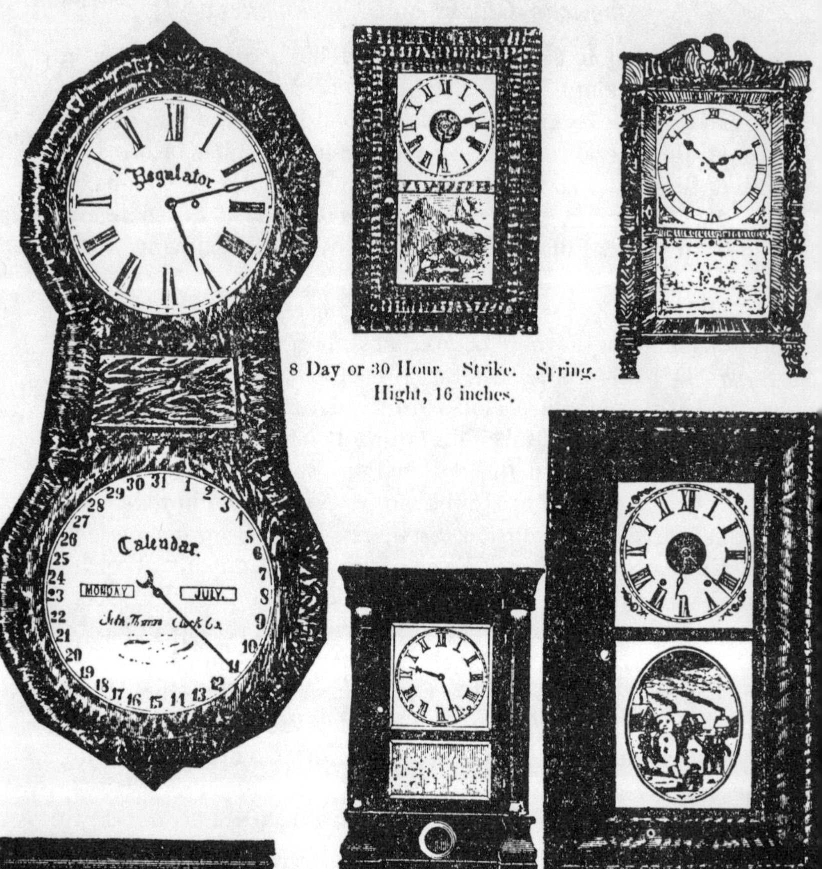

TOP ROW: Calendar office and counting-room clock, 1876; kitchen clock, 1856–86; and a carved pillar-and-scroll of the 1820s. CENTER: Small pillar clock, *c.* 1865; large O-G with snowman panel, 1862. LEFT: Pillar clock in the line from late 1840s to 1880s. All Seth Thomas clocks from the manufacturer's catalogues. It should be noted that Seth Thomas not only made complete calendar clocks but that the firm also made movements for other calendar clock companies which flourished in the 1870s and 1880s.

TOP: E. N. Welch double O-G of 1869. Made in one-day and eight-day; eighteen inches high. Welch drop octagon wall clock; twelve-inch dial; twenty-five inches high. Date is 1869. BELOW: Welch double O-G, twenty-six inches high; one-day weight clock, 1869. Fourteen-inch-high cottage clock by Welch, made in one-day or eight-day spring types. All clocks from catalogue of E. N. Welch Manufacturing Company, 1869.

so many different cases that one wishes the industry had also fathered a Lewis Carroll, who would have written the entire story à la *Alice in Wonderland.* This chapter on the Thomas, Hoadley, Ives, Marble, Hart, Wilcox, Marsh, Welch, Case, Birge, Terry, Barnum, Atkins, Whiting, Brown, Foresville, Terryville, Thomaston, and other aspects of Connecticut clockmaking could be continued for another hundred pages without exhausting the historical resources already recorded by Lockwood Barr, Carleton Buell, Penrose Hoopes, and Edward Ingraham. These men have literally tabulated the Connecticut clock story in its every ramification.

Therefore this chapter shall attempt nothing more than to picture, with captions as brief as possible, a parade of Connecticut clocks taken directly from the catalogues and other illustrated literature of the makers. It is a pity that P. T. Barnum's name is connected with Connecticut clockmaking under a cloud and the shadow of suspicion. He should have made a success of his clockmaking. In Connecticut, from 1805 to 1855, clockmaking was a three-ringed circus, at Bristol, Plymouth, and New Haven. There was a midway with side shows, freaks, wonders, and natural curiosities. There were fakirs, confidence men, pickpockets and touts. Daily there were races with huge stakes for the winners. The entire nation was the market and, after Chauncey Jerome had shown how to crash the English market, there were other nations, with other markets to tap—with Connecticut clocks.

It was a great age in terms of business development; a greater age in terms of clock production. Some of the clocks are pictured here. Those shown demonstrate also why, on many an occasion, you will find clocks not pictured here. The "lines" were changed from year to year. Minor changes were made in case and in movement design while batches of clocks were going through a factory. Clock panels were made in so many patterns that even today no less than one thousand, all different, stencils used in their making are preserved in one lot that has come down from one tablet painter. Some tablets were hand-painted even down to 1855. Elijah Darrow, who had been an art instructor, got his former pupils, young girls and married women, to paint clock dials and tablets.

There have been collections of all different Connecticut clocks

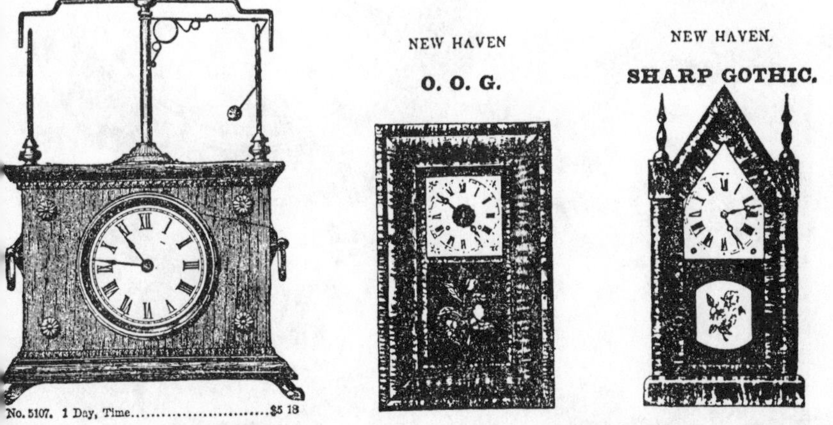


TOP, AND BOTTOM LEFT: Three clocks from the 1885 catalogue of the New Haven Clock Company. Note that tablets or panels in clock doors are decalcomania transfers and not hand painted. The flying pendulum, of course, is a variant of the old "foliot" balance as first used on clocks. BOTTOM CENTER AND RIGHT: Two clocks from the catalogue of the New Haven Company, 1865.

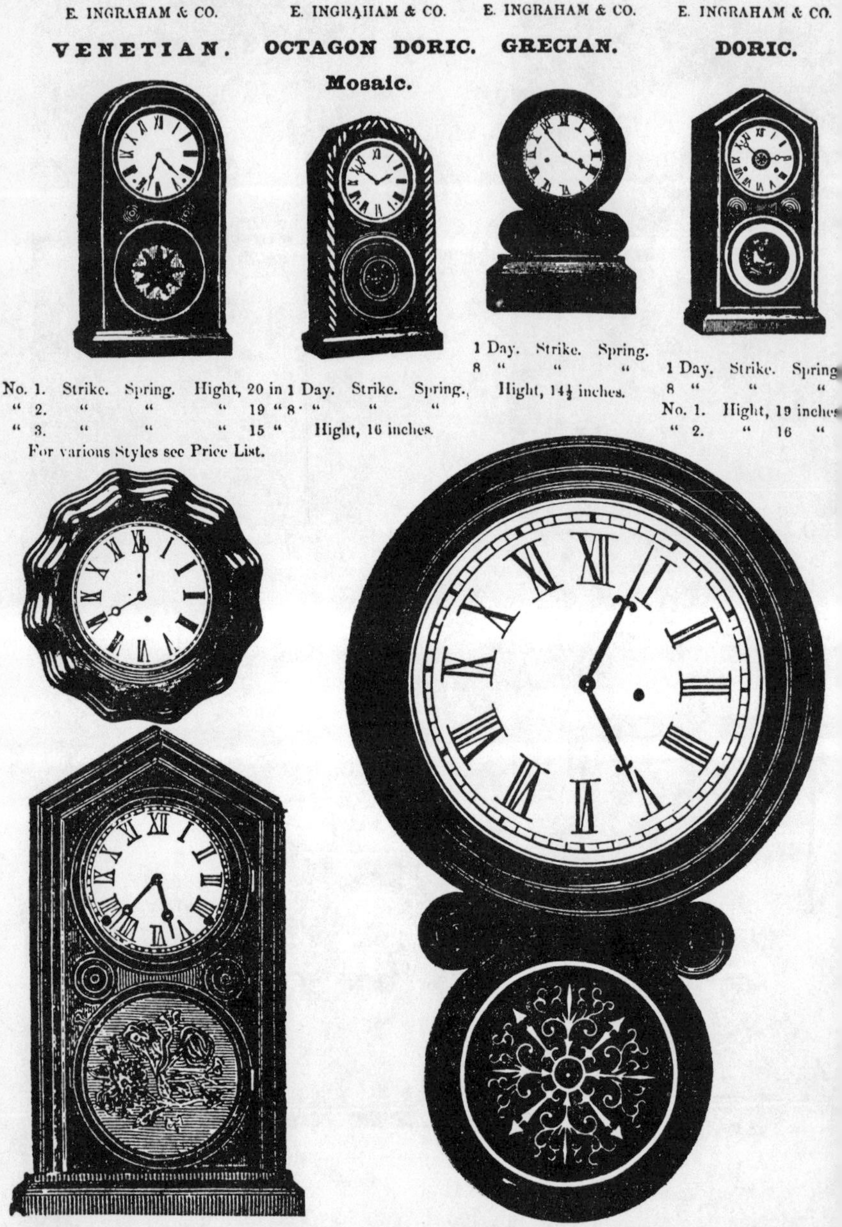

E. INGRAHAM & CO.

**VENETIAN.**

No. 1. Strike. Spring. Hight, 20 in
" 2. " " " 19 "
" 3. " " " 15 "
For various Styles see Price List.

E. INGRAHAM & CO.

**OCTAGON DORIC.**

**Mosaic.**

1 Day. Strike. Spring.
8 " " "
Hight, 16 inches.

E. INGRAHAM & CO.

**GRECIAN.**

1 Day. Strike. Spring.
8 " " "
Hight, 14½ inches.

E. INGRAHAM & CO.

**DORIC.**

1 Day. Strike. Spring
8 " " "
No. 1. Hight, 19 inches
" 2. " 16 "

TOP: A galaxy of no less than twenty-five small clocks in the Ingraham line of 1876 supplies us with these little items. BOTTOM, LEFT: An Ingraham clock of the 1870s. Over it a corrugated gallery clock with twelve-inch dial (spring-driven). RIGHT: Ingraham's Ionic wall clock, spring-driven, with twelve-inch dial. Date is about 1865.

started from time to time by many courageous souls. Some have collected one thousand examples. Not a single one of them has ever felt he could say, "at last I have every one." Like buttons, Connecticut clocks of the period here considered exist in so many varieties, types, and minor styles that to say the number is infinite is almost permissible. Our pictures do not extend to infinity but they do point the way.

TOP LEFT: Atkins' corner clock, *c.* 1860. TOP RIGHT: Atkins small column clock of 1866. BOTTOM LEFT: Two small clocks by Waterbury, 1880. RIGHT: Waterbury sunflower clock, 1887. All pictures from makers' catalogues.

TOP, LEFT: Welch calendar clock, ten-inch dial; one-day. *c.* 1876. TOP, RIGHT: E. N. Welch O-G clock of 1870s, twenty-nine inches high; eight-day weight. BOTTOM ROW: New Haven and E. N. Welch small clocks, ranging from twenty-six inches to fourteen inches high. Date is late 1850s and early 1860s. All pictures from catalogues of the makers.

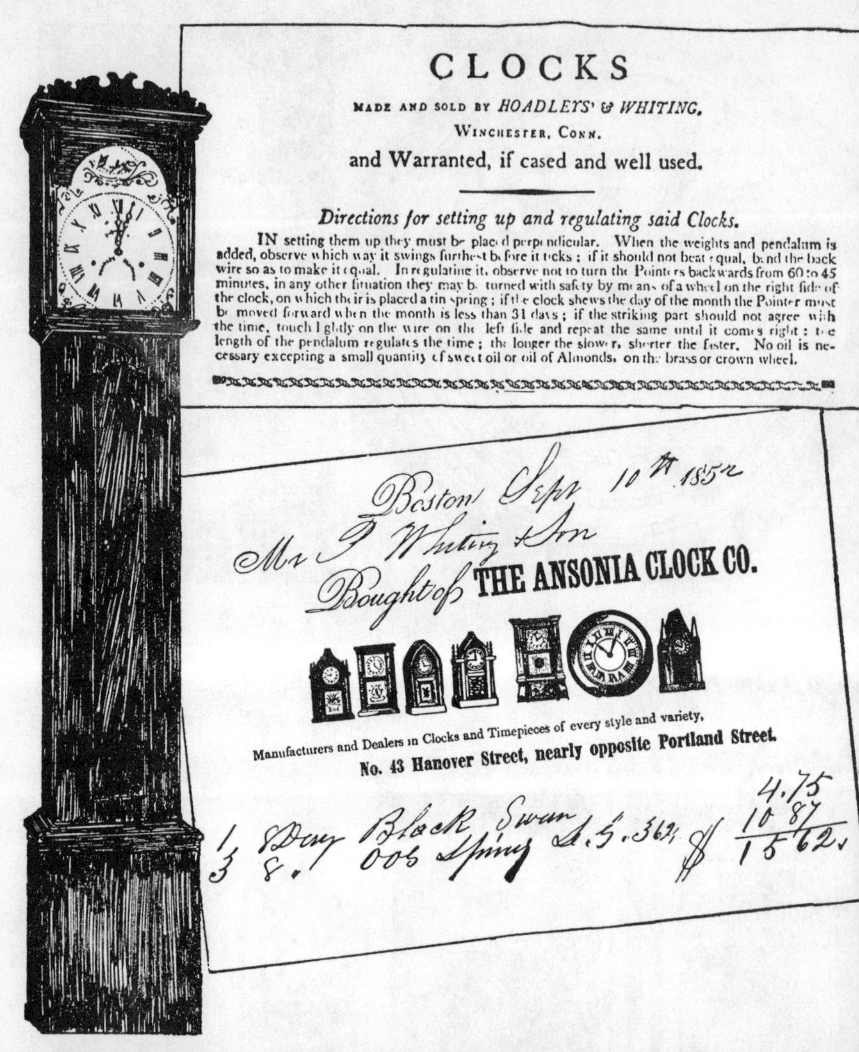

# CLOCKS

MADE AND SOLD BY *HOADLEYS' & WHITING,*

WINCHESTER, CONN.

and Warranted, if cased and well used.

---

*Directions for setting up and regulating said Clocks.*

IN setting them up they must be placed perpendicular. When the weights and pendalum is added, observe which way it swings furthest before it ticks; if it should not beat equal, bend the back wire so as to make it equal. In regulating it, observe not to turn the Pointers backwards from 60 to 45 minutes, in any other situation they may be turned with safety by means of a wheel on the right side of the clock, on which their is placed a tin spring; if the clock shews the day of the month the Pointer must be moved forward when the month is less than 31 days; if the striking part should not agree with the time, touch lightly on the wire on the left side and repeat the same until it comes right: the length of the pendalum regulates the time; the longer the slower, shorter the faster. No oil is necessary excepting a small quantity of sweet oil or oil of Almonds, on the brass or crown wheel.

Boston Sept 10th 1852

Mr J. Whiting & Son

Bought of THE ANSONIA CLOCK CO.

Manufacturers and Dealers in Clocks and Timepieces of every style and variety,

No. 43 Hanover Street, nearly opposite Portland Street.

1 8 Day Black Swan 4.75

3 8. OOS Spring S. S. 3.62½ 10.87

$ 15.62

Tall-case clock by S. Hoadley, Plymouth. Time and strike, with seconds dial under XII. Case is walnut, seven feet high. Owned by Mrs. Virginia Haughwout, the Richard Bland House, Williamsburg, Virginia. Clock paper of little-known firm of Hoadleys' & Whiting, *c.* 1815, and a bill for four eight-day clocks by Ansonia Clock Company's Boston store, 1852. Both from collection of Francis B. Platt, Schenectady, N.Y.

CHAPTER

ALMOST every newspaper in our United States between the years 1800 and 1860 considered each advancement in the mechanical arts, sciences, and philosophy as important news. Since it is also a fact that the newspapers of those days had to reflect the desires of subscribers or suspend publication, it is safe to assume that mechanical, scientific, and philosophical news was something the public wanted. When the Massachusetts *Ploughman,* a rural newspaper, ran the following piece of news on June 19, 1847, we can be sure it was looked at with some wonder, some envy, and perhaps with some skepticism.

"*Electric Clock.*—The clock is enclosed in a neat oak case, about four and a half feet in height and one foot four inches wide. Its face is of ample dimensions, very plain in appearance, and is furnished with second, minute, and hour hands in all respects similar to those of the usual construction. The pendulum is the same length as that of the ordinary old-fashioned eight-day clocks. Here, however, analogy ceases. It is true there are some wheels and pinions to move the hands and afford accurate indications of the divisions and progress of time, but these are few in number and do their work in a manner totally different from those in other kinds of clocks. The electric clock has neither weight nor spring, nor power of any other kind, within itself, to keep it in motion, and it therefore never requires winding up.

"Whence, then, does the electric clock derive its power of continuous motion? Wait a little—we will try to explain it.

"There are two very small copper wires fixed in the angles of the clock case, which communicate with similar wires at the back of the pendulum bar, and are thence continued to a coil of the same kind of wire enclosed in a circular brass box, which box

LEFT: The "Grisi" model, cast-iron cased clock, 1869. RIGHT, TOP: Cast-iron clock known as the Washington. RIGHT, BOTTOM: The wide-awake. All of these cast-iron cased clocks are of Connecticut make, although the makers' names do not appear on them. They were made for distribution and sale by The American Clock Company, a nation-wide catalogue house.

Blinking-Eye Clocks Popular in 1870s. TOP LEFT: The Continental. BOTTOM LEFT: Sambo. ABOVE: Topsy. All of these figural cases are of cast iron; when the clock is running the eyes blink. Connecticut made, not marked with maker's names, but from catalogue of Waterbury Clock Company. Courtesy of Francis B. Platt, Schenectady, N.Y.

constitutes what is usually termed the bob of the pendulum. The box being hollow, in the direction of its axis, the cavity thus formed admits of the insertion of two sets of permanent magnets, whose similar poles are placed near to, but not in contact with, each other. These magnets are kept in their places by being enclosed in brass boxes secured to the sides of the clock case. The pendulum is so adjusted that it has, of course, perfect freedom of motion; whilst in its oscillations it passes alternately the poles of the magnet just mentioned.

"Leaving the clock for a few minutes, we now observe two copper wires, the ends of which are in contact with those within the case. Continuing their course along the wall, these wires pass out of doors, descend below the surface of the earth, and, at a short distance from the house, are connected, the one with a few bushels of coke and the other with five or six plates of zinc. These materials are buried in a hole in the earth, about four feet square, and five feet deep, the coke being placed at the bottom with a layer of earth above it, and then the zinc plates are laid thereon, and the whole covered up, thus forming a galvanic battery. Here consists the power which imparts motion to the clock; a current of electricity being induced by the coke and zinc, which, although of low intensity, is unlimited as to quantity, the source whence it is derived being the earth itself. The pendulum being set in motion and the current of electricity through the wires established, a beautiful arrangement of simple mechanism immediately comes into operation, by means of which the circuit is broken and renewed at each alternate oscillation. Thus by the skill of the inventor the combined agencies of galvo-electricity, electro-magnetism, and permanent magnetism are made to produce an uniform and, so to speak, perpetual motion of the pendulum; and we obtain a time measurer of such extraordinary accuracy that we believe it will bear comparison, in this respect, with the best constructed chronometer.

"If it be desired to have other clocks in different parts of the house, that we have been describing requires only to be connected with them by a copper wire, and the circuit completed to the battery; and they will all be kept going by the motion of one pendulum, and record exactly the same time. So also the public clocks in a town, could, by similar means, be made to synchronise.

TOP LEFT: Tucker bronze clock with Connecticut movement. TOP RIGHT: Noiseless clock, Connecticut make, running under a glass bell or dome. BOTTOM LEFT: The baseball or ballplayers' clock; bronze case; Connecticut movement. BOTTOM RIGHT: Parlor mantel clock in bronze case. The bronze clocks date from 1869; the noiseless clock is 1885. The "oil derrick" of the noiseless clock supports the pendulum which swings above the movement.

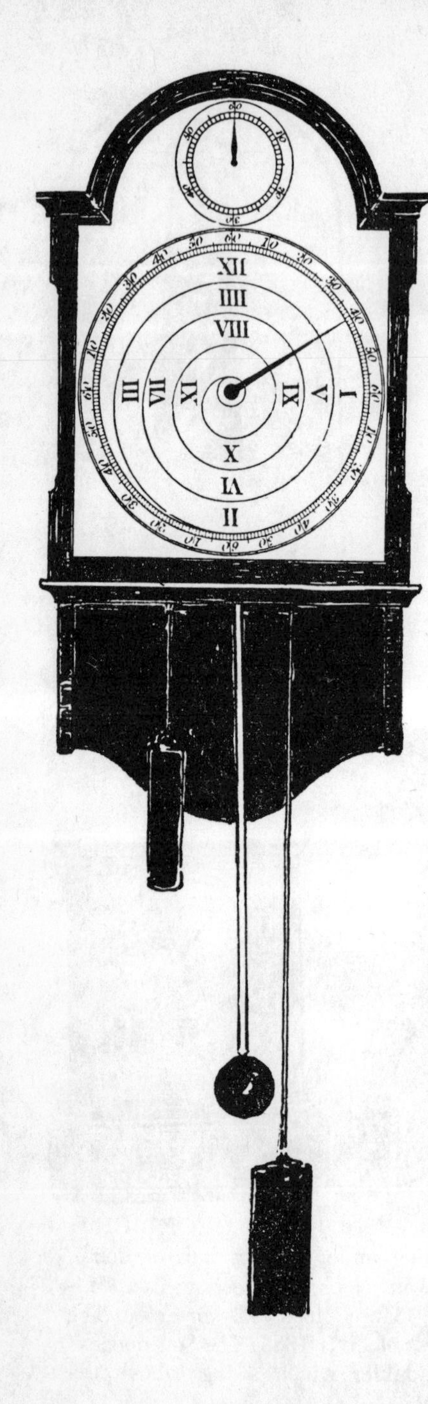

LEFT: The clock invented by Benjamin Franklin, *c.* 1750, described in text. ABOVE: A rare original drawing of John Fisher, clockmaker of York, Pa., from the Collection of George Hay Kain, Jr.

"Such is the electric clock, invented by Mr. Alexander Bain, of Edinburgh—a gentleman deservedly known in the scientific world."

In 1866 S. A. Kennedy, who had been associated with Samuel F. B. Morse in electric telegraphy, invented an electric clock using the magnetic principle. This clock, in the form of an ornate tall wall clock, was marketed in 1867. It was not operated by an "earth battery" as advocated by Alexander Bain, but by a wet battery of the type then used in telegraphy. Perhaps the Kennedy electric clock would have been a success had it been hitched to a perpetual earth battery.

Electric clocks are mentioned here only because they have been considered something new. In the Bain story, if one studies it well, lies the germ of the idea of an electric master clock with synchronized subsidiary clocks tied to it as a system. When something of this sort was made possible by the use of synchronous motor clocks, it was not because the synchronous motor was new but because central power plants, generally, were master-clocking their alternating current at sixty cycles. The electric clock took this country by storm in the 1920s. Most of these electric clocks were synchronous. Most of them were non-self-starting; they had a little lever to snap in order to start the motor which was, actually, the only mechanism within the clock. The only self-starting synchronous clock then made was the Warren Telechron. Self-starting was its big feature. Its motor would not run one bit more accurately than any other synchronous clock motor. All such motors just had to stay in step with the sixty-cycle generators at the central stations.

The Sangamo, and later the Hamilton-Sangamo electric clock, was originally a fine timepiece of brass, electrically wound, with a Hamilton watch escapement of seven-jewel type. It was an expensive clock as electric clocks were then priced. Some of the cases were after originals by Simon Willard, made by Erskine-Danforth. Later, Hamilton-Sangamo produced a non-self-starting synchronous motor clock and finally were ready to go into production on a new synchronous movement which, in starting itself, did not use the synchronous principle at all. This invention, perfected by Sangamo engineers who by that time considered them-

IMMEDIATELY ABOVE: Washington memorial clock by Dubuc of Paris, said to have been imported *c.* 1805 by John Shaw of Annapolis, Md. Many of these clocks were imported and it is doubtful if Shaw was the only importer. Clock is of ormulu, or gilt-brass. UPPER RIGHT: French clock of white marble and bronze. Thousands of clocks of this type were imported between 1810 and 1850. Lumas Watson of Cincinnati was making clocks of this type, of wood and ivory, in 1830s. From Arthur Sussel.

TOP, LEFT: Cast-iron clock of 1870s; Connecticut movement and case; eighteen inches high. TOP, CENTER: French carved wood clock, Louis Seize period. At least one million clocks in this style, in stamped wood cases were made and sold by Connecticut clock companies between 1880 and 1900. TOP, RIGHT: The Columbus Clock, all-wood, ancient-type movement, stamped wood front; made to sell as souvenir at Columbian Exposition, 1893. BOTTOM: Jigsaw artist's dream, the Fleetwood, with Seth Thomas movement. Sold complete, or with movement and patterns, by Pomeroy of Hartford, 1886–1900.

selves clockmakers (yes, some of them were from Connecticut), used a motor of the induction hysteresis type, of very low power, to start a motor of synchronous type and of greater power. The induction motor kicked the synchronous motor into action and this at once engaged the induction motor and carried it with it in synchrony with the sixty-cycle alternating-current impulses. Thus did clockmaking early in the twentieth century repeat its history of a century ago in Connecticut. Many Connecticut clock companies, including Seth Thomas, entered the electric clock field. Some entered it to their sorrow. Others, in surviving the depression of 1931, have kept electric clocks, along with spring-driven clocks, in their lines.

Sometime in the 1760s our great American scientist and philosopher, Franklin, invented a clock having only three wheels. We can trust Mr. Franklin to be concerned with simplification. His timepiece, herein pictured, had a single hand which, in making one circuit of the dial, made that circuit in precisely four hours. Four sixty-minute divisions mark the time track. The dial looks as scientific as an astronomical instrument, yet it is really simple. Note that VIII is under IIII and that both are under XII. When the hand points precisely upward it is either twelve o'clock, four o'clock, or eight o'clock. When the hand is at the first fifty mark beyond this column of figures it is either twelve-fifty, four-fifty, or eight-fifty. When the hand points to I it is one o'clock, five o'clock, or nine o'clock. This clock had a second dial in the tympanum or arch. It was not wound up with a "winch" as they then designated clocks wound with keys or levers, but by drawing on the cords which hauled the weight upward around a power-imparting drum. The inconvenience of this clock was that, at night, one could not tell which of any of the three hours was true time. Franklin is said to have remarked "who would care"? We would rather own one of these Franklin clocks than any other clock pictured in this book. It is the most "modern" of all the timepieces mentioned or displayed.

Another very ingenious timepiece, this one of the nineteenth century, is the "wagon-spring" clock invented by Joseph Ives of Bristol. This clock, dispensing with both weights and coiled springs, used the tremendous power stored in a depressed-leaf spring as used in wagons. Ives mounted a special spring of this

Proof from a wood block used in printing paper clock dials, *c.* 1840. This proof is from the catalogue of a woodcut-making firm which offered dial printing blocks to clockmakers. The original proof of this dial measures slightly more than seven inches square; obviously a dial for a small mantel clock. Paper dials were used from *c.* 1790. The paper proof was pasted on a wood panel or a square of sheet iron. Spandrels were colored and the entire dial then varnished.

ABOVE, LEFT: Kennedy Electric clock, battery operated, 1867. ABOVE, RIGHT: Paper clock dial of 1792. These dials were sold in "books" of twenty-four, forty-eight, and ninety-six papers, ready for pasting on wood panels or iron plates. Some were printed in France, some in the Netherlands, and some in the United States. BELOW, RIGHT: Bronze statuettes offered by Seth Thomas Clock Company in 1880s. Ariosto, Petrarch, Tasso, and Dante.

type in a cast-iron frame and conveyed the power to the movement by means of a metal sprocket chain and rocking arms. This great amount of stored power, released slowly, enabled Ives to design a clock that would run for thirty days at one winding. He also made thirty-hour and eight-day clocks with this novel power feature. Ives seems to have built his first wagon-spring models about 1816–18. Not many of these clocks were made until Ives himself set up shop in Brooklyn, Long Island, in 1825. Then he began making and marketing the clocks with his name on the dial and with his locale designated thereon as New York. It has been said that the cases used by Ives in this period, and which appear on wagon-spring clocks made up to the 1830s, show decided Duncan Phyfe influence. Who knows? A re-examination of the Phyfe account books may well disclose that this master's shop, then employing fifty to one hundred workmen, may have made cases for Ives. In spite of the competition with coiled springs as motive power for clocks, the wagon-spring clock invented by Ives was made up to the 1860s. Ives received several patents on this unique clock idea. The last one is dated 1859. He deserves great credit for discovering a principle whereby a spring would do the work of a weight. It will be remembered, from notes in another chapter, that the first spring applications to a clock involved a complicated conical section known as a fusee. Ives did not use a fusee, but his combination of levers, chains, and cams did convert the pressure of a long-leaf spring into the steady pull of a heavy weight. Birge & Fuller and Atkins, Whiting & Company are known to have made wagon-spring clocks under the Ives patent.

Most surviving cased examples are either in (1) hexagonal or round cases with pendulum box, to serve as regulators or wall clocks; (2) in mantel clock cases that are variants of the pillar-and-scroll; (3) in pointed Gothic cases. Some Ives thirty-hour clocks are fitted with a single leaf spring. This is, actually, a small spring steel "bow" about the size of Dan Cupid's famed weapon. Certain of these movements are in a variant of the "acorn" case known as the "hourglass" case. The striking mechanism of Ives's wagon-spring clock was driven by one side of the spring, the time-keeping mechanism by the other. The clocks were fitted with nine and one-half inch pendulums, the rod of which was a flat piece of pine.

Catalogue page of bronze clocks. All cases cast and all movements made by Connecticut companies. Movements by New Haven, Ingraham, Seth Thomas, and Ansonia. Dates of introduction range from 1869 to 1876. Sold by American Clock Company, a wholesale distributor.

UPPER LEFT: Edward Prevear of Leominster, Mass., offered this "sun-transit" to clock and watchmakers in 1868. Seventy-one users from Maine to California endorsed it. All other pictures on this page are electrically wound clocks by the Standard Electric Time Company of New Haven, Conn. They all date 1888. The inventor of this system of electric clocks was C. H. Pond. As many clocks as desired could be connected with a master clock and all would keep time synchronously.

About 1845 Ives invented another unique type of clock movement. He fashioned the plates, wheels, et cetera from tin-plate! We have seen how Chauncey Jerome's thirty-hour brass clock revived the Connecticut clock business and boomed the rolled brass industry. It is to Joseph Ives, however, that the real credit for making rolled brass should go. He experimented with brass clocks long before Jerome, and his, not Jerome's, brass clocks really started the industry. Jerome was close to Ives and had full knowledge of Ives's inventiveness. When Jerome claimed to have invented the looking-glass clock, he may well have used the technique of thinking by which any borrower of an idea can become its father. One sees the thing or idea in concrete form and says, "Oh yes, I've been thinking of doing the same thing." Jerome was a casemaker when Ives conceived the tall looking-glass case for his eight-day brass clock. There, in one package, was an idea factory for Jerome. He later "invented" his thirty-hour brass clock and almost at once invented a smaller looking-glass clock case!

If these comments seem anticlimactic after what has been said about Jerome in Chapter VII, let it be remembered that invention of a case or clock movement in the hurly-burly of Connecticut clockmaking during the first half of the nineteenth century was simply a matter of changing slightly the ideas of another man, or a group of other men, and lo, you were an inventor and a clock genius. Ives was a genius. So was Jerome. Ives was a creative genius. Jerome had, with his other attributes, a genius for taking, and getting, credit.

Bronze clocks, that is bronze cased clocks, were produced in Connecticut in some numbers. Most of them were produced after 1865 although the idea was expressed earlier and seems to have resulted in several examples made between 1845 and 1855. French influence by direct example is perhaps responsible for the bronze-cased clock. The wholesale clock dealer and the big retail clock store were phenomena born of mass production and intensive selling methods. These dealers, wholesale and retail, learned by experience that the more varied the assortment of clocks the greater the number of potential customers, either for a new clock, another clock, or two or more clocks. A clock in every room in the house as a slogan was not born in the 1920s. It was clock-selling philosophy in the 1850s. Among the examples of bronze-

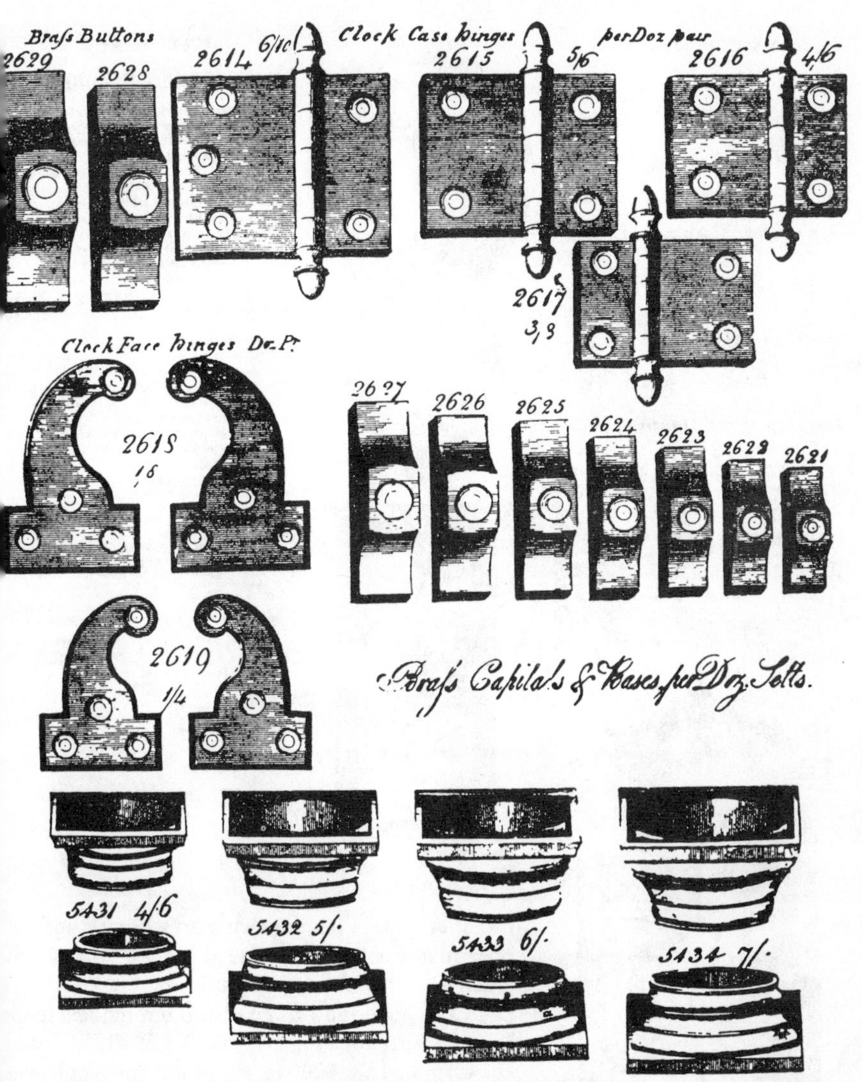


Clock hardware for American clockmakers, offered in the catalogue of a Birmingham Syndicate, *c.* 1788. Hardware of this type is found on many tall-case clocks made after 1790.

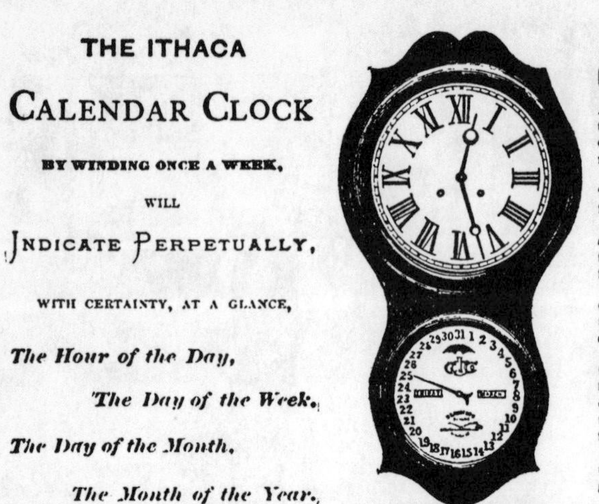

THE ITHACA

CALENDAR CLOCK

BY WINDING ONCE A WEEK,

WILL

INDICATE PERPETUALLY,

WITH CERTAINTY, AT A GLANCE,

*The Hour of the Day,*

*The Day of the Week,*

*The Day of the Month,*

*The Month of the Year,*

Manufactory: Ithaca, Tompkins Co., New York.

The manufactures of this Company are protected by the extension of the original Akins & Burritt patent, dated Sept. 19th, 1854, for 7 years from Sept. 19th, 1868, and by the two patents of H. B. Horton, dated April, 18th, 1865, and August 28th, 1866, comprising in all 20 patent claims on the calendar machine alone; and also by the patent of H. B. Horton and M. L. Wood, for testing and proving Calendar Clocks by power, dated 11th June, 1867.

THE ITHACA

Calendar Clock Company,

After 18 years experience on the part of persons in their employ or connection, in the Invention, Development and Manufacture of CALENDAR CLOCKS, are now prepared to offer to the public the

**Most Reliable Calendar in the World,**

The great superiority of which can be demonstrated in the following essential points among others:

FIRST—The parts by which the changes are made are held securely fast at all times, and the changes being made instantly once in 24 hours, there is no time in which the parts can be displaced by jar or touch.

SECOND—The time movement is never in any appreciable degree taxed or drawn upon by the Calendar the force required to make the calendar changes being so slight that

**The Power of an Ordinary Watch**

is sufficient for the purpose. This very essential point has been gained by dividing the labor through a period of 18 hours, and by diminishing the amount of labor to be performed by the beautiful simplicity attained in the mechanical arrangement.

This Company take pleasure in bringing their manufactures before the public, knowing that they offer a good article at a low price.

The different styles will be adapted for use in *Dwellings, Offices, Stores, Banks, Insurance Offices, Steamboats, Ships*, and in short, wherever a record of time is desirable. It is the intention of the Company to use none but

**Superior 8 Day Time Movements,**

so that the Clock shall be perfectly reliable in every particular. And to insure the perfection of the Calendar they have devised and patented a very ingenious machine by which they test every Calendar before offering it for sale, by running it through a period of 5 years, the 24 hour change being made once in 5 seconds by steam power.

They invite attention particularly to the very fine REGULATOR movement used in all their different styles of Bank Clocks. This movement is sufficiently close as a time keeper to answer the purpose of an expensive Regulator costing from $200 to $500, in very many Jewelry establishments where economy is an object and when put into their best style of case, the Clock will compare favorably even in appearance with the more expensive ones.

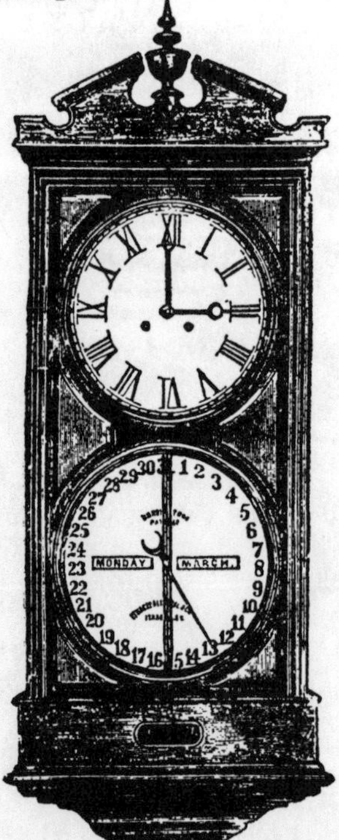


Calendar clocks for the rich man's library and the poor man's cottage, produced by the Ithaca Calendar Clock Company. Pictured here is catalogue page and cover and three of the ten models made by the Ithaca Company. TOP CENTER: Wall clock, priced at $20, in rosewood; in black walnut at $18. BOTTOM, CENTER: Farmer's model, priced at $11 plain and $13 with alarm attachment. BELOW, LEFT: A superior Library or bank model, offered at $40. Certain collectors in the category of specialists now seek examples of these calendar clocks. The Ithaca Company ceased operations in the 1890s.

cased clocks with Connecticut movements illustrated in this chapter is the "baseball" clock. This timepiece was made in the 1860s, perhaps immediately after the war between the States. Baseball, in almost every American city and town, was then a popular participant sport. This clock, thus far at least, seems to have escaped the notice of collectors of American sporting antiques. It is every bit as interesting as the famed Currier & Ives baseball print.

Comical clocks in cast iron cases were made by the Waterbury Clock Company and other Connecticut makers. There are three examples illustrated which at one time were thought to be foreign-made clocks. They are completely American both as to subject and manufacture. The cases were cast in Connecticut foundries, painted in Connecticut shops, and fitted with Connecticut movements of a special kind. All of these are "blinking-eye" clocks. Two of them, Sambo and Topsey, are obviously out of Christie's Minstrels and *Uncle Tom's Cabin*, respectively. The Continental is supposed to represent a Continental soldier. All three are one-day clocks. Other fancy cast-iron cased clocks, and some clocks in papier-maché cases, were made in Connecticut and perhaps also by New York City makers. Chauncey Jerome made some clocks in cast-iron cases, some plated with bronze or brass, and some painted. Rectangular mantel or shelf clocks of the 1870s were made of iron painted to simulate marble. Such clocks were usually topped with a bronze ornament. These clocks are related, but from the wrong side of the tracks, to the Dubec bronze clocks which were shipped to the United States in some numbers between 1800 and 1820. These are known as "Washington Memorial" clocks, and there are at least seven varieties, six of which pose a full-length bronze Washington beside a bronze box containing a clock movement. One of them has only a bust of Washington on an upright rectangular case. The 1876 Seth Thomas catalogue contains, in addition to pictures of cased clocks, a galaxy of clock ornaments including small busts of Venus, Tasso, Ariosto, Dante, Petrarch, Goethe, Schiller, and other notables.

A "corner clock" was made by the Atkins Manufacturing Company of Bristol in the 1850s. The case of this clock was designed for placement on a shelf set in the angle of two walls. The corner pillars are topped by a molding with angled corbels and the base is similarly constructed as to shape. This clock is illustrated. From

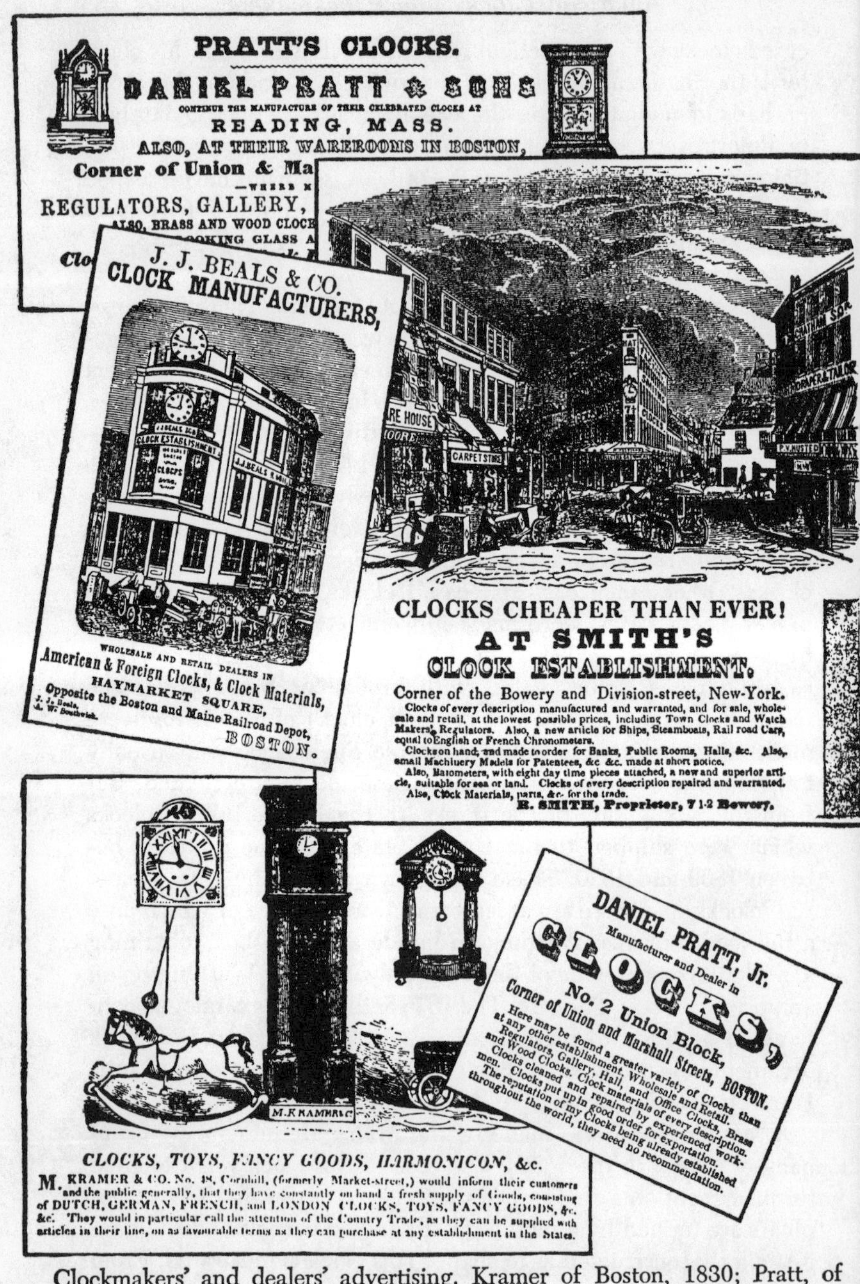


Clockmakers' and dealers' advertising. Kramer of Boston, 1830; Pratt, of Reading, Mass., and Boston, 1847 and 1849; J. J. Beals, Boston, 1849; Smith of New York, 1842.

*The useful Alarm-Bell.*] This is originally a Dutch invention, and by which a person may be enabled to rise at any time of the night; or know how time goes as well as by a clock, or watch, by observing the following directions

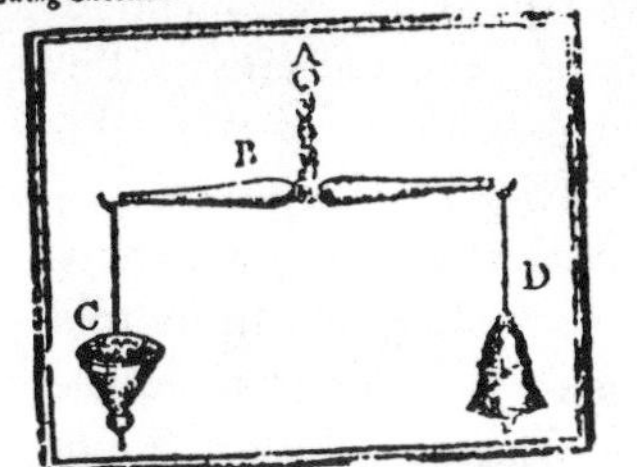


A is a small chain in the middle of a beam, and by which it hangs. B is a kind of a beam, like those belonging to scales. C a vessel made of either glass or tin, in the form described, which is to be filled with fine dry sand, the quantity to be more or less, according to the time you would rise: the vessel C is to have a small hole at the bottom, as in an hour glass, thro' which the sand is to pass. D is along at the opposite end of the beam B. When the vessel C is empty, the bell D is to be a very little heavier than C, by which means, after the sand is all discharged, the bell D becoming more weighty than C, the ballance instantly falls on that side, and the bell continues ringing for some time, and by which noise the person is called at the time required.

## DR. DAVID RITTENHOUSE.

THIS distinguished Astronomer and Philosopher, was a native of Pennsylvania, and for a long time a resident of this City. In early life he blended the pursuits of Science with the active employments of a Farmer, and Clock and Watch-Maker. In 1769, he united with several Members of the "American Philosophical Society," by invitation from that Body, and he, on that occasion, distinguished himself, by his ASTRONOMICAL CALCULATIONS, and by the comprehension of his mind. He succeeded Dr. FRANKLIN, as President of the "American Philosophical Society." He espoused the cause of American INDEPENDENCE. He discharged the duties of TREASURER of Pennsylvania, and DIRECTOR of the NATIONAL MINT, as well as his other public and private Duties, with entire satisfaction. He DIED, in the 64th Year of his Age, universally lamented.

Doctor RITTENHOUSE was eminently conspicuous in all his Mechanical Efforts. He produced several beautiful Time-Pieces, containing the Machinery of a Musical Clock, with a miniature Planetarium.

### THE RITTENHOUSE ASTRONOMICAL CLOCK.

This CLOCK is on an enlarged scale, containing Six Dials, one above the others, showing the Motions of all the Planets,—one in the centre, showing the Seconds, Minutes, Hours, Days of the Month, and Age of the Moon,—and one in each corner, showing the Phases of the Moon,—the Sun slow, and fast, and the position of the Orbit of the Earth.

This great Philosophical Curiosity was made for the late Mr. JOSEPH POTTS, who paid *Six Hundred and Forty Dollars* for it. In 1774, it was purchased by the late Mr. THOMAS PRIOR, of whom General HOWE was anxious to purchase it, he having offered *One Hundred and Twenty Guineas* for it, while the British were in possession of this City. The Ambassador of the Spanish Court, offered Mr PRIOR *Eight Hundred Dollars* for it, which he intended as a *present*, to the King of Spain.

After Mr. Prior's death, this valuable Clock passed into the hands of the late Professor BARTON, and after remaining for a long time, almost neglected, it was recently purchased by Dr. JAMES SWAIM, a gentleman of this City, who, we are gratified to learn, places a just estimate on this superior evidence of American Science and Skill.

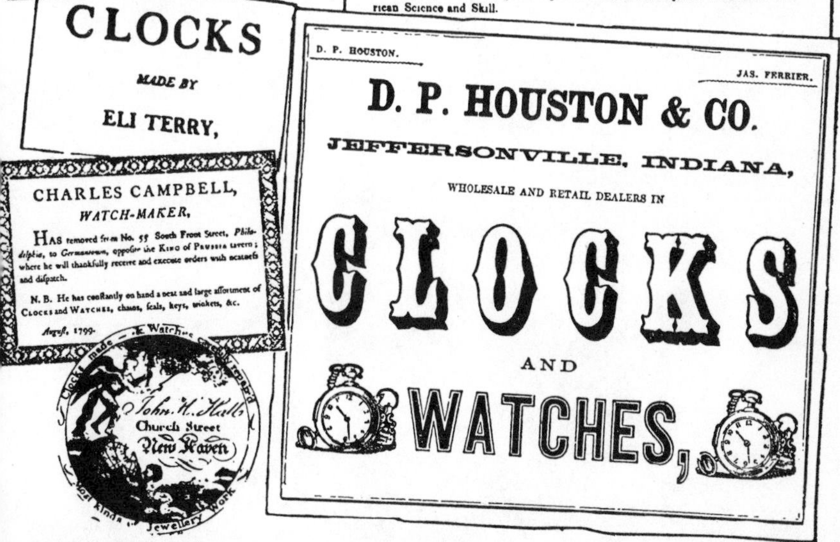


TOP: Directions for making a sand "alarum" from *The Golden Cabinet*, Philadelphia, 1793; eulogy on David Rittenhouse, stating that the now famous astronomical clock, pictured in Chapter X, originally made for Mr. Joseph Potts, and priced at $640, was "recently purchased" by Dr. Swaim. From *A History of Philadelphia*, by Daniel Bowen, 1839. BOTTOM: Small clock papers by Eli Terry and Charles Campbell; watch paper engraved by A. Doolittle, for John Hall of New Haven, *c.* 1789; Advertisement by Houston & Co., Jeffersonville, Indiana, from *Progress of the Republic*, 1856. Houston & Co. were wholesale distributors of Connecticut clocks.

a scanning of early catalogues, it appears that other Connecticut makers also produced corner clocks. Among the pictures in this chapter is a drawing of the Columbus clock, made of wood for the Columbian Exposition 1893, by the Bostwick & Burgess Manufacturing Company of Norwalk, Ohio. With this clock, we arrive at the end of as much of the American clock story as can be told here. It is hoped the words and pictures in Chapters I to X, the list of American clockmakers and the Glossary, Index, Bibliography which make up Chapters XI and XII, will serve to satisfy the hunger of many collectors in respect of information on American clocks and clockmakers, and to whet the appetite of others for the more detailed information that is waiting for them in books listed in the Bibliography. That this book may also serve as a paving stone for the writer of the final definitive history of American clocks and clockmaking is the fervent desire of the author.

CHAPTER

The following chapter is made up of thirty-two pages of half-tone illustrations of American clocks, now either reposing in private or public collections or in the hands of antiques dealers.

More than two hundred photographs, in addition to those pictured, have been supplied to us for this work. It is a matter of much regret that all of the pictures could not be included. The variety of clocks made by American makers, especially between the years 1800 to 1860, becomes more and more amazing as one studies the catalogues of the manufacturers and the photographs of clocks in collections. Almost daily new and hitherto unnoted, if not unknown, examples come to light. In editing the great mass of photographs submitted, an effort has been made to select outstanding examples of the most generally known types of clocks.

The captions which appear on each page with the photographs describe as briefly as possible the clocks pictured. In some cases the owners failed to give sizes and other pertinent information which many readers would like to have. Therefore, these omissions were unavoidable.

Special comment is, perhaps, in order concerning certain of the clocks in this chapter. The clock masterpiece of America, by David Rittenhouse, which is the first one pictured, is also mentioned on page 157 where comment about it, printed in 1839, is reproduced in facsimile. The clock beside it, by Dr. Christopher Witt of Germantown, Pennsylvania, is really a tall clock. It is seven feet eight inches high to provide for an unusually long fall of the heavy weights which drive it for eight days. It has a one and a quarter second pendulum. The clock pictured on page 165 has a very interesting record. These two views of the same clock show it with two different dials, the change being made, apparently, after it became the property of Henry Ford. An even more important clock by the same makers, C. & D. Forrer of Lampeter Square, Lancaster, Pennsylvania, is shown at the extreme right on page 187.

On page 173 is pictured an original pillar-and-scroll clock by Heman Clark of Plymouth, Connecticut, which must have been made in, or before, 1813, and at least three years before the so-called "original" pillar-and-scroll case was made for Eli Terry's thirty-hour, all-wood movement. There will, perhaps, be some weeping and wailing over the discovery of this clock with its original engraved label. Many who have emphatically credited the invention of the pillar and scroll to Eli Terry will want to defend their position and may even consider ignoring this signpost which points to the fact that, to the best of our present knowledge, H. Clark, or Heman Clark of Plymouth, Connecticut, made eight-day, brass movement pillar-and-scroll clocks before Eli Terry received his patent on his thirty-hour, all-wood movement.

No one who has believed Terry invented the pillar and scroll need defend his position. We have credited Terry with the invention and continued that crediting until the H. Clark pillar-and-scroll clock was discovered. Now we will remain convinced that Clark's is the first pillar and scroll until an earlier example by another maker is found. The science we use in collecting antiques must forever be just what science is to the scientist—what seems to be true in light of what we now know.

LEFT: America's finest clock, the masterpiece by David Rittenhouse, now owned by Drexel Institute of Technology, Philadelphia. Photograph by courtesy of the Philadelphia Museum of Art, Philadelphia. Clock described in text, Chapter III. RIGHT: Tall clock by Dr. Christopher Witt of Germantown, Pennsylvania, may date as early as 1725 or after 1750. This clock is seven feet eight inches tall and almost twenty inches wide. Ginsburg & Levy.

LEFT: Tall-case clock by Daniel Rose, Reading, Pennsylvania, *c.* 1780–1800. Eight-day, hour-strike, mahogany case. Owned by John L. Ruth. RIGHT: Tall-case clock by John Heintzelman, Manheim, Lancaster County, Pennsylvania, *c.* 1795. Moon-phase indicator under center. Eight-day, hour-strike, rope-wind. Walnut case. John L. Ruth.

LEFT: Exceptionally fine tall-case clock by Jacob Hostetter, Hanover, Pennsylvania. The many hands on the dial indicate "eastern" and "western" time and the time at Melbourne and Berlin. Case is mahogany, inlaid. This clock has a whispering gong that sounds every two minutes. Hour strike is on two tones of bells. Date is *c.* 1790–1800. RIGHT: Tall clock by Jacob Spangler, York, Pennsylvania, *c.* 1810–1820. Mahogany case, eight-day. L. S. Spangler.

Two tall-cased clocks from Maryland. LEFT: Mahogany-cased example by A. & W. Johnston, Hagerstown, *c.* 1800. RIGHT: Clock by George Woltz, Hagerstown. *c.* 1780. Mahogany case. L. S.

LEFT: Masterpiece of clock-case making by Jacob Bachman of Lampeter Square, Lancaster, Pennsylvania, housing a movement by C.&D. Forrer of the same locale. This clock, when sold at auction some years ago, bore the replacement dial here pictured with maker's name wrongly spelled "Farrar." The case was attributed to Randolph or Gostelow, of Philadelphia. RIGHT: Now in the Henry Ford Museum, the Forrer clock dial looks like this. It is still wrong, and the name is still Farrar instead of Forrer.

LEFT: Tall-case clock by Jacob Godshalk, Philadelphia. Brass dial, brass movement, hour strike, eight-day, moon phase (numerals are on the disk, not on the dial), sweep second hand, mahogany case. Date is *c.* 1768–1770. Owned by John L. Ruth. RIGHT: Tall-case clock in Sheraton-style case by Silas Hoadley. The Gothic arch cut in door and fitted with glass pane is probably a much later vandalism. Date may be 1808 to 1825. Essex Institute.

Two magnificent eight-day tall clocks in curly maple cases. LEFT: Clock by Jacob Eby, Manheim, Lancaster, Pennsylvania, in rare swell or bow-front case, having hour, day of month, and sweep second hands, moon phase, and hour strike. Date is *c.* 1800. Joe Kindig, Jr. RIGHT: Clock by Aaron Willard, approximately same date, or later. Separate second dial, moon-phase slot, and hour strike. Shreve, Crump & Low Company.

LEFT: Tall clock by John Fisher, York Town, Pennsylvania, *c.* 1765–1770. Brass dial, with sweep second hand, moon phase, and day-of-month slot. Time and strike. Walnut case. York County Historical Society. RIGHT: John Fisher's masterpiece, now at Yale University. This clock received special mention in the Baltimore press, 1790. Joe Kindig, Jr.

LEFT: One of the finest early American tall clocks known, made by Peter Stretch of Philadelphia, *c.* 1740. Note elaborately carved hood on the walnut case, and the belled dome. The style is William and Mary with admixture of classic columns. Brass dial, moon phase, second-indicating hand on dial, day-of-month slot, time and strike. Joe Kindig, Jr. RIGHT: Clock by Daniel Burnap of East Windsor, Connecticut. Engraved brass dial with second indicator and moon phase in slot. Case is by Chapin, the famed cabinetmaker. C. W. Lyon, Inc.

LEFT: Tall-case clock by Jacob Gorgas, near Ephrata, Lancaster County, Pennsylvania. Case and movement original, dial a replacement of *c.* 1840. Original dial would be of brass with molded spandrels. Second indicator, time, and strike. Case is walnut. Date *c.* 1765–1775. Owned by W. Earle Fulton. RIGHT: Tall-case clock by Silas Hoadley. Case of Sheraton style is not improved by the somewhat heavy and plain corner columns on the waist. Essex Institute.

LEFT: Seth Thomas, eight-day, brass movement, small tall-case clock. It is only sixty inches high. Believed to have been experimental, *c.* 1815–1820. Case is of that period. Formerly in E. L. Ford collection, now owned by John L. Ruth. RIGHT: Exquisitely proportioned small tall-case clock by John Bailey of Hanover, Massachusetts. It is only fifty inches high. Date is *c.* 1800–1810. Owned by L. S. Spangler. Both clocks are examples of the type now called "Grandmother." The Seth Thomas clock is time only; the Bailey is time and strike, with moon phase.

LEFT: Tall-case clock by George Hoff, Lancaster, Pennsylvania, *c.* 1765–1770. Brass thirty-hour movement, copper dial with chapter ring, and spandrels of pewter. Rope wind. Walnut case. John L. Ruth. RIGHT: Tall clock made by G. S. H. Bellerose of Three Rivers, Canada, either for, or as a memorial to, General Brock, killed in the War of 1812. Case is mahogany, inlaid. Date may be 1800 to 1820. L. S. Spangler.

LEFT: Pillar-and-scroll cased, eight-day brass movement by Heman Clark, Plymouth, Connecticut, *c.* 1810–1813. Case is 32⅜ inches high over all and 17½ inches wide. Pillars taper from 23/32 of an inch at base to 17/32 at top. Under this clock is the engraved label pasted inside the case. Owned by Mr. and Mrs. Frank Beaven. RIGHT: Eli Terry pillar-and-scroll cased thirty-hour wooden movement clock, *c.* 1816–1817. Case is 29½ inches high over all and 17¼ inches wide. This clock by Terry has centered pendulum (earlier models had off-center pendulums) and the dial carries a second hand where the exposed escape wheel appears on earlier models made six months before this one. The glass over-dial is convex in order to clear the center staff.

ABOVE, LEFT: Pillar-and-scroll clock by Ethel North (Note: Ethel North was a man, not a lady clockmaker!) *c.* 1820. Owned by L. S. Spangler. UPPER RIGHT: Modified pillar-and-scroll made by Marsh, Williams & Co., Dayton, Ohio, in 1830s. Stenciled dial, walnut wheels, ivory bearings. These makers were proud of having the only clock factory in the West. Owned by Frank V. Wray, Portland, Oregon. LOWER LEFT: Eli Terry pillar case with Masonic cresting. Probably a special casing job to capture the Masonic Lodge trade. C. W. Lyon, Inc.

TOP LEFT: Experimental clock by Eli Terry, 1816. Movement, weights, gong, and pendulum exposed through clear glass panel on which dial is painted. TOP RIGHT: Experimental Eli Terry clock, *c.* 1816, with dial exposing only escapement and pendulum. Two-part door with painted panel. These 1816 clocks came out before Terry's pillar-and-scroll. BOTTOM LEFT: Seth Thomas pillar-and-scroll. This has Terry's "patent" movement similar to that in clock at top left. The Thomas label is engraved, as are all the other labels in the clocks here pictured. The Seth Thomas pillar-and-scroll may be the same date, 1816, as the Terry above, right. Thomas purchased the Heman Clark shop in 1813. Thomas may have used the Clark pillar-and-scroll design before Eli Terry. L. S. Spangler and General Time Instruments Corporation.

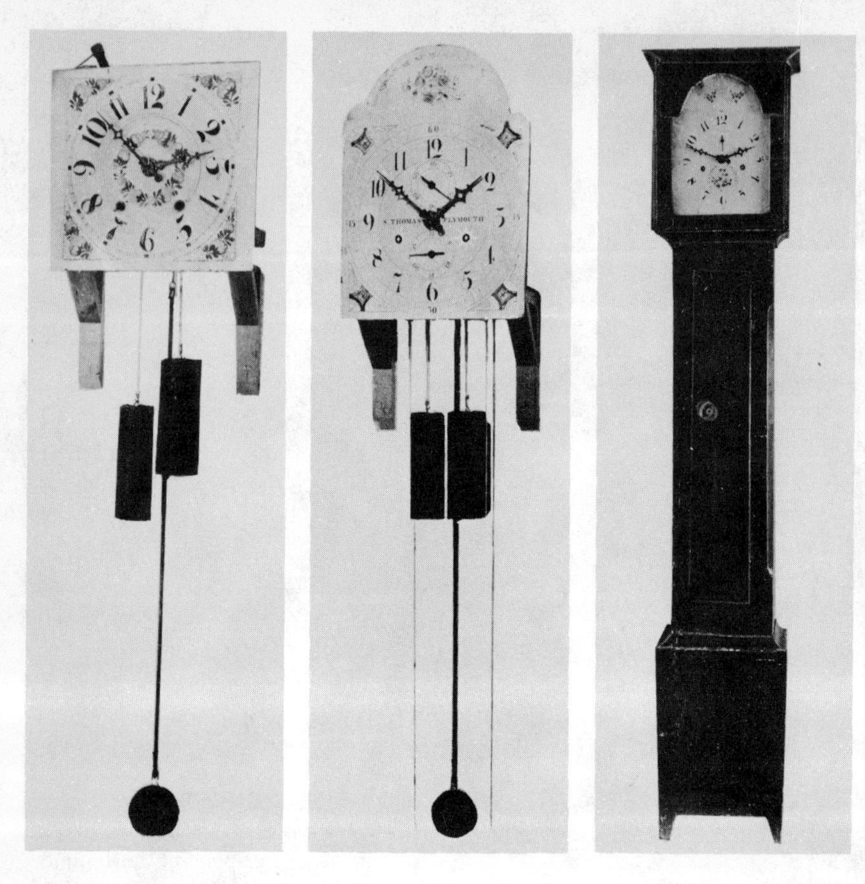

ABOVE, LEFT: Thirty-hour all-wooden movement hang-up clock with strike made by G. Daniels, Cincinnati, *c.* 1820, as a model for L. Watson, clockmaker, of same city. ABOVE, CENTER: Seth Thomas hang-up clock, *c.* 1812. It is a thirty-hour clock with time, second, month date, and strike. Wooden movement. Similar movements, cased by the purchasers in any cases they could have made, are identifiable by the dials and signature, S. Thomas, Plymouth. Weights are tin cans filled with stones! ABOVE, RIGHT: Thirty-hour wooden-movement tall-case clock made by Ephraim Downs for L. Watson, Cincinnati, 1818. Weights are tin cans filled with stones. Time, strike, and second indicator. All clocks on this page from the collection of Alden H. Wyatt, Joplin, Missouri.

UPPER LEFT: Mural or wall clock of "Parliament" type in pine case, japanned. Around the rim is lettered the motto *"Ab Hoc Momento Pendet Aeternitas, 1763."* Purchased by Samuel Dexter, 1764, for the First Parish, Dedham. Owned by the Dedham Historical Society. Maker unknown. UPPER RIGHT: Clock by Charles Young, Chambersburg, Pennsylvania, *c.* 1760s. See Chapter III. From Joe Kindig, Jr. LOWER LEFT: Portable clock by Peter Oosterhoudt, Kingston, New York, *c.* 1790. Time and strike, with repeater. Author's collection.

UPPER LEFT: Eli Terry experimental movement with exposed escapement and pendulum, in pillar-and-scroll case. Probably 1816. Owned by L. S. Spangler. UPPER RIGHT: Eli Terry Jr., carved Pillar-and-Crest clock, Plymouth, Connecticut., *c* 1820s. Made for the Canadian market. Same clock was made with carved American eagle. Mr. and Mrs. Frank Beaven. LOWER LEFT: Hanging mirror clock by Samuel Abbott, Boston, *c.* 1825–1830. L. S. Spangler.

UPPER LEFT: "Hour-glass" clock by Joseph Ives; one-day wagon-spring movement. The spring is a single leaf bow. UPPER RIGHT: Forestville Manufacturing Company "acorn" clock of dainty and delicate proportions. The painted glass tablet depicts the residence of J. C. Brown, important executive of the company. LOWER LEFT: Forestville Manufacturing Company late acorn type. All of these clocks are time and strike. L. S. Spangler, Hagerstown, Maryland.

ABOVE, LEFT: Atkins Clock Co., thirty-day wagon spring, made under Joseph Ives's patent, 1853–1858. Original case, with label. Time only. UPPER RIGHT: C. & L. Ives eight-day brass-movement shelf clock; plates of riveted brass strips; pendulum swings in the center column behind which is a mirror. Date is *c.* 1830–1836. LOWER LEFT: Double steeple or "two-story Gothic" clock by Birge & Fuller, Bristol, Connecticut, *c.* 1844. Movement is the Ives eight-day wagon spring with roller pinions. From the collection of Albert Bosshart, Jr., Clifton Springs, New York.

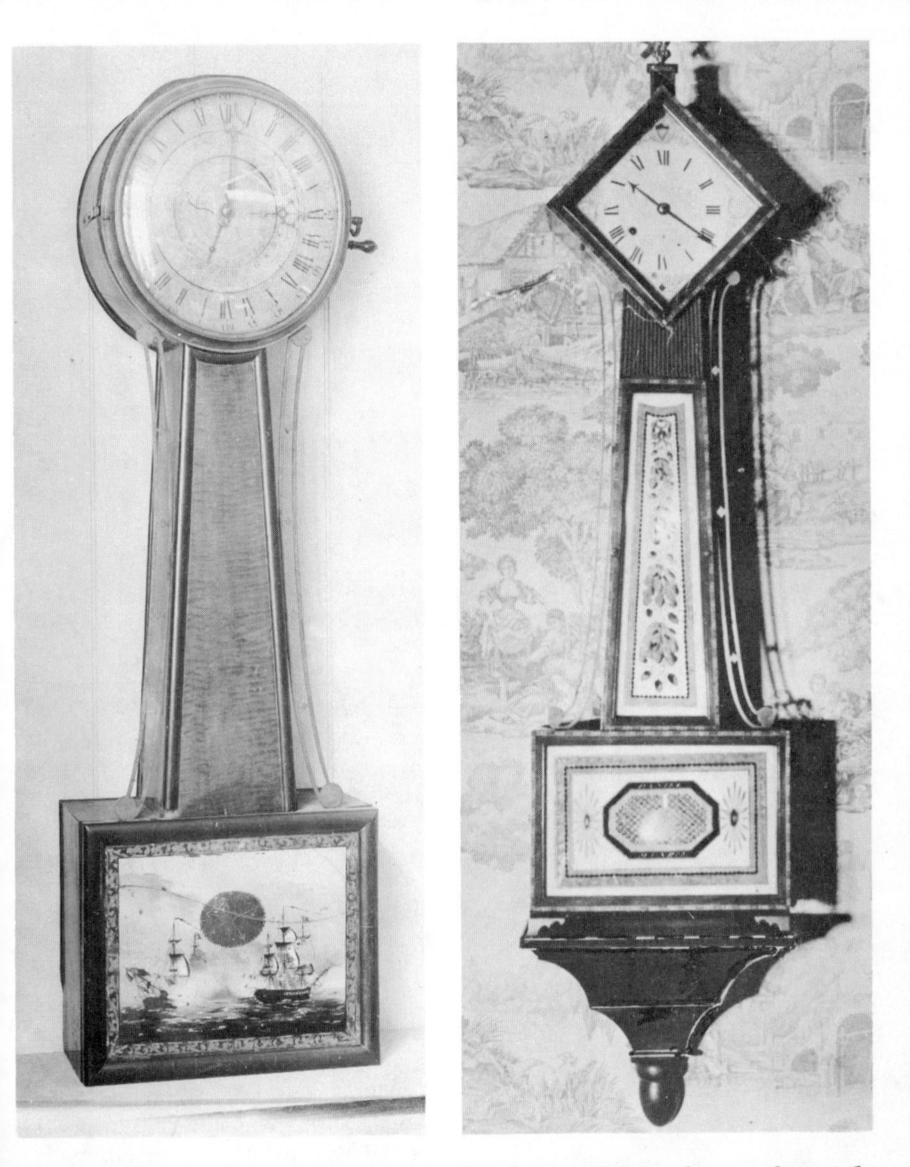

LEFT: Banjo clock by James Ferguson, London, *c.* 1770, perhaps earlier, and certainly not later than 1776. The glass panel in the bottom is not original; bottom probably had wood panel. Essex Institute. RIGHT: "Diamond-head" banjo, a rare variant of the Willard-type banjo. Made originally as a mantel clock, it is shown resting on a bracket shelf for use as a wall clock. C. W. Lyon, Inc. The Ferguson banjo has twenty-four-hour dial and astronomical indicator.

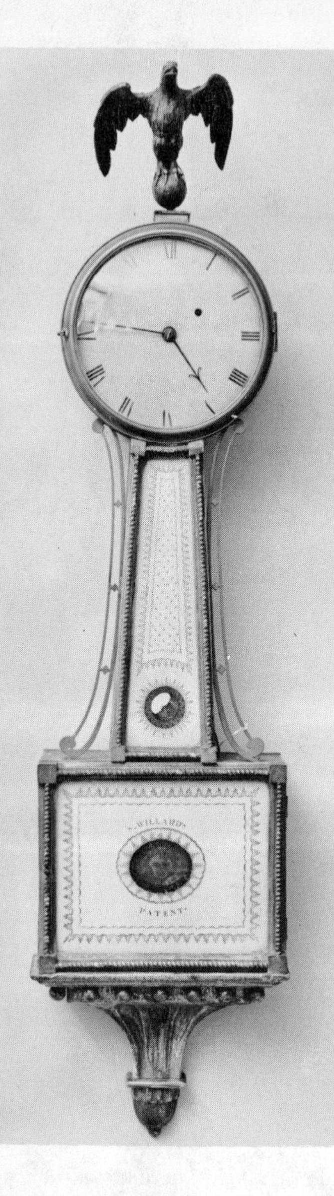

LEFT: Simon Willard presentation banjo with cream-and-gold panels, or tablets, painted on glass, and partially gilded (parcel-gilt) casing. The eagle is probably a finial added after 1816. The clock may date from *c.* 1800–1810. RIGHT: Shelf or mantel banjo of lyre form with painted panel. Case part forming lyre is beautifully carved. The domed tower finial houses the striking hammer; gong is the dome. Made by Sawin & Dyar, Boston, *c.* 1815–1820. C. W. Lyon, Inc.

ABOVE: Aaron Willard shelf clock with half-kidney paneled door. Case style is Sheraton. ABOVE, RIGHT: Violin clock by Seth Thomas, after 1855. Courtesy of the Philadelphia Museum of Art. RIGHT: Lyre wall clock by Forestville Manufacturing Co. in the collection of L. S. Spangler.

TOP, LEFT: Exceptionally important mantel type "case-on-case" clock by William Fitz, Portsmouth, New Hampshire, *c.* 1765–1770. Brass dial, time only. TOP, RIGHT: Simon Willard, wall clock; brass dial, time, and strike. Probably one of Willard's very earliest fine wall clocks. LOWER RIGHT: Mantel clock with half kidney front, by James South, Charlestown, Massachusetts, *c.* 1800–1810. I. Sack.

UPPER LEFT: Heman Clark, Plymouth, Connecticut, double-pillar without scroll, *c.* 1810–1811. Eight-day brass movement, time and strike and second dial. Dr. Amos G. Avery. Clock measures 26 inches high by 16¾ wide. UPPER RIGHT: Unique Simon Willard timepiece of *c.* 1790, brass dial with engraved tab bearing maker's name. Casing is *c.* 1835. I. Sack. LOWER LEFT: Case-on-case mantel clock by James Dakin, Boston, *c.* 1800–1810. Case is beautifully made. Dial is metal, painted. I. Sack.

LEFT: S. Willard "light house" clock, 28 inches high to top of finial on glass dome. Mahogany base and column; brass ornaments. "PATENT" painted on column, *c.* 1800–1810. I. Sack. CENTER: S. Willard "presentation" banjo of almost unique qualities. Note the side brackets and the bottom bracket. Mr. and Mrs. Roland Vaughn. RIGHT: Pillar or "coffin" clock by an unknown maker, but of New England origin. Case is inlaid. Date *c.* 1800–1810.

LEFT: Magnificent tall-case clock by Thomas Walker, Fredericksburg, Virginia, *c.* 1770. Brass dial with rocking ship, second hand, and day-of-month slot. Time and strike. I. Sack. CENTER: Tall clock by James Perrigo, *c.* 1795–1820 (by either Perrigo, father or son), owned by Dedham Historical Society. RIGHT: Superlatively cased tall clock by Christian Forrer, Lampeter Square, Lancaster, Pennsylvania, *c.* 1766. Case by Bachman; brass dial, sweep second hand, day-of-month slot, and moon phase. This is a finer example than the Forrer clock in Ford Museum Collection. Lancaster County Historical Society.

UPPER RIGHT: "Paper" or label from a clock by A. Munger, Auburn, New York, *c.* 1825–1835, showing a strip of the wallpaper with which Munger always lined his cases. BALANCE OF PAGE: Clocks from the great collection of Willis R. Michael, Red Lion, Pennsylvania. Notable are the Aaron Willard "case-on-case" clock flanking display to right, the candle-stand clock by Terryville Manufacturing Co. at left, and the tall-case clock by William Crane.

TOP LEFT: Pennsylvania pillar-and-scroll by J. D. Custer, Norristown. C. E. Landis, Newburgh, New York. CENTER: Off center pendulum pillar-and-scroll by Seth Thomas. RIGHT: Organ grinder, Gambrinus, and lion "blinking-eye" clocks. Francis B. Platt, Schenectady, New York. BOTTOM LEFT: Stovepipe clock by Asa Munger, Auburn, New York. C. E. Landis, Newburgh, New York. CENTER AND RIGHT: Face and movement view of Joseph Ives's wagon-spring clock in Phyfe-type case.

LEFT: Tall-case clock by Ellis Chandlee, Nottingham, Pa., *c.* 1799. Walnut case ninety-five inches high. Owned by James C. Lincoln. Pictured by courtesy Edward Chandlee, author of *Six Quaker Clockmakers.* TOP CENTER: Mirror panel clock by Markham & Case, Columbia, S. C. From William McKoy, Chester, S. C. TOP RIGHT: "Off center" Seth Thomas, *c.* 1816, in pillar-and-scroll case. From John L. Ruth. IMMEDIATELY ABOVE: Clock advertisement by Leslie & Price, Philadelphia, 1795.

TOP LEFT: Solid acorn cased eight-day "equalized power-spring clock warranted not to fail" by J. C. Brown, Bristol, Connecticut, 1850. The Edward Ingraham Collection has several such examples. This one is signed "Forestville Manufacturing Co." TOP RIGHT: A flat pillar-and-scroll case by Jerome, Darrow & Co., Bristol, Connecticut, *c.* 1825. A variant of this casing, taller, with the bottom tablet almost the size of center tablet, was made by J. Taber of Saco, Maine. Thirty-hour, noisy or "groaner" type movement. Time and strike. Owned by Dudley S. Ingraham, Bristol, Connecticut. LEFT: Case by Dr. Titus Merriman. (Other examples are pictured in line drawings elsewhere in this volume.) Scores of this basic style case, no two alike, were found a century after their making. Originally used examples are excessively rare. This from the collection of Edward Ingraham of Bristol, Connecticut. It is 30 inches high and 11 inches wide.

TOP LEFT: Magnificently cased shelf clock designed by Elias Ingraham, master cabinetmaker who founded the E. Ingraham Clock Company. This case made *c.* 1829 for movements by Ephraim Downs. Edward Ingraham of Bristol, Connecticut. TOP RIGHT: Eight-day brass-movement shelf clock by Chauncey & Noble Jerome, 1834–1839. Dudley S. Ingraham, Bristol, Connecticut. Both are large clocks, over 37½ inches high. Both are time and strike. BOTTOM, LEFT: Small shelf clock with "all-over" transfer glass panel forming dial opening and "tablet." Made by New England Clock Co., Bristol, Connecticut, 1851. Time only, 11 inches tall. Edward Ingraham.

CHAPTER

PERHAPS the first list of American clockmakers was compiled by Mrs. Hudson Moore for her pioneer volume *The Old Clock Book*, published by Frederick A. Stokes, 1911, and reprinted in 1936 by the Tudor Publishing Company. The second list, an enlargement of Mrs. Moore's, was compiled by Wallace Nutting for his *Clock Book* and again enlarged for inclusion in his *Furniture Treasury*, Volume III. Britten lists certain American clockmakers in his large volume of world-wide scope. Numerous local historical societies have published monographs on the clockmakers of towns and counties. Some state and national institutions have published lists compiled from newspapers of record in certain cities and regions, trade account books, and so forth.

Names of clockmakers (or any other artisans for that matter) derive from one or more of the following data sources: (1) Work of record—in this case actual clocks, bearing name of maker on dial, frequently the place of making, infrequently the date or a number and, on even rarer occasions (save in the case of factory-made clocks), a paper pasted inside the case giving maker's name, sometimes the name of the printer of the paper or label, and at times the label of the maker of the case. Often the style of the case is a clue to the approximate date the clock was made but the type and kind of movement and type and kind of dial are generally more conclusive guides to the date of making, if not the date of casing. (2) Tax lists and other civil records of counties and states, when preserved. (3) Newspaper advertising of and by clockmakers. (4) Editorial mention of clocks and clockmakers in newspapers and periodicals. (5) Church records (births, marriages, baptisms, burials, et cetera). (6) Account books of stores, shops, tradesmen, and artisans who had dealings with clockmakers, and account books of individuals revealing transactions with clockmakers; actual account books of clockmakers and of brass founders who dealt with them. Account books of decorators, stencil cutters, and specialists also yield valuable data in respect of special services rendered to clockmakers. (7) Town and city directories.

These sources are generally at the service of any and all individuals desirous of doing research work on lists of clockmakers. In compiling the following list of some three thousand names of clockmakers at work in the American colonies and federal states, all previously recorded clockmakers were checked with one or more of the above listed sources. Acknowledgment and many thanks are hereby extended to the New York Public Library, the New York Historical Society, and to the American Antiquarian Society, for permission to check innumerable city and town directories of early dates and hundreds of files of early newspapers. The directory check included the directories of Chicago, St. Louis, Detroit, Indianapolis, Louisville, Cincinnati, Cleveland, Pittsburgh, and scores of directories from Eastern cities and towns. This check was not, however, the most comprehensive effort in the research undertaking for this book. The co-operation of more than five hundred historical societies in the United States was solicited in order to determine the names of any actual clockmakers at work prior to 1860 and to scan all local sources in order to isolate such names. One hundred fourteen historical societies finally co-operated in the undertaking. Deep and profound thanks are extended to these organizations, every one of which deserves mention here and is so mentioned at the end of the list of clockmakers.

The checking and rechecking of clockmakers' names revealed many discrepancies with previously published lists. Therefore, in order to keep this present list within the realm of reasonable accuracy, the following standards have been set:

Dates, except when specific dating is possible, are given in, or within, decades. Thus a clockmaker listed as working "1800s to 1820s" may have worked from 1800 to 1829 or, within these decade limits, worked from 1809 to 1821. If the date is simply "1800s," then the time of working is within that decade, whether it was one year or ten.

Every city and town did not, in the early years of directory publishing, have a new directory each year. Sometimes these compendiums were published at five- and even ten-year intervals. Most directories were compiled the year preceding date of issue. We have found certain clockmakers listed in directories dated 1830 who, according to civil and other records, had died the year before or had moved to other locales. When a date is preceded by c. (*circa*) it means "around" that date or about that date. When one date only is given, that date represents the year, and the only year, concerning which information was found. When the first date is specific, followed by a date designating a decade, then the first date marks the now-known beginning of work but indicates that the end of the work period is not yet certain. When the date begins with a decade and ends with a specific date, the reverse is true. Where no date or dates can be given, the symbol "n.d." (no date) is used. Similarly, when no place is known, the symbol "n.p." (no place) is given. On occasion "n.p." is followed by a probable place and "n.d." by an approximate date. At times, where neither of these devices are used, additional information such as "tall clocks" is given. This is intended for use in broad-gauge guidance. Tall clockmaking, generally, ceased about 1840. Very few, indeed, were made after that date. Hence a "no-date" maker whose work is represented by a tall clock was most likely working not later than 1840. Yet some makers, in small towns and in pioneer districts, made tall clocks up to the 1860s.

Some of the names in the list of clockmakers bear witness to the fact that not all our clockmakers stayed put in one place. Many of them worked in several places, and some of them moved from fifty to one thousand miles in the course of their life's work. Also, if space permitted, we could list the other trades and services these clockmakers followed and rendered. Almost one thousand of those listed were also either silversmiths, goldsmiths, watchmakers, cameo cutters, seal-makers and engravers, plate engravers, jewelers, and makers of mathematical and other instruments—way-wisers, smoke jacks, keys, locks, guns, spinning wheels, and baby cradle rockers.

None of the names in the list (or at least so aver some one hundred and sixty-seven separate researchers) is given unless there is a clock of record bearing the name of the man, the firm, or the company, or there is mention of work as a clockmaker in one of the sources mentioned in this preface to the list. Yet this present list, admittedly, is woefully incomplete. Even as we go to press an additional thirty-nine names are being set for inclusion in it. It is planned that new editions of this book will have the accumulated additions to the list added. Every reader is invited to (1) check the list with any clocks owned, or data held, and to report any differences or additions that should be made. Address the author in care of the publishers, New York City, and (2) report any names of clockmakers in any city or town anywhere in the United States known to have worked prior to 1876. By such co-operative effort we may someday have a list of clockmakers which we may boast of as being 90 per cent correct and inclusive.

We wish to thank the following students and clock collectors for supplying names of hitherto unlisted clockmakers in many sections of our country: Edward Ingraham, John L. Ruth, Lockwood Barr, Roy Fitzgerald, Robert L. Gage, Frank P. Boyer, James A. Blaisdell, David C. Hill, Albert L. Partridge, George DeCou, Philip H. English, L. S. Spangler, Willis R. Michael, Alden H. Wyatt, John J. Bowman, Mark E. Shanaberger, George B. Davis, Rhea Mansfield Knittle, Hamilton K. Wheeler, Samuel H. Barrington, Richard C. Newcomb, J. E. Coleman, George B. Cutten, Clinton A. McGlamery, M. H. Van Dyk, Roy A. Cann, Arthur E. James, William D. McCain, William J. Hamilton, Arthur U. Stevenson, Herbert Rand, Charles A. Carruth, Edward E. Chandlee, Edward M. Mitchell, Albert Bosshart, Jr., Joseph S. Henderson, Amos G. Avery, Paul G. Darrot, Frederick Smith, Frank V. Wray, Stewart Dow, Mrs. Frank Beaven, Allene Gebhard, Abbie E. Kendall, Mrs. William Mansfield, Gertrude Hassler, Elsie A. Choate, Hazel M. Griffin, Edith J. Backus, Edith Beard Cannon, Caroline Crutcher, Vette Watson, Ethel M. Ryan, Kathryn Kent, Allen Wise, Donald F. Staib, Hiram E. Deats, Joe Kindig, Jr., Samuel W. Jennings, Andrew Shiland, John Schenk, Harold A. Barnhart, Francis B. Platt, George D. Smith, and William A. McKoy.

ABBETS, JAMES: Albany, N.Y., 1760
ABBEY, DAVID: Pittsburgh, Pa., 1830s
ABBOTT, MOSES: Sutton, N.H., 1820s
ABBOTT, S.: Boston, 1820s–1830s

ABEL: ABBEL: ABELE: see Appel
ADAMS, CHARLES: Erie, Pa., 1860s
ADAMS, JONAS: Rochester, N.Y., 1830s
ADAMS, NATHAN: Danvers, Mass., 1780s to 1790; Boston, 1790s–1820s
ADAMS, SAMUEL: Boston, 1825
ADAMS, THOMAS: Baltimore, 1800s
ADAMS (WILLIAM) & EATON (SAMUEL): Boston, 1815–1820
ADAMS, WILLIAM: Boston, 1810–1825
AGAR, EDWARD: New York, 1760s. Maker and dealer
AIKINSON (OR ATKINSON), P.: Concord, Mass., 1790s
ALBERT, JOHN: Huntington Twp, York (now Adams) County, Pa. Tall clocks, n.d.
ALBRIGHT, R. E.: Flushing, L.I., 1850s
ALDEN & ELDRIDGE: Bristol, Conn., 1820
ALLEBACH, JACOB: Philadelphia, 1820s–1840s
ALLEBACH, M. B.: Philadelphia, 1790s–1800s. Also recorded in 1770s
ALLEN, ALEXANDER: Rochester, N.Y., 1850s–1860s. Manufacturer
ALLEN, JAMES: Boston, from 1680s to *c.* 1700
ALLEN, JARED: Rochester, N.Y., 1840s
ALLEN, JOHN: New York City, 1790s–1800s
ALLEN, WILLIAM: Annapolis and Port Tobacco, Md., 1773–*c.* 1780s
ALLYN, JOHN: Hartford, Conn., *c.* 1650. *See* Van Allyn
ALMY & WALL: *See* Wall, William A.
ALMY, JAMES: New Bedford, Mass., 1830s
ALRICHS, JACOB: Wilmington, Del., *c.* 1795–1800s. Tall case and shelf clocks
ALRICHS, JONAS: Wilmington, Del., 1780s–1797. Tall clocks only
ALRICHS & M'CLARY: Wilmington, Del., 1810–1813
ALTMORE, MARSHALL: Philadelphia, 1830s
AMANA CLOCKS: Made by members of a European sectarian group at Buffalo, N.Y., 1843–1855; and at Iowa County, Iowa, thereafter. Sect is still active in Iowa. A clock by the Amana group at Buffalo is shown on page 116
AMANT, FOSTER: Philadelphia, 1790s
AMES, HORACE: New York City, 1850s
AMIDON, L.: Bellows Falls, Vt., 1850s–1860s
ANDERSON, DAVID D.: Marietta, Ohio, 1825–1835
ANDERSON, DAVID M.: Waynesburg (now Honeybrook), Pa., 1830–1860
ANDREWS, ELON: Utica, N.Y., 1820s
ANDREWS, F. C.: New York City, 1840s

ANDREWS, L. M. & F. C.: Bristol, Conn., 1837–1843. Manufacturers
ANDREWS, N. & T.: Meriden, Conn., 1830s. Manufacturers
ANGSTAT, ADAM: N.d., n.p. Tall clock
ANNIN, M.: New York City, 1786
ANSONIA (BRASS &) CLOCK CO.: Ansonia, Conn., from 1855
ANTAME, JOSEPH A.: Philadelphia, last half eighteenth century
ANTHONY, ISAAC: Newport, R.I. Dealer, 1730s
ANTHONY, L. D.: Providence, R.I., 1848
APPEL, JOHN ELIAS: Dover, Pa., 1760s–1780
APPLEWHITE, WILLIAM: Columbia, S.C., 1820s; Camden, S.C., 1830s
ARCHER, WILLIAM: New York City, 1820s–1830s
ARMSTRONG, THOMAS: Brooklyn, N.Y., 1830s–1840s
ARNOLD, JACOB: Philadelphia, 1840s
ARNOLD, JARED: Amber, N.Y., 1825–1840s
ASBY, JAMES: Boston, 1770s, advertised 1771 and 1773
ASH, LAWRENCE: Philadelphia, 1762
ASHBY (OR ASBY) JAMES: Boston, 1760s–1770s
ASHTON, SAMUEL: Philadelphia, 1790s
ASKEW, JAMES: Charleston, S.C., 1770s–1790s
ATHERTON, OTIS: New York City, 1790s
ATKINS, ALDEN A.: (also ATKINS & ALLEN and ALDEN A. ATKINS & Co.) Bristol, Conn., Manufacturer, 1837–1846
ATKINS & ALLEN: Bristol, Conn., 1820s
ATKINS & CO., I.: Bristol, Conn., 1847–1857
ATKINS & NORTON: Bristol, Conn., n.d.
ATKINS CLOCK MFG. CO.: Bristol, Conn., 1855–1857
ATKINS CLOCK CO.: Bristol, Conn., 1859–1879
ATKINS & DOWNS: Bristol, Conn., 1831–1832. Eight-day wooden movement shelf clocks
ATKINS, ELDRIDGE G.: Bristol, Conn., 1838–1842
ATKINS, IRENUS: Bristol, Conn., 1830–1856. Brass mantel and wagon spring
ATKINS, JOEL: Middletown, Conn., 1770s
ATKINS & CO., MERRITT: Bristol, Conn., 1847–1856
ATKINS & PORTER: Bristol, Conn., 1840–1846
ATKINS, ROLLIN: Bristol, Conn., 1825
ATKINS, R. & I.: Bristol, Conn., 1833–1837
ATKINS & SON: Bristol, Conn., *c.* 1870
ATKINS & WELTON: Bristol, Conn., 1835–1836
ATKINS, WHITING & CO.: Bristol, Conn., 1850–1854. Fine brass and wagon spring
ATKINSON, ANNA MARIA LEROY: Lady clockmaker, Lancaster, Pa.,

1740s. Married Wilmer Atkinson, cutler, 1749. Made clocks at Lancaster with name of husband on dial. She was daughter of Abraham LeRoy, (Swiss) clockmaker of Lancaster. Finally moved to Baltimore with husband. May be the Anna Maria Atkinson listed as clockmaker, Baltimore, 1790s to 1810s

ATKINSON, JAMES: Boston, 1745–1756

ATKINSON, LEROY: Baltimore, 1820s–1830s

ATKINSON, M. & A.: Baltimore, 1800s

ATKINSON, M. & W.: Baltimore, 1780s–1790s

ATKINSON, WILMER: *See* Atkinson, Anna Maria LeRoy. Worked at Lancaster, Pa., 1740s–1750s. Cutler by trade. Clocks with his name made by his wife

ATMAR, RALPH: Charleston, S.C., *c.* 1790s–1810s

ATTMORE, MARSHALL: Philadelphia, 1820s–1840

ATWOOD & BRACKETT: Littleton, N.H., 1850s–1860s

ATWOOD, B. W.: Plymouth, Mass., 1860s

AUSTIN, BENJAMIN: Kalamazoo, Mich., 1840s

AUSTIN, ISAAC: Philadelphia, 1785–1805. Near Chester, Pa., *c.* 1780

AUSTIN, ORRIN: Waterbury, Conn., 1820s

AVERY, JOHN: Boston, 1720s

AVERY, JOHN: Preston, Conn., 1740s to 1794

AYERS, ALEX: Lexington, Ky., 1790s–1810s

AYERS, HAMILTON: New Holland, Lancaster County, Pa., *c.* 1820–1840

AYERS, SAMUEL: Lexington, Ky., 1790s–1820s

BABBITT, H. W.: Providence, R.I., 1848

BABCOCK & CO.: Philadelphia, 1830s

BABCOCK, GEORGE: Providence, R.I., 1830s–1850s. Probably a dealer

BACH, VALENTINE: Frederick, Md., 1790s

BACH, VALENTINE: Hagerstown, Md. Advertised in 1798

BACHELDER, EZRA: Danvers, Mass., 1790s–1840

BACHMAN, JACOB & JOHN: Father and son, Lampeter, Lancaster, Pa., were not clockmakers but superior cabinetmakers making cases for Lancaster County clockmakers. On occasion they would trade cases for movements, case the movements so traded, and sell clocks with the name Bachman on the dial. Worked (Jacob) 1766–1790s, (John) 1790s–1840s. John also had a son John who worked 1818–1850s. All made clock cases and marketed clocks with their names on dials

BACKES, J. P.: Charleston, S.C., 1850s

BACON, JOHN: Bristol, Conn., 1834–5

BACON, SAMUEL: Annapolis, Md., 1752
BADDER, ISAAC: Dayton, Ohio, 1820s–1840s
BADGER, JAMES: Brooklyn, N.Y., 1840s
BADMAN, JOSEPH: Colebrookdale, Pa., 1780s
BADOLLET, PAUL: New York, 1790s
BAGNALL, BENJAMIN: Boston, *c.* 1710–1740. One of the early New England makers of tall-case clocks
BAGNALL, BENJAMIN JR.: Boston, 1760s–1770s
BAGNEL, SAMUEL: Boston, 1740–1760
BAILEY & BROTHER: Utica, N.Y., 1840s
BAILEY, CALVIN: Hanover, Mass., 1800s–1810s
BAILEY, E. S.: Abbeville, S.C., 1840s; Newberry, S.C., 1850s–1860s
BAILEY, G. S. & CO.: Danbury, Conn., 1860s
BAILEY, GAMALIEL: New York City, 1820s; Cincinnati, Ohio, 1830s–1840s
BAILEY, JOHN: Hanover, Mass., *c.* 1770s; Lynn, Mass., 1780s–1790s
BAILEY, JOHN, JR.: New Bedford, Mass., 1790s–1820s
BAILEY & OWEN: Abbeville, S.C., 1840s–1850s
BAILEY & PARKER: Rutland, Vt., 1850s–1860s
BAILEY & WARD: New York, 1830s
BAILEY, WILLIAM: Philadelphia, *c.* 1816–1840s
BAILEY, WILLIAM, JR.: Philadelphia, 1816–1822
BAILY, EMMOR: London Grove (Chester County), Pa., 1790s
BAILY, JOEL: Bradford (Chester County), Pa., 1775–1790
BAKER, ALEXANDER: New York, 1850s
BAKER, BENJAMIN: Philadelphia, 1820s
BAKER, ELEAZER: Ashford, Conn., 1780s to 1830s
BAKER, GEORGE: Providence, R.I., 1824–1848
BALCH, BENJAMIN: Salem, Mass., 1790s–1800s; Boston, 1810s–1830s
BALCH (JAMES) & SON: Salem, Mass., 1830s
BALCH & LAMSON: Salem, Mass., 1840s
BALCH & SON: Boston, 1830s
BALCH, CHARLES: Newburyport, Mass., from *c.* 1810. ( ? )
BALCH, DANIEL: Newbury, Mass., 1760s–1780. Also worked at Haverhill, Mass. An original bill for a Daniel Balch clock is dated Newbury, 1768
BALCH, DANIEL, JR.: Newbury and Newburyport, Mass., *c.* 1780s–1820s
BALCH, EBENEZER: Wethersfield and Hartford, Conn., 1740s to 1790s
BALCH, JAMES: Salem, Mass., 1820s–1860s
BALCH, JOSEPH: Wethersfield, Conn., 1782–1794
BALCH, MOSES: Lowell, Mass., 1830s

BALCH, THOMAS: Newburyport and Salem, Mass., 1820s–1830s
BALDWIN & JONES: Boston, *c.* 1810–1820
BALDWIN, ANTHONY WAYNE: Lampeter Square, Lancaster, Pa., 1810–1850
BALDWIN, EBENEZER: Nashua, N.H., 1810s–1830s
BALDWIN, GEORGE: Sadsburyville (Chester County), Pa., 1802–1844
BALDWIN, HARLAN: Sadsburyville (Chester County), Pa., 1800s
BALDWIN, JABEZ: Boston, 1800s
BALDWIN, JEDDEDIAH: Hanover, N.H., *c.* 1790–1800; Rochester, N.Y., *c.* 1830s
BALDWIN, S. S. & SON: New York, 1820s–1830s
BALDWIN, THOMAS F. H.: Downingtown and Coatesville, Pa., 1830–1859
BALER, JOHN: Northampton, Pa., n.d.
BANKS, EDWARD: Portland, Me., 1830s.
BANSTEIN, JOHN: Philadelphia, *c.* 1790
BARBER, JAMES: Philadelphia, 1840s–1850s
BARBES & WELCH: Bristol, Conn., n.d.
BARBORKA, J.: Iowa City, Iowa, 1870s–1900s. Mostly tower clocks
BARKER, B. B.: New York, 1780s–1800s
BARKER, WILLIAM: Boston, 1800–1813
BARKLAY, J. & J. S.: Baltimore, 1810s–1820s
BARNES, B. D.: Oswego, N. Y., 1850s–1860s
BARNES & BACON: Bristol, Conn., 1834–1840
BARNES & BAILEY: Berlin, Conn., 1830s
BARNES & CO., PHILIP: Bristol, Conn., 1836–1837. Lockwood Barr reports this firm as successors to Barnes & Bartholomew; firm made up of Henry Merriman, George Merriman, and Rensselear Upson
BARNES & CO. (Thomas Jr., Wm. Johnson, & Willys Roberts, a son of Gideon): Bristol, Conn., *c.* 1819–1823. Made tall clocks
BARNES & JEROME: Bristol, Conn., 1833
BARNES & WATERMAN: Bristol, Conn., 1811–1812
BARNES, BARTHOLOMEW, & CO.: Bristol, Conn., 1830s
BARNES, DARROW & CO.: Bristol, Conn., 1838–1840
BARNES, EDWARD M.: Bristol, Conn., 1834–1845
BARNES, L. M. & CO.: North Adams, Mass., 1850s–1860s
BARNES, STEPHEN: New Haven, Conn., 1840s–1850s
BARNES, THOMAS: Bristol, Conn. Most active *c.* 1810–1820, but apparently working over long period, 1795 to 1850
BARNES, TIMOTHY: Litchfield, Conn., 1760s–1820; at Clinton, N.Y., *c.* 1825

Barnes, Thomas, Jr.: Bristol, Conn., 1811–1840

Barnes, William H.: New Haven, Conn., 1840s–1850s

Barnhart, Simon: Kingston, Ross County, Ohio, 1840s–1850s

Barns, John: Anne Arundel County, Md. Bond servant workman with Kensey Johns, 1756

Barnhill, Robert: Philadelphia, n.d.

Barnitz, A. E.: York, Pa., 1850s

Barr, John: Port Glasgow, Wayne County, N.Y., n.d. Prior to *c.* 1840

Barragant, Peter: Philadelphia, 1820s–1830s

Barrell, Colborn: Boston, 1770s

Barrow, Samuel: Philadelphia, 1771

Barrows, James M.: Tolland, Conn., 1830s

Barry, Standish: Baltimore, *c.* 1784–1810

Bartholomew & Barnes: Bristol, Conn., 1830s

Bartholomew, Brown & Co.: Bristol, Conn., 1833–1834

Bartholomew, E. & G.: Bristol, Conn., 1820s

Bartholomew, George W.: Bristol, Conn., 1833–1845

Bartholomew, Hills & Brown: Forestville, Conn., 1830s. (Became E. N. Welch Manufacturing Co.)

Barton, Benjamin: Alexandria, Va., 1830s

Barton, John: Haverhill, Mass., n.d.

Barwell, Bartholomew: Maker and dealer, New York, 1749–1760

Bassett, George F.: n.p. *c.* 1797. Hudson River Valley locale indicated

Bassett, J. & W. H.: Cortland, N.Y., 1810s–1820s; Albany after 1820s

Bassett, N. B.: Albany, N.Y., 1810s

Batchelder, Andrew: Danvers, Mass., 1800s–1840s

Batchelder, Ezra: Danvers, Mass., 1780s–1820s

Batchelor & Bensel: New York, 1840s

Bateman, Joseph: Norristown, Pa., n.d. Tall clocks

Bateman, Valentine: Reading, Pa., n.d. Tall clocks

Bateson, John: Boston, 1720s

Bath, Barten: New York, 1840s

Batterson, James: Philadelphia, *c.* 1705; Boston, 1707–1710; Charleston, S.C., from *c.* 1711 to 1727

Battles, A. B.: Utica, N.Y., 1840s

Baugh, Valentine: Abingdon, Va., 1820s

Baur, John N.: New York, 1820s–1840s

Bayley (*See also* Bailey), Calvin: Hanover, Mass, 1800s

Bayley, John: Hanover, Mass., 1770s to 1810s

Bayley, John: Hingham, Mass., 1810s

Bayley, Joseph: Hingham, Mass., 1800s

BAYLEY, LEBBENS: Maine (n.p.), 1800s. Mention found of man as clockmaker; clocks reported but not seen; newspaper items do not mention places
BAYLEY, SIMEON: Philadelphia, 1790s
BEACH & BYINGTON: Plymouth, Conn., late 1840s
BEACH & HUBBEL: Bristol, Conn., 1860s. Marine clocks
BEACH & SANFORD: Hartford, Conn., 1785–1788
BEACH & WARD: Hartford, Conn., 1790–1798
BEACH, MILES: Litchfield, Conn., 1760s–1785; Hartford, 1788–1790, and again Hartford, 1797–1813
BEACH, MILES & SON: Hartford, Conn., 1813–1825
BEACH, WILLIAM: Hartford, Conn., 1820s–1830s
BEALS, J. J.: Boston, 1830s–1840s and later. An extensive dealer
BEALS, J. J. & W.: Boston, 1840s. Dealers
BEARD & CO., E. C.: Louisville, Ky., 1830s–1870s. Also dealers
BEARD (D.) & WEAVER (C.): Appoquinimink, Del., 1770s–1790s
BEARD, DUNCAN: Appoquinimink, Del., *c.* 1750s–1797. Tall clocks and some spring-driven mantel or shelf clocks
BEARD, D. & C.: Appoquinimink, Del., 1780s–1790s
BEARDSLEY, H. P.: Curonna, Mich., 1860s
BEATLEY, RALPH: Chelsea, Mass., 1840s
BEATTY, GEORGE: Harrisburg, Pa., 1808–1850
BECKER, CHARLES: Cleveland, Ohio, 1830s. Listed as manufacturer, 1836
BECKER, JACOB: Hanover, Pa., 1820s
BECKWITH, DANA: Bristol, Conn., 1818–1823
BEER, ALFRED: Versailles, Ind., 1850s–1880s
BEER, ROBERT: Olean, Ind., 1820s to 1825; Versailles, Ind., after 1825
BEIGEL, HENRY: Philadelphia, 1810s
BEITEL, JOSEPH: Nazareth, Pa., n.d. Tall clocks
BELK, WILLIAM: Philadelphia, 1790s–1800s
BELKNAP, EBENEZER: Boston, 1820s–1830s
BELKNAP, JEREMIAH: n.d. n.p.
BELKNAP, WILLIAM: Boston, *c.* 1800s–1820s
BELL, JAMES: New York, 1800s–1820s
BELL, JOHN: New York, *c.* 1730s
BELL, M.: Manteo, N.C., late 1880s
BELL, WILLIAM: Philadelphia, 1800s
BEMIS, AUGUSTUS: Paris, Me., *c.* 1812
BENEDICT & BURNHAM: Waterbury, Conn., 1850s; became Waterbury Clock Co.
BENEDICT & SCUDDER: New York, 1820s–1830s

BENEDICT, S.: New York, 1820s
BENEDICT, S. W.: New York, 1820s–1830s
BENHAM, AUGUSTUS: New Haven, Conn., 1840s–1850s
BENJAMIN, BARZILLA: New Haven, Conn., 1820s
BENJAMIN, JOHN: Stratford, Conn., *c.* 1750–1790
BENNETT & THOMAS: Petersburg, Va., 1820s
BENNETT, T. N.: Canandaigua, N.Y., 1850s–1860s
BENNY, JONATHAN: Easton, Md., 1790s
BENSEL, LEONARD J.: New York 1880s. Night clocks
BENTLEY, ELI: West Whiteland (Chester County), Pa., 1774–1778; York, Pa., 1780; Littlestown, Pa., and Taneytown, Md., to 1800s
BERAULT, JOHN: New York City, 1810s
BERRY, JAMES: New York City, 1780s–1792
BERWICK, ABNER: Brunswick, Me., 1820s
BESSONET, JOHN: New York City, 1790s
BEST, THOMAS: Lebanon, Ohio, 1820s
BEVANS (or BEVENS), WILLIAM: Philadelphia, 1810s; Norristown, Pa., *c.* 1815–1820
BICHAUT, JAMES: Boston, 1729
BIDDLE, OWEN: Philadelphia, 1760s–1770s. Maker; dealer in blanks and parts
BIEGEL, HENRY: Philadelphia, 1810s
BIERSHING, HENRY: Hagerstown, Md., 1815–1843
BIGGER & CLARKE: Baltimore, 1783
BIGGER, GILBERT: Baltimore, 1784–1800s
BIGGER, WILLIAM: Baltimore, 1802
BILL, JOSEPH: Middletown, Conn., 1840s
BILLINGS, ANDREW: Poughkeepsie, N.Y., 1790s–1820s
BILLINGS, JONATHAN: Reading, Mass., 1830s
BILLINGS, JOSEPH: Reading, Pa., 1770s–1780s
BILLON & CO.: Philadelphia, 1790s
BILLON, CHARLES: Philadelphia, 1810s. Saint Louis, Mo., 1820s
BILLON, A. C. & CO.: Davenport, Iowa, 1850s
BILLOW, CHARLES (& CO.): Boston, 1790s
BILLS, ELIJAH: Colebrook River, Conn., n.d., but between 1820–1840
BILY BROTHERS: Spillville, Iowa. Wood carvers, still working 1947, casing but not reported making clocks
BINGHAM & BRICERLY (or BRIERLY), Philadelphia, 1770s–1800s
BIRDSEY, E. C. & CO.: Meriden, Conn., 1830s
BIRGE & IVES: Bristol, Conn., n.d.
BIRGE, CASE & CO.: Bristol, Conn., 1833–1834
BIRGE & CO.: Bristol, Conn., 1848

BIRGE & FULLER: Bristol, Conn., 1844–1847. Wagon-spring clocks
BIRGE, GILBERT & CO.: Bristol, Conn., 1835–1837
BIRGE, JOHN: Bristol, Conn., 1830–1860
BIRGE, MALLORY & CO.: Bristol, Conn., 1838–1843
BIRGE, PECK & CO.: Bristol, Conn., 1849–1859
BIRNIE, LAWRENCE: Philadelphia, 1774–1777
BISBEE, J.: Brunswick, Me., 1790–1820s
BISHOP & BRADLEY: Plymouth, Conn., 1820s–1830s. Also at Watertown, Conn.
BISHOP & NORTON: Bristol, Conn., 1853–1855
BISHOP, HOMER: Bristol, Conn., late 1830s or early 1840s
BISHOP, MORITZ: Easton, Pa., 1780s–1800s
BISHOP, RUFUS: Mount Joy, Lancaster County, Pa., 1850s
BISSELL, D.: East Windsor, Conn., *c.* 1830s
BIXLER, CHRISTIAN: Lancaster, Pa., 1753–1800
BIXLER, CHRISTIAN, JR.: Reading, Pa., 1785–1820
BIXLER, CHRISTIAN, III: Easton, Pa., 1790–1830
BLACK, JOHN: Philadelphia, 1840s
BLAIR, ELISHA: Brooklyn, N.Y., 1840s
BLAISDELL, ISAAC: *See also* Blasdell, Amesbury, Mass., and Chester, N.H., 1760s–1780s
BLAISDELL, RICHARD: Chester, N.H., *c.* 1790s
BLAKE, E. G.: Farmington, Me., 1850s
BLAKESLEE, JEREMIAH: Plymouth, Conn., 1840s
BLAKESLEE, M. & E.: Plymouth, Conn., 1830s
BLAKESLEE, M.: Plymouth, Conn., 1820s
BLAKESLEE, R., JR.: New York City, *c.* 1830s–1850
BLAKESLEE, RILEY: Plymouth, Conn., 1800s
BLAKESLEE, ZIBA: Newtown, Conn., 1790s–1830s. Also had a brass foundry and made clock parts in blanks
BLAKESLY, HARPER: Cincinnati, 1820s
BLASDEL *See also* Blaisdell, DAVID: Almsbury (Amesbury), Mass., 1750s–1790s
BLASDELL, EBENEZER: Chester, N.H., 1790s–1810
BLISS & CREIGHTON: New York, 1840s. Offices also at Boston, Baltimore, and Philadelphia
BLOOMER & SPERRY: New York, 1840s
BLUMER, JOSEPH: Northampton, Pa. (now Allentown), 1798–1820s
BLUNDY, CHARLES: Charleston, S.C., 1750s
BLUNT, E. & G. W.: New York, 1840s
BOARDMAN & DUNBAR: Bristol, Conn., 1810s
BOARDMAN & WELLS: Bristol, Conn., 1832–1843

BOARDMAN, CHAUNCEY: Bristol, Conn., 1811–1850s, alone and in other firms
BOARDMAN, SMITH & CO.: Bristol, Conn., 1832
BODE, W.: Philadelphia, 1790s
BODELY, T.: Boston, 1720s
BOEHME, CHARLES L.: Baltimore, 1799–1812
BOGARDUS, EVERARD: New York, 1690s
BOIS DE CHESNE, JOHN F.: Charleston, S.C., 1750
BOLLES, THOMAS N.: n.p., 1790s–1810s
BOLOQUET, MARCEL: New Bern, N.C., 1750s–1760s. Swiss *émigré* clockmaker
BOND, CHARLES: Boston, 1825
BOND, WILLIAM & SON: Boston, 1815–1840s
BONFANTI, JOSEPH: New York, 1820s. Making questioned; a dealer
BONNAUD, M.: Philadelphia, 1790s
BONNET, JOHN M.: Zanesville, Ohio, 1850s–1860s
BOSS & PETERMAN: Rochester, N.Y., 1840s
BOSTON CLOCK CO.: Boston, 1880s
BOTSFORD, PATRICK: New Haven, Conn., 1840s–1850s
BOTSFORD, S. N.: Whitneyville, Conn., 1850s
BOUGHEL, JOSEPH: New York, 1780s
BOUJU, JOSEPH: Saint Louis, Mo., 1820s
BOUVRIER, M.: Baltimore, Pittsburgh, and Zanesville, Ohio, in order named, during 1800s to *c.* 1827
BOWER (or BAUER) HIRAM (or HENRY): Philadelphia, 1790s–1800s
BOWER, MICHAEL: Philadelphia, 1790s
BOWER, WILLIAM: Charleston, S.C., 1772–1773
BOWMAN, JOSEPH, SR.: New Holland and Elliotts Corner, Lancaster County, Pa., 1790s–1820s
BOWMAN, JOSEPH: Strasburg, Lancaster County, Pa., 1822–1850
BOWNE, SAMUEL: New York, 1750s
BOYCE, B. M.: *See* Pratt, Daniel, Jr.
BOYD, JOHN: Sadsbury, Chester County, Pa., 1831–1867
BOYD, JOHN: Lowell, Mass., 1860s
BOYNTON, CALVIN: Buffalo, N.Y., 1850s–1860s
BOYNTON, JOHN E.: Manchester, Iowa, 1860s
BRACE, RODNEY: Torrington, Conn., 1790s; N. Bridgewater, Mass., after 1800s. Had Isaac Packard as a partner in later venture
BRACE & PACKARD: *See* Brace, Rodney
BRADBURY, JACOB: New York, 1840s
BRADLEY & BARNES: Boston, 1850s
BRADLEY & HUBBARD: Meriden, Conn., 1850s

BRADLEY, B. & Co.: Boston, 1850s; took over the Jerome Branch
BRADLEY, D. W.: New York, 1850s
BRADLEY, FREDERICK: New York. Casemaker. Clocks bearing his name or "paper" not made by him; only cased by him
BRADLEY, LUCIUS: Watertown, Conn., 1800s–1810s
BRADLEY, NELSON: Plymouth, Conn., 1840s
BRADLEY, RICHARD: Hartford, Conn., 1840s
BRADLEY, Z. & SON: New Haven, 1840s
BRAND, JOHN (and/or), JAMES: Boston, from 1710s. Both names appear on clocks and in advertisements of the 1710 decade
BRANDEGEE, E.: Berlin, Conn., 1830s
BRANDT, AIME & CHARLES: Philadelphia, 1802–1813; Aime alone, 1817–1825
BRANDT (or BRANT), ADAM: New Hanover (now Hanover), Pa., 1750s–1760s
BRANDT (or BRANDS) & MATHEY: Philadelphia, 1797
BRANDT, BROWN & LEWIS: Philadelphia, 1790s
BRANDT, JACOB: New Hanover, Montgomery County, Pa., *c.* 1790s–1810s
BRASHER (BRASHEAR), A.: New York, 1750s
BRASIER (BRAZER), A.: Philadelphia, 1790–1820
BRASTOW, ADISON & Co.: Lowell, Mass., 1830s
BREADY, C. L.: Philadelphia, 1800s
BREARLY, JAMES: Philadelphia, 1790s–1810s
BRECKENRIDGE, J. M.: Meriden, Conn., 1830s; New Haven, 1840s–1870s
BRECKWELL, JOHN: Pikeland, Chester County, Pa., 1830s
BREESE, LYMAN: Wellsburg, Va., 1830s
BRENKELAER, JAN: New York (?) or Hudson valley. n.d.; n.p. Various researchers report mention and tradition dating this maker from *c.* 1660 to 1750s
BRENNAN, BARNABAS: Philadelphia, 1840s
BRENEISER (also BRENEISEN), SAMUEL: Reamstown and Adamstown, Lancaster County, Pa., working 1835–1860
BRENFER (also reported as BRENFTER) W.: Connecticut, n.p., *c.* 1790–1810
BRENT, ADAM: New Hanover. Reported at place so named, in Pennsylvania, and at similar place name in Massachusetts. Tall-case clocks known
BREWER, ISAAC: Philadelphia, 1810s–1820s
BREWER, WILLIAM: Philadelphia, 1770s–1790s
BREWSTER, ABEL: Canterbury, Conn., 1796–1805

BREWSTER, CHARLES E.: Portsmouth, N.H., *c.* 1830–1840s

BREWSTER & WILLARD: Portsmouth, N.H., 1830s–1840s. Partnership, probably for selling, of Charles E. Brewster and one of the Willards of Roxbury

BREWSTER, ELISHA: Bristol, Conn., 1831–1862; various companies as hereunder:

BREWSTER & BROWN (1839–1840)

BREWSTER & CO., ELISHA (1840–1843)

BREWSTER & CO. (1861)

BREWSTER & SON, E. C. (1855)

BREWSTER & INGRAHAM (1844–1852)

BREWSTER MANUFACTURING CO. (1852–1854)

BREWSTER, GEORGE G.: Portsmouth, N.H., *c.* 1850s

BRIGDON, GEORGE S.: Norwich, Conn., 1810s–1830s

BRIGGS, JOHN C.: Concord, N.H., 1840s–1850s

BRINKERHOFF, DIRCK: New York, 1740s–1750s. Believed to have been a maker, dealer, and importer

BRISTOL BRASS & CLOCK CO.: Bristol, Mass., 1850–1900

BRISTOL CLOCK CO.: An export company organized by Chauncey Jerome

BRITTAIN, JOSEPH: Bakerstown, Allegheny County, Pa., 1830s

BRODERSON, EMIL: Cincinnati, with Duhme & Co., 1860s. A Danish expert

BROGAN, JOHN: New York, 1810s

BROKAW, AARON: Rahway and Elizabeth, N.J., 1780s–1840s

BROKAW, ISAAC: Bridgetown and Elizabethtown, N.J., 1760s–1780s

BROKESMIELD, JOSEPH: Cincinnati, 1830s

BRONSON, I. W.: Buffalo, N.Y., 1820s–1830s

BROOKS, B. F.: Utica, N.Y., 1840s

BROOKS, F. O.: Madison, Ind., 1860s

BROWN, ALBERT: Columbia, Lancaster County, Pa., 1850s

BROWN & GOODRICH: Bristol, Conn., 1810s–1830s

BROWN & KIRBY: New Haven, 1840s

BROWN & CO., SAMUEL: New York, 1820s–1830s

BROWN (J. R.) & SHARPE: Providence, R.I., 1840s–1850s. Advertising of this firm (now Brown & Sharpe) in 1840s states they were clockmakers and manufacturers of precision tools for clock and watchmakers

BROWN, DAVID: Providence, R.I., 1820s–1840s

BROWN, JOHN: Lancaster, Pa., 1820–1840

BROWN, JONATHAN: Bristol, Conn., 1833–55. Had various partners, silent and named. Was one of principals of Forestville Mfg Co. Also as BROWN, J. C. & CO.: Forestville, Conn., 1842–1849

BROWN, J. H.: Des Moines, Iowa, 1856
BROWN, JOSEPH R.: Providence, R.I., 1847
BROWN, LAURENT: Rochester, N.Y., 1840s
BROWN, ROBERT: Baltimore, 1820s. In 1830 ROBERT BROWN & SON
BROWN, SAMUEL: New York, 1810s
BROWN, S.: Norristown, Pa., 1850s
BROWN, WILLIAM: York, Pa., 1840s–1850s
BROWNE (or BROWN), GAWEN: Boston, 1752–1773
BRUFF, JAMES: New York, 1760s
BRYANT, E. D.: New York, 1850s
BRYANT, THOMAS: Rochester, N.Y., 1830s
BUCHER, JESSE: Dayton, Ohio, *c.* 1825–1840
BUERK, J. E.: Boston, 1860s. Made watchman's time-detector clocks
BUDD, JOSEPH: Mount Holly and New Mills (now Pemberton), N.J., n.d. Tall clocks
BULKLEY, JOSEPH: Fairfield (no state), *c.* 1775–1815
BULL, JOHN: York, Pa., first half nineteenth century
BULL, J. P.: Newark, N.J., 1850s
BUNDY MANUFACTURING CO.: Binghamton, N.Y. Made time-recording clocks using Seth Thomas movements. Last quarter nineteenth century
BUNKER, BENJAMIN: Nantucket, Mass., 1770s–*c.* 1820
BUNNEL & SCOVILL: Owego, Tioga County, N.Y., 1820s–1830s
BUNNEL, EDWIN: Bristol, Conn., 1850s. Dealer and trader
BURDICK, M. H.: Bristol, Conn., 1840s–1850s
BURDICK, H. M.: Cleveland, Ohio. Distributor of clocks and watches at wholesale
BURGER, JOSEPH: New York; dial maker who sold some dials with his name on them and hence is sometimes noted as maker. No records of his ever having made clocks could be found
BURGI (or BURG), JACOB: Lancaster, Pa., *c.* 1750
BURKELOW, SAMUEL: Philadelphia, 1790s
BURKMAR, THOMAS: Boston, 1770s
BURNAP, DANIEL: East Windsor (and other places), Conn., 1780–1836. Master who taught Eli Terry
BURNHAM, ENOCH: Paris, Rumford, and Portland, Me., 1806–1830s
BURNS, HUGH: Philadelphia, 1811
BUROT, A.: Baltimore, 1810s–1827
BURR & CHITTENDEN: Lexington, Mass., 1830s. Had a factory "employing 3, making 3–500 clocks a year." Burr removed to Chicago *c.* 1840. These are Connecticut movement clocks cased at Lexington, Mass.

BURR, C. A.: Rochester, N.Y., 1841–1842. Probably dealer only
BURR, EZEKIEL & WILLIAM: Providence, R.I., 1790s
BURR, JONATHAN: Lexington, Mass., 1830s; Chicago, Ill., 1840s
BURRAGE, JOHN: Baltimore, 1769
BURRITT, JOSEPH: Ithaca, N.Y., 1830s
BURROWS, DOWDNEY: Philadelphia, 1768
BURROWES, THOMAS: Strasburg, Lancaster County, Pa., 1787–1810
BURT & CADY: Kansas City, Mo., 1860s
BURWELL & CARTER: Bristol, Conn., 1859–1861
BURWELL, ELIAS: Bristol, Conn., 1859–1867
BUSH, GEORGE: Easton, Pa., 1810s–1830s
BUSH, HENRY: Cincinnati, 1830s
BUSH, MICHAEL: Easton, Pa., n.d. made tall clocks
BUTLER & BARTLETT: West Chester, Pa., 1830s
BUTLER, NATHAN: Utica, N.Y., 1800s
BYAM, C. C.: Amesbury, Mass., 1850s–1860s
BYINGTON & CO.: Bristol, Conn., 1843–1849
BYINGTON & GRAHAM: Bristol, Conn., 1852–1853
BYRAM, EPHRAIM: Sag Harbor, L.I., N.Y., 1850s

CABLE, STEPHEN: New York City, 1840s–1850s
CACHOT, FELIX: Bardstown, Ky., 1813–1839. Cachot was an ex-Trappist monk
CADWELL, EDWIN: New York City, 1840s
CAIN, C. W.: New York City, 1830s
CAIRNS, JOHN: Providence, R.I., 1780s
CAIRNS, JOHN, JR.: Providence, R.I., 1830s–1840s
CALAME, OLIVIER: Frederick, Md., 1810s–1820s
CALENDAR CLOCK CO.: Several firms of record bear this name at Glastonbury, Conn., and New York City, operating *c.* 1850–1870
CALLENDAR & AUGER: Meriden, Conn., 1850s–1860s
CAMP, EPHRAIM: Salem Bridge, Conn., n.d. First quarter nineteenth century
CAMP, HIRAM: Bristol, Conn., with Chauncey Jerome, 1829. New Haven. Genius who reorganized Jerome's wreck and founded New Haven Clock Co.
CAMPBELL, BENJAMIN: Hagerstown, Md., 1775–1792; Uniontown, Pa., 1792–1830. This clockmaker lived to the ripe old age of ninety-four. Born 1749 at New London Crossroads, Chester County, Pa.
CAMPBELL, CHARLES: Philadelphia, 1797
CAMPBELL, ISAAC: Philadelphia, 1813–1824
CAMPBELL, JOHN: Hagerstown, Md., 1770s

CAMPBELL, R.: Baltimore, 1820s–1830s
CAMPBELL, THOMAS: New York City, 1810s
CAMPBELL, WILLIAM: Carlisle, Pa., 1765–1795; Philadelphia, 1795–1800s
CANBY & NIELSON: West Chester, Pa., 1810s
CANBY, CHARLES: Wilmington, Del., 1790s–1830s. Tall, shelf, and wall clocks. Also a dealer
CANFIELD & FOOTE: Middletown, Conn., 1790s
CANFIELD, SAMUEL: Middletown, Conn., 1780s–1790s; Lansingburgh, N.Y., 1790s to 1800s
CANNON, WILLIAM: Philadelphia (apprentice record), 1730s
CAPPER, M.: Philadelphia, 1790s
CAREY, JAMES: Brunswick, Me., 1800s–1840s
CARLETON, JAMES H.: Haverhill, Mass., n.d.
CARLETON, JOHN C.: Bradford, Vt., first half nineteenth century
CARLETON, MICHAEL: Haverhill, Mass. Early in 1900 this man was credited with making a clock owned by Z. Symmes who died in 1708! We cannot locate him at that date, but find meager records indicating 1800–1820
CARMAN, SAMUEL: Brooklyn, N.Y., 1840s
CARNEY, HUGH: Walcottville, Conn., n.d.
CARPENTER, ANTHONY: Lancaster County, Pa. (New Holland), 1820s. A son, also named Anthony, made clocks with father. *See also* Fraser
CARPENTER, C. H.: Middleboro, Mass., 1860s
CARPENTER, JOSEPH: Norwich, Conn., 1769–1804
CARR, FRANK B.: Fall River, Mass., 1860s
CARR, J. P.: New York City, 1810s
CARR, LYMAN: Manchester, N.H., 1850s–1860s
CARR, T. P.: New York City, 1810s
CARRELL, DANIEL: Philadelphia, 1780s; Charleston, S.C., 1790s–1800s
CARRELL, JOHN & DANIEL: Philadelphia, 1785
CARRYL (also as CARROLL), PATRICK: New York City, 1750s
CARSON, GEORGE: York, Pa., 1800s–1820s
CARTER, W. W. & L. F.: Bristol, Conn., 1863–1868
CARVALLO, N.: Charleston, S.C., mid eighteenth century
CARVER, JACOB: Philadelphia, 1780s–1800
CARY, JAMES: Brunswick, Me., 1800s to 1840. Taught Dennison, the great watchmaker
CASE & BIRGE: Bristol, Conn., 1830s
CASE & ROBINSON: Bristol, Conn., 1845–1855. Also toy and gadget makers

CASE, DYER, WADSWORTH & CO.: Augusta, Ga., assemblers of Seth Thomas parts to avoid Yankee peddlers' tax in 1830s

CASE, ERASTUS: Bristol, Conn., 1830s

CASE, HARVEY: Bristol, Conn., 1830s

CASE, WILLARD & CO.: Bristol, Conn., 1835

CASTAN, STEPHEN: Philadelphia, 1810s

CASTENS, J. M.: Charleston, S.C., *c.* 1760s–1770s

CASWELL, A.: New York, 1850s

CATE, SIMEON: Sanbornton, N.H., 1820s–1830s

CATER, STEPHEN: Charleston, S.C., mentioned 1744–1748

CATHCART, A. H.: Marshall, Mich., 1860s

CATHERWOOD, JOHN: Charleston, S.C., mentioned in 1750s–1760s

CATLIN, JOEL: Augusta, Ga., 1820s

CAVE, JOSEPH: West Goshen & West Chester, Pa., 1819–1835

CECIL, CHARLES: Philadelphia, 1800s–1810s

CELLERS, JOHN: Chillicothe, Ohio, 1810s

CHADWICK, JOSEPH: Boscawen, N.H., 1810s–1830s

CHAMBERLIN, CYRUS: New Haven, Conn., 1840s–1850s

CHAMBERLIN, WILLIAM: Towanda, Pa., 1838–1850s

CHAMPNEY & FELTON: Troy, N.Y., 1850s

CHANDLEE & HOLLOWAY: Baltimore, 1810s–1824

CHANDLEE & SONS: Nottingham, Pa., after 1770s

CHANDLEE, BENJAMIN: Son-in-law of Abel Cottey, first Quaker clockmaker of Philadelphia. Chandlee worked at Nottingham, Pa., 1714–1740. *See* Bibliography

CHANDLEE, BENJAMIN, JR.: Nottingham, Pa., 1740s–1790. Part of his property was in Maryland after running of Mason-Dixon line. Also had small brass foundry

CHANDLEE, BENJAMIN, III: Baltimore, Md., 1810s–1820s

CHANDLEE, ELLIS (also ELLIS CHANDLEE & BROTHERS): Nottingham, Pa., 1780s to 1810s. Brothers' firm 1790–1797

CHANDLEE, ELLIS & ISAAC: Nottingham, Pa., 1790s

CHANDLEE, GOLDSMITH: Nottingham, Pa., Maryland, and Winchester, Va., working after 1770

CHANDLEE, ISAAC: Nottingham, Pa., 1770s–1813

CHANDLEE, JOHN: Wilmington, Del., 1790s–1810s

CHANDLER, ABIEL: Concord, N.H., 1830s–1860

CHANDLER, TIMOTHY: Concord, N.H., 1785–1840; Pomfret, Conn., 1780–1785

CHAPIN, AARON: Hartford, Conn., 1820s–1830s

CHAPMAN, C. H.: Easthampton, Mass., 1850s–1860s

CHAPPEL (SAMUEL) & SARTWELL (JAMES): Busti, near Jamestown, N.Y., and Chautauqua, N.Y., 1830s–1840s. Hang up tall-case movements; wag-on-wall

CHASE, JOHN F.: Newark, N.J., 1850s

CHASE, TIMOTHY: Belfast, Me., 1820s–1840

CHAUDRON & RASCH: Philadelphia, 1830–1840s. Also CHAUDRON & CO. This firm made clocks, imported clocks, and were fine silversmiths

CHAUDRON, EDWARD: Philadelphia, 1799–1813; PETER, 1790s–1820s; SIMON, 1799–1813. This group, seemingly worked independently and together

CHENEY, ALCOTT: Middetown, Conn., 1818–1840s

CHENEY, ASAHEL: Northfield, Mass., 1780s. Son of Benjamin

CHENEY, BENJAMIN: East Hartford and perhaps other points in Connecticut, 1746–1780. Taught Benjamin Willard who, in turn, is said to have taught Simon Willard

CHENEY, BENJAMIN: Berlin, Conn., 1810s or 1820s to 1835. Son of Elisha

CHENEY, ELISHA: Berlin, Conn., 1793–1833. Vandalia, Ill., 1834–1840s. Believed also to have worked at Springfield, Ill. Record is hazy

CHENEY, MARTIN: Windsor, Vt., 1790s. Son of Benjamin

CHENEY, O.: Berlin and Middletown, Conn., 1835–1850

CHENEY, RUSSEL: Putney & Thetford, Vt., 1790s–1800s

CHENEY, TIMOTHY: East Hartford, Conn., 1750s–1790s. Brother of Benjamin

CHESHIRE CLOCK CO.: Cheshire, Conn., 1880s. Owned by A. E. Hotchkiss

CHESTER, GEORGE: New York City, from *c.* 1735

CHESTER, RICHARD: Hanover, Pa., 1790s–1816

CHILD, JOHN: Philadelphia, 1810s–1830s

CHILD, T. W.: Boston, 1820s

CHIPPERFIELD, N. W.: New York City, 1850s

CHITTENDEN (AUSTIN) & BURR (JONATHAN): Lexington, Mass., "factory" operating in 1830s. Probably a casing and assembly shop for Connecticut movements

CHOLLOT, JOHN: Philadelphia, 1810s–1820s

CHRIST, DANIEL: Kutztown, Pa., 1800s

CHURCH, EDWARD: New Haven, 1840s–1850s

CHURCH, JOSEPH: Hartford, 1820s–1830s

CHURCH, LORENZO: Hartford, 1840s

CITO, J. C.: Boston, 1810s or 1820s. Probably a dealer

CLAGGETT, H.: Newport, R.I., 1720s–1740s

CLAGGETT, THOMAS: Newport, R.I., *c.* 1740–1790. There is a record of seizure of shop to satisfy claims of casemaker, John Townsend, 1783

CLAGGETT, WILLIAM: Boston and Newport master clockmaker, Boston, 1714–1716 and Newport, R.I., 1716 to *c.* 1749

CLARK, AMOS: Lewisberry, York Co., Pa., 1790s–1810s

CLARK & CO., F.: Augusta, Ga., 1820s

CLARK & HUTCHINSON: Philadelphia, 1810–1815

CLARK & LATHAM: Charleston, S.C., 1770s–1790s

CLARK & TURNER: Fayetteville, N.C., 1820s

CLARK, BENJAMIN & EDWARD: Philadelphia, 1790s–1810s. Worked together and as individual makers. Some clocks marked B. & E. Clark

CLARK, BENJAMIN: Wilmington, Del., 1830–1850

CLARK, DANIEL: Waterbury, Conn., *c.* 1812–1820

CLARK, DAVID: Charleston, S.C., 1760s–1780s

CLARK, ELLIS: Philadelphia, 1810s–1840s

CLARK, EPHRAIM: Philadelphia, 1780–1800s

CLARK, GILBERT & BROWN: New York City, 1840s

CLARK, GILBERT & CO.: Winchester, Conn., first half of nineteenth century

CLARK, HEMAN: Plymouth Hollow (now Thomaston), Conn. Apprentice of Eli Terry to 1806. Said to have purchased Terry's first hang-up clock shop. Erected a shop *c.* 1809–1810 wherein he made brass eight-day shelf clocks in pillar-and-scroll cases and in pillar cases without the scroll top. Operated this plant to 1813 when he sold it to Seth Thomas. *See* text for further data on Heman Clark, Chapter VI

CLARK, JOSEPH: New York City, advertised in 1768; removed to Danbury, Conn., 1786. Made chime, repeater, and common eight-day tall clocks with moon's age, sweep second hands, and day-of-month feature. Also a silversmith and framer of miniatures in silver and gold cases. Left Danbury in 1811

CLARK, J. W. & CO.: Philadelphia, 1810s

CLARK, RICHARD: Charleston, S.C., advertised in 1767

CLARK, ROBERT: Charleston, S.C., advertised in 1785

CLARK, SYLVESTER: Salem Bridge, Conn., 1830s

CLARK, THOMAS: Boston, advertised in 1764

CLARK, WILLIAM H.: Palmer, Mass., 1850s–1860s

CLARKE, AMBROSE: Baltimore, advertised in 1784

CLARKE (or CLARK), CHARLES: Philadelphia, 1805–1810

CLARKE, GEORGE: Providence, R.I., 1820s
CLARKE, GEORGE H.: New York City, n.d.
CLARKE, GEORGE R.: Utica, N.Y., 1820s
CLARKE, GILBERT & CO.: Winsted and Winchester, Conn., 1840s–1850. Lucius Clarke and William L. Gilbert
CLARKE, JOHN: New York City, 1770s–1790s. Philadelphia, 1790s–1800s
CLAUDE & FRENCH: Annapolis, Md., 1780s
CLAUDON, J. G.: Charleston, S.C., *c.* 1760s
CLAYTON (or CLATON) C.: Philadelphia, n.d.
CLAYTON, JOHN: Charleston, S.C., advertised 1743
CLAYTON, ROBERT: Aeronaut and clockmaker of Cincinnati, 1830s
CLEAVELAND, WILLIAM: Salem & Putnam, Ohio, *c.* 1800s to 1810s
CLEMENS, MOSES: New York City, 1740s
CLEVELAND, BENJAMIN N.: New York City and Newark, N.J., 1790s–1830s
CLEVELAND, WILLIAM: Salem, Mass., *c.* 1778–1800. Uncle of William
CLEVELAND, WILLIAM: New London, Norwich, and Salem; working *c.* 1792–1820s. Grandfather of President Grover Cleveland. *See also* Trott & Cleveland
CLERC, HENRY: New York City, 1810s
CLORNBY (may be LORNBY, C., or J. C.): n.p. Clocks reported with Clornby on dials, in capital letters, with space, but no period, after *C*
COCKS (COX), JAMES: New York City, 1810s
COCHRAN, GEORGE: West Chester, Pa., 1799–1807
COCHRANE, THOMAS: New York City, 1810s
COE, BENJAMIN: Alexander, N.Y., 1850s–1860s
COE, RUSSEL: Meriden, Conn., 1850s
COHEN, THOMAS: Chillicothe, Ohio, 1800s, 1810s; Saint Louis, Mo., 1840s–1850s
COLE, DAVID: New York City, 1840s
COLE, J. C.: Rochester, N.H., 1810s–1820s
COLE, S.: Great Falls, N.H., 1830s–1850. Son of J. C. Cole
COLLINS, J.: Goffstown, N.H., *c.* 1820s–1830s
COLLINS, WILLIAM: New York City, 1850s
COLVIN, WALTER: Trenton, N.J., advertised in 1785
CONANT & SPERRY: New York City, 1840s
CONANT, ELIAS: Bridgewater, Mass., 1770s–1810
CONANT, ELIAS: Lynn, Mass., 1810s
CONANT, W. S.: New York City, 1820s
CONN PROTECTIVE CLOCK CO.: Bristol, Conn., 1849

Conrad, Osborn: Philadelphia, *c.* 1810s to 1830s. Also Osborn Conrad and Company, 1830s
Converse, Pascal: New Haven, 1840s–1850s
Cook & Stillwell: Rochester, N.Y., 1840–1850
Cook, E.: Rochester, N.Y., 1820s
Cook, Frederick B.: Columbia, Lancaster County, 1828–1832; York, Pa., 1832–1842
Cook, Richard: *See* Kock, Richard
Cook, William: Baltimore, 1810s–1820s
Cook, Zenas: Waterbury, Conn., 1811 to 1820
Coolidge, Henry: New Haven, Conn., advertised 1787
Cooper, Charles: Lebanon, Pa., 1800–1820
Cooper, Robert: Philadelphia, n.d.
Cooper, T.: Olneyville, R.I., 1848
Cope, Jacob: n.p., n.d.
Copeland, Robert: Baltimore, Md., 1790s–1800s
Corey, P.: Providence, R.I., 1848
Corgee, Arthur: Philadelphia, 1820s
Corl, Abraham: East Vincent & Coventry, Chester Co., Pa., 1808–1830
Corliss, James: Weare, N.H., 1800s
Cornell, Walter: Newport, R.I., 1790s–1820s
Cornwell, Nathan: Darien, Georgia, 1820s
Cortland Clocks: A company of unlisted makers at Cortland, N.Y., working in 1840s, perhaps using Connecticut movements, conducted a sort of peddling cartel, selling clocks in neighborhood
Cottey, Abel: Philadelphia, 1682–1711. For many years a clock by Cottey made *c.* 1707 was considered the earliest known American-made clock
Cowan, William: Richmond, Va., 1820s
Cowley, L. D.: LeGrange, Ind., 1860s
Cox & Clark: New York City, 1830s. Probably dealers
Cox, Benjamin: Philadelphia, 1810–1815
Cozens, Josiah: Philadelphia, *c.* 1820
Cranch, Richard: Boston and Braintree, Mass., 1770–1775. Probably a dealer
Crane, Aaron D.: Newark, N.J., 1830s–1850s. Made one-year clocks
Crane, John E.: Lowell, Mass., 1840s–1850s. Model maker. Clock-making doubtful
Crane, Jonas: Newark, N.J., 1850s
Crane, Simeon: Canton, Mass., n.d.
Crane, William: Canton, Mass., 1780s

CRAWLEY, ABRAHAM: Boston, 1816
CREHORE, CHARLES C.: Casemaker of high repute; worked for Willards
CRISSWELL, ISAAC: Philadelphia, 1840s–1850s
CRITCHET, JAMES: Candia, N.H., 1800s
CRITTENDEN, SIMEON: Hawley, Mass., 1820s–1850s
CROCKER, O.: E. Meriden, Conn., 1830s
CROSBY & WASHBURGH: New York City, 1850s
CROSS, THEODORE: Boston, 1760s–1770s
CROUCHLEY, THOMAS W. H.: New York City, 1840s
CROW, GEORGE: Wilmington, Del., 1750–1770
CROW, JOHN: Wilmington, Del., 1790s. May have been dealer only
CROW, THOMAS: Wilmington, Del., 1788; Philadelphia, 1790s; West Chester, Pa., 1808–1811
CROWLEY & FAIR: Philadelphia, 1823
CROWLEY, JOHN: Philadelphia, n.d. Shelf and mantel clocks *c.* 1813–1823
CROWTHER, WILLIAM: New York City, 1820s
CRUM & BARBER: Unionville, Conn., 1830s–1840
CUMMENS, WILLIAM: Roxbury, Mass., 1790–1834
CUMMINGS, JOHN: Katskill and Albany, N.Y., 1780s
CUMMINGS, S.: Concord, N.H., 1790s
CURE, LEWIS: New York City and Brooklyn, 1830s–1840s
CURRIER & FOSTER: Salem, Mass., *c.* 1790s–1820
CURRIER, EDMUND: Salem, Mass., 1820s–1830s
CURTIS & DUNNING: n.d.; n.p.
CURTIS, J. & CO.: Cairo, N.Y., 1820s–1830s
CURTIS, LEMUEL: Concord, Mass., and Burlington, Vt. Worked at Concord, 1814–1818 and Burlington to 1856. Made some of the finest banjo and variants thereof ever made. The peer of all the Willards and master of most
CURTIS, LEWIS: Farmington, Conn., 1795–1820; St. Charles, Md., 1820–1835; Hazel Green, Wis., 1836 to 1840s
CURTIS, SOLOMON: Philadelphia, 1790s–1800s
CURTIS, W.: Newburyport, Mass., 1800s
CUSHING, G. H.: Braintree, Mass., 1800s–1810s
CUSTER, DANIEL: Reading, Pa., 1810–1820s
CUSTER, ISAAC D.: Norristown, *c.* 1830s–1850s
CUSTER, JACOB D.: Norristown, Pa., 1825–1860. Made superlatively fine Pennsylvania-type pillar-and-scroll clocks—finer than any by Terry but also far more expensive. Custer's shelf and mantel clocks are now considered to be as good as any of the Terry designs if not superior

Dadin, Louis: Charleston, S.C., 1840s

Daft, Thomas: Philadelphia, 1775–1780s; New York City, 1786–1790s

Daggett, James: Saint Louis, Mo., 1820s

Daggett, T.: Providence, R.I., 1848

Dakin, James: Boston, *c.* 1790s–1810s

Dalziel, John: New York City, 1790s

Dana, George: Providence, R.I., 1800s to 1824

Dana, Peyton & Nathan: Providence, R.I., 1800s. Peyton or Payton Dana active as late as 1848

Danner, Alexander: Casemaker of Lancaster, Pa., 1785–1840. Had a factory for making cases (tall) for many Lancaster clockmakers including the Schreiners, Heintzlemans, Hoffs, Zahms, and others

Darby & Harder: New York City, 1840s

Darlington, Benedict: Westtown, Pa., 1814

Darrow, Elijah: Bristol, 1822–1840s; partner with the Jeromes and with Chauncey Jerome. Also produced many clock tablets

Dart, Lewis: Jersey City, 1850s

Davenport, James: Salem, Mass., 1780s

Davidson, B.: Norwich, Conn., 1770s. Probably also a dealer. Son by same name worked at New Haven in 1820s

Davies, Thomas: Utica, N.Y., 1820s

Davis & Babbitt: Providence, R.I., 1810s

Davis Clock Co.: Columbus, Miss., 1880s

Davis, D. P.: Roxbury, Mass., 1840s–1850s. With E. Howard

Davis, Gabriel (also Davies): Churchtown and Manheim, Lancaster County, Pa., 1780s–1790s

Davis, John: Stratford and/or Fairfield, Conn., 1750s

Davis, John: Churchtown and New Holland, Lancaster County, Pa., 1800s to 1810s. Philadelphia in 1820s

Davis, Peter: Jaffery, N.H., n.d.

Davis, Samuel: Pittsburgh, Pa., 1810–1820

Davis, Toklas & Co.: San Francisco, 1880s

Davis, William: Boston, 1683–1690s

Dawson, Jonas: Philadelphia, 1810s

Day, D. N. & R.: Westfield, Mass., 1820s–1840s

Day, Israel: Baltimore, 1802

De Berard: Utica, N.Y., 1820s

De Bruhl (or De Bruls), M. S.: Charleston, S.C., *c.* 1760s

De Forest & Co.: Salem Bridge, Conn., 1830s

De Goy, Lewis: Boston, 1790s

De Huff, A.: York, Pa., to 1850s

DELAPLAINE, JAMES: New York City, 1780s–1800s
DE LONGUEMAIRE, ————: Charleston, S.C., 1690s–1700s
DELOSTE, F.: Baltimore, 1810s
DEMILT, BENJAMIN: New York City, 1800s–1820
DEMILT, SAMUEL: New York City, 1840s
DEMILT, THOMAS: New York City, 1800s–1820. Also as T. & B. Demilt. Removed to Philadelphia *c.* 1820
DENNISON, AARON: Roxbury, Mass. Primarily watchmaker. Partner of E. Howard
DERBY, CHARLES: Salem, Mass., 1840s–1850s
DERBY, JOHN: New York City, 1810s
DE RIEMER & MEAD: Ithaca, N.Y., 1830s
DE SAULES & CO.: New York City, 1830s
DEUCONNER, G.: Philadelphia, 1810s
DEULL, JAMES: Philadelphia, n.d.
DEVERELL, JOHN: Boston, 1780s–1800s
DEWITT, GARRIT: Sparta, Georgia, 1830s–1850s
DEXTER, H.: Stockbridge, N.Y. Cased Connecticut movements, 1830s–1840s
DEXTER, DANA: Roxbury, Mass., 1860s
DEXTER, JOSEPH: Providence, R.I., 1820s
DE YOUNG, MICHAEL: Baltimore, 1830s
DICKEY, THOMAS: Marietta, Lancaster County, Pa., 1810–1820; Middletown, Pa., *c.* 1820. Harrisburg, Pa., after 1820
DICKINSON, JOHN: Philadelphia, 1822
DICKINSON, RICHARD: Mt. Holly, N.J., 1760s
DIEHL, JACOB: Reading, Pa., 1790s–1820s
DIKEMAN, EDWARD B.: Grand Rapids, Mich., 1837–1860s
DISTURNELL, WILLIAM: New Haven, Conn., 1784–1786; Middletown, Conn., 1786–1790s
DITTMEIR, JOHN: Rochester, N.Y., 1860s–1870s
DIX, JOSEPH: Philadelphia, n.d.
DOBBS, H. M.: New York City, 1790s–1800s
DODD, ABNER: Newark, N.J., 1830s
DODGE & WILLIAMS: Providence, R.I., 1799–1802
DODGE, EZRA: New London, Conn., 1787–1798; Providence, R.I., in 1820s
DODGE, GEORGE: Salem, Mass., 1830s
DODGE, NEHEMIAH: Providence, R.I., 1790s–1820s
DODGE, SERIL: Providence, R.I., 1780s
DOLL, JOSEPH: Lancaster, Pa., 1800s–1820s; Harrisburg, Pa., after 1821

Dominick, Frederick: Philadelphia, 1768–1774

Dominy, Nathaniel: East Hampton, L.I., 1764–1809

Doods, Joseph: n.p., n.d.

Doolittle, Enos: Hartford, 1790s–1800. Also made blanks for other clockmakers at his bell foundry

Doolittle, Isaac: New Haven, Conn., 1742–1797. Also made cast brass blank parts for other makers. Made clock and tower bells

Doolittle, Isaac, Jr.: New Haven, Conn., 1780–1820

Doolittle, Lucius: New York City, 1850s

Dorsey, Philip: Baltimore, 1790s–1800s

Doty, John F.: Albany, N.Y., 1810s

Doughty (Douty), Henry: Philadelphia, 1770s

Douglass, John: New Haven, 1800s–1820s

Douglass, Thomas: Niles, Michigan, 1860s

Doull, James: Charlestown, Mass., 1790s–1820s; Philadelphia after 1825

Dover, Thomas: Dayton, Ohio, 1820s–1830s

Dowdney, Durrows: Philadelphia, 1760s–1770s

Dowle, Robery: New York City, 1790s

Dowling, G. R. & B.: Newark, N.J., 1830s

Downes, A.: Charleston, S.C., late eighteenth century

Downs, Anson: Bristol, Conn, 1830s

Downs, Ephraim: Bristol, Conn., 1825–1842. Before that at Waterbury, 1811, with and/or for L. Harrison and at Cincinnati with Lumas Watson, 1816 to 1820

Dring, Thomas: West Chester, Pa., 1760–1780

Drown, R. W.: Newburyport, Mass., 1800s to 1820s

Droz (also Droze) & Sons: Philadelphia, 1810s–1820s

Droz, Charles A.: Philadelphia, 1810s

Droz, Ferdinand Humbert: Cleveland, Ohio, 1850s–1860s. Also at Pittsburgh, 1840s. Son of Humbert Droz, Philadelphia

Droz, Humbert: Philadelphia, 1790s–1810s

Drysdale, William: Philadelphia, 1810s–1840s

Dubois & Folmar: New York City, 1810s

Dubois, Gabriel: New York City, 1810s

Ducommun, Henry: Philadelphia, 1800s to 1840s

Dudley, Benjamin: Newport, R.I., 1785–1820s

Duffield, Edward: Philadelphia, 1740s–1760s; Lower Dublin, 1760s–1780s

Duffner, Vincent: Cincinnati, Ohio, 1830s–1840s

Dunbar, Butler: Bristol, Conn., 1810s–1830s; Springville, Pa., 1830s–1840

DUNBAR & MERRIMAN: Bristol, Conn., 1810s. (*See* Merriman, Titus)
DUNBAR, JACOBS & WARNER: Bristol, Conn., *c.* 1850
DUNHEIM, A.: New York City, 1770s
DUNLAP, ARCHIBALD: New York City, 1800s
DUNN, ROBERT: New York City manufacturer, 1840s
DUNNING & CRISSEY: Rochester, N.Y., 1840s
DUPUY, JOHN: Philadelphia, 1765–1780
DUPUY, ODRAN: Philadelphia, 1730s
DURGIN, F.: Andover, N.H., n.d.
DUSENBERRY, D. C.: Middletown, N.Y., *c.* 1790s–1820s
DUTCH, STEPHEN: Boston, 1800s–1810s
DUTTON, DAVID: Mt. Vernon, N.H., 1820s–1830s
DUTTON, REED: Milford, N.H., early nineteenth century; probably a dealer or trader
DYAR, WARREN: Lowell, Mass., 1830s
DYER, JOSEPH: Concord, Mass., to 1820; Middlebury, Vt., after 1820
DYSART, JAMES P.: Lancaster, Pa., 1850s

EASTERLY: *See* Esterlie
EASTMAN, ABEL B.: Concord, N.H., 1790s–1800s; Belfast, Me., 1800s–1810s; Haverhill, Mass., 1810s–1820s
EASTMAN, ABEL B.: May be duplication of above, or a son. Haverhill, Mass., 1820s
EASTMAN & CAREY: Brunswick, Me., 1805–1810
EASTMAN, ROBERT: Brunswick, Me., 1800s
EATON, ELON: Grand Rapids, Mich., 1860s
EATON, JOHN H.: Boston, 1820s
EBERMAN, C. F.: Lancaster, Pa., 1850s
EBERMAN, JACOB: Lancaster, Pa., 1795–1820
EBERMAN, JOHN (SR.): Lancaster, Pa., from 1760 to 1790s
EBERMAN, JOHN (JR.): Lancaster, Pa., 1773–1830
EBERMAN, JOSEPH: Lancaster, Pa., 1800–1844
EBY, CHRISTIAN: Manheim, Lancaster County, Pa., 1830s
EBY, GEORGE: Manheim and Sporting Hill, Lancaster County, Pa., 1830s–1850s
EBY, JACOB: Manheim and Sporting Hill, Lancaster County, Pa., *c.* 1800–1840s
EDGERTON, MATTHEW: New Brunswick, N.J. Cabinetmaker who made cases and cased movements, 1790s–1820s
EDMANDS & HAMBLETT: Boston, 1860s. Electric and electromagnetic clocks

EDMUNDS, JAMES: Charleston, S.C., advertised 1745

EDMUNDSON, THOMAS: York County, Pa., 1790s–1800. Elisha Kirk apprentice

EDSON, JONAH: Bridgewater, Mass., 1810s–1830s

EDWARDS, ABRAHAM: Ashby, Mass., 1780s–1830s; CALVIN, same place, same period

EDWARDS, A. & C. (partnership of Abraham and Calvin): Ashby, Mass. Manufactured one hundred or more clocks per year; wooden movement tall-case or hang-up clocks. Working in 1790s—before Eli Terry did his multiple producing of wooden movements

EDWARDS, JOHN: Ashby, Mass., *c.* 1810–1812

EDWARDS, NATHAN: Acton, Mass., 1800s–1810s

EDWARDS, SAMUEL: Gorham, Me., 1808–1830s. Prior to Gorham at Ashby, Mass., 1800–1808

EFFEY, WILLIAM: Davenport, Iowa, 1850s

EGGERT, D. & SON: New York City, 1840s

ELIOT, WILLIAM: Baltimore, 1790s

ELLICOTT, ANDREW: Solebury, Pa., 1774–1780. Was professor at West Point, 1812–1820

ELLICOTT, JOSEPH: Buckingham, Pa., 1760–1780s. Removed to Maryland where he founded the place known as Ellicotts Mills. His clocks are exceptionally fine, tall-cased examples, some with chimes of fourteen bells playing up to twenty-four tunes

ELLIOT, B. R.: Farmington, Me., 1850s

ELLIOT, HAZEN: Lowell, Mass., 1830s

ELLIOTT, J.: Plymouth Meeting (or so reported) Pa.. 1770s

ELLIOTT, LUTHER: Amherst, N.H., 1840s–1850s

ELLIOTT, ZEBULON: New York City, 1810s

ELLSWORTH, DAVID: Windsor, Conn., 1763–1820

ELMORE, M. W.: Ottawa, Kansas, 1860s

ELVINS, WILLIAM: Fells Point, Md., 1780–1799. Then at Baltimore

ELY, HUGH: New Hope, Pa., 1799–1803. Trenton, N.J., 1803–1820s

ELY, JOHN: Mifflinburg, Pa., 1800s–1830s

EMBREE, EFFINGHAM: New York City, 1780s–1790s

EMERSON, DUDLEY: Lyme, Conn., from *c.* 1787

EMERSON, D.: Lyme, Conn., 1780s–1790s

EMERSON, T. P.: LaFayette, Ind., 1860s

EMERY, JESSE: Weare, N.H., 1800s

EMMETT, EDWARD T.: Boston, advertised in 1764

EMMONS, ERASTUS: Trenton, N.J., 1800s–1820s

EMPIRE CLOCK COMPANY: Noble Jerome's enterprise of 1854, at Bristol, Conn.

ENDT, THEODORE: Philadelphia, 1740s. Father of John of New York and Philadelphia

ENGARD, SAMUEL: Philadelphia, 1830s–1840s

ENT (also ENDT), JOHN: New York City, advertised 1756. Philadelphia, 1760s–1790s

ERB, JOHN: Conestoga, Lancaster County, Pa., 1835–1860. Also at Safe Harbor

ESSEX, JOSEPH: Boston from 1712

EST, JOHN: New York City, 1750s–1760. Probably a dealer

ESTELLE, SAMUEL: Germantown, Ohio, 1870s

ESTERLIE, JOHN: Clockmaker of New Holland, Lancaster County, Pa., 1810–1830. In 1814 had a branch shop at Maytown, same county, and later a shop at Lebanon, Pa.

EUBANK & JEFFERIES: Glasgow, Ky., 1820s

EUBANK, JOSEPH (and JOSEPH & JAMES): Glasgow, Ky., 1819–1830

EUREKA MANUFACTURING CO.: Bristol, Conn., 1830s–1840s and perhaps to 1868

EVANS, ALFRED: Kirkwood, N.Y., 1840s–1860s. Known as a vendor, perhaps not a maker

EVANS, DAVID: Philadelphia, 1760–1772; Baltimore, 1773–1785

EVANS, S.: New Castle, Del., after 1740

EVANS (S.) & FURNISS (WILLIAM): New Castle, Del., early 1740s

EVANS, SEPTIMUS: Warwick, Pa., *c.* 1810

EVANS, THOMAS: New York, 1750s–1760s

EVANS, WILLIAM: Philadelphia, 1810s–1820s

EVERSOLE, H. E.: Logansport, Ind., 1860s

EVES, WILLIAM: Cincinnati, 1830s

EVITS, R.: Kalamazoo, Mich., 1840s

EYRE, JOHAN: Philadelphia, n.d.

EYSTER (*see also* OYSTER), P.: Hazy tradition has it that this man was working at Lancaster, Pa., late eighteenth century. Not verified, but probably correct

FABER, S.: New Bedford, Mass., 1810s–1820s

FADELEY, J. M.: Louisville, Ky., 1840s

FAFF, A. P.: Philadelphia, 1830s

FAHRENBACH, P.: Boston, 1850s

FALES, G. S.: New Bedford, Mass., 1810s to 1820

FALES, JAMES: New Bedford, 1810s–1830s

FALES, JAMES, JR.: New Bedford, 1830s

FARIS, CHARLES: Annapolis and Baltimore, Md., 1780s–1800

FARIS, HYRAM: Annapolis and Baltimore, Md., 1790s

FARIS, WILLIAM: Philadelphia prior to 1759; Annapolis, Md., 1760–1800

FARIS, WILLIAM, JR.: Annapolis and Baltimore, Md., 1780s. Later Edenton, N.C., and Havana, Cuba

FARMER, M. G.: Salem, Mass., 1840s

FARNHAM, S. S.: Oxford, N.Y., 1840s

FARNUM, HENRY & RUFUS: Boston, 1780s

FARR, JOHN C.: Philadelphia, 1840s

FASBENDER, J. H.: Charleston, S.C., mid to late eighteenth century

FASIG, CONRAD: Reading, Pa., *c.* 1790s–1820s

FAULKNER, JAMES: New York City, 1840s

FAVRE, CHRISTIAN: Lampeter, Lancaster County, Pa. Misspelling of Forrer, which see.

FAVRE, JOHN JAMES: Philadelphia, 1797

FAY, HENRY: Albany, N.Y., 1850s

FEDDERSEN, H. F.: Lancaster, Pa., 1850s

FEHLINGER, SAMUEL: Gettysburg, Pa., 1800s

FELIX, J.: Columbia, Lancaster County, Pa., 1840s–1850s

FELLOWS, ABRAHAM: Troy and Waterford, N. Y., 1810s–1835

FELLOWS, JAMES: Lowell, Mass., 1830s

FELLOWS, READ & OLCOTT: New York City, 1820s–1830s. Probably dealers

FELLOWS, STORM & CARGILL: New York City dealers, 1830s

FENLESTER, A.: Baltimore, 1800s

FERRIS, W.: Philadelphia, 1810s

FERRIS, BENJAMIN: Philadelphia in 1810s; Wilmington, Del., 1813

FERRIS & MCELWEE: Philadelphia, 1810s

FERRIS, ZIBA: Wilmington, Del., 1806–1850. Tall, shelf, and wall clocks. Maker died, 1875

FERTIG, BENJAMIN: Philadelphia, 1810s

FERTIG, JACOB: Vincent, Chester County, Pa., 1802–1823

FESSLER, JOHN: Frederick, Md., 1780–1820

FESSLER, JOHN, JR.: Frederick, Md., 1820s–1840s

FESSLER, JOHN: Frederick, Md., 1780s–1820s. Recent data indicate that this man, or another named John, was working at Frederick up to 1840s

FETON, J.: Philadelphia, 1820s–1840s

FIELD, JOHN: Poughkeepsie, N.Y., 1790s–1820. Also a brass founder

FIELD, PETER: New York City, 1800s; Peter Field, Jr., also worked at New York City to 1830

FIFFE, H.: n.p., n.d.

FILBER or FILBERT, JOHN: York, Pa., 1790s–1810; Lancaster, Pa., 1810–1820; York after 1820

FINLEY, JOHN: Charlestown, Md., 1754

FINNEY, JOHN: Believed to be same as Finley, same city, same date

FISH, ISAAC: Utica, N.Y., 1840s

FISHER, GEORGE: Frederick, Md., 1830s–1850

FISHER, GEORGE: Lancaster, Pa., 1780s–1800s. Advertised for a journeyman helper, 1800, and offered clock parts, tools, et cetera for sale

FISHER, JOHN: Lampeter Square, Lancaster, Pa., 1749–1756. Thereafter at York, Pa., where he became the town's first and finest clockmaker. His masterpiece (now owned by Yale University) was publicized in 1790 in the Baltimore *Gazette.* Fisher died in 1808 possessed of one organ clock, one musical clock, one time clock, and eleven other timepieces in work. Portrait, hitherto unpublished, of this maker appears on page 142

FITCH, JOHN: Clock and watchmaker, inventor of steamboat, and general hard-luck man who was an itinerant, restless soul. Stayed put longest at Windsor, Conn., 1764–1769; Trenton, N.J., 1770–1776, and Philadelphia, 1780s–1790

FITCH, JONAS: Pepperell, Mass., 1770s–1800s

FITE, JOHN: Baltimore, 1800s–1810

FITTS, GEORGE: Bangor, Me., 1830s–1860s

FITZ, WILLIAM: Portsmouth, N.H., 1760s–1780s

FIX, GEORGE: Reading, Pa., 1820s–1840s

FIX, JOSEPH: Reading, Pa., 1820s–1840s

FLETCHER, CHARLES & THOMAS: Importers, Philadelphia, 1830s

FLING, DANIEL: Mt. Holly, N.J., and Philadelphia, 1810s

FLOWER, HENRY: Philadelphia, 1750s

FLOYD, THOMAS: Charleston, S.C., advertised 1767–1770s

FOARD: *See* FORD

FOLGER, WALTER: Nantucket, Mass., 1787–1820. A gifted amateur maker

FOLMAR, A.: New York City, 1810s

FOOTE, CHARLES: Bristol, Conn., 1852–55

FOOTE, WILLIAM: Middletown and East Haddam, Conn., 1790s–1820

FORBACH, JOSEPH: New York City, 1850s

FORBES & TUCKER: Concord, N.H., 1830s–1840s; probably dealers

FORBES, JOHN: Philadelphia, 1760s–1770s; Hartford, Conn., after 1771

FORBES, W.: Bristol, N.H., 1840s

FORD, GEORGE: Lancaster, Pa., 1811–1840

FORD, GEORGE, JR.: Lancaster, Pa., 1825–1845

FORD, PETER: York, Pa., *c.* 1783–1819. Also spelled Foard in records

FORD, SOUTHERLAND: Charleston, S.C., 1740s

FORESTVILLE MANUFACTURING CO.: Bristol, Conn., 1835–1839. Some clocks bear papers or labels with name also of Hills, Brown & Co and J. C. Brown & Co.

FORESTVILLE CLOCK MANUFACTORY: Same company operating under management of J. C. Brown. Made the now much desired acorn clocks, some bearing a tablet picturing J. C. Brown's residence. Operating to 1855

FORRER, CHRISTIAN & DANIEL: Lampeter Square, Lancaster, Pa., 1754–1777. Apprentices to Jean François Guillerat of Delamont, the Grand Val, Switzerland, came to the colonies in 1754 and opened shop near Lancaster, Pa. Finest Forrer clocks are in cases by their fellow Swiss, the fine cabinetmaker Bachman (which see in this listing). Fine C. & D. Forrer clock in Ford museum is misnamed "Farrar" on the newly painted dial. Forrers remained in business only to the 1770s. They had a sizable fortune from Switzerland, nearly ten thousand pounds, and from 1777 invested in real estate, farms, ferries, and other properties

FOSTER, J. C.: Portland, Me., 1830s

FOSTER, ———: Amherst, N.H., 1840s

FOSTER, NATHANIEL: Newburyport, Mass., 1818–1830s

FOSTER, THOMAS: With Nathaniel Foster at Newburyport, Mass., in 1820s

FOWELL, JOHN: Boston, 1805

FOWELL, NATHANIEL: Boston, 1803

FOWLE, J. H.: Northampton, Mass., 1850s–1860s

FOWLE, NATHAN: Charleston, S.C., mid-eighteenth century

FOX, ASA: Buffalo, N.Y., 1810s

FOXCROFT, J. A. (also FOXCROFT & CLARK): Baltimore, as individual, 1820s–1830s and as partnership, 1830 to 1838–9

FRAGERCRANS, P.: Princeton, Ill., 1860s

FRANCIS (BASIL) & VUILLE (ALEXANDER): Baltimore, 1760s

FRANCIS, BASIL: Baltimore, 1760s–1772; Albany, N.Y., 1772–1780s

FRANCIS, FIELD & FRANCIS: Toymakers of Philadelphia who are reported as making clocks. May have made only toy clocks

FRANCK, PHILIP: New Berlin, Pa., 1800s–1850s

FRANKLIN & MARSHALL: Seneca Falls, N.Y. Cased Connecticut movements in cases designed by Munger of Auburn, N.Y.

FRARY, OBEDIAH: Southampton, Mass., 1740s–1770s

FRASER, JACOB: New Ephrata (now Lincoln), Lancaster County, Pa., 1830s–1860s

FRASER, SAMUEL & WILLIAM: New Ephrata and Lincoln, Lancaster County, Pa., continuously from 1855 to 1940. WILLIAM worked 1855–1900; SAMUEL, 1880 to 1940. This business was founded 1834 by William Fraser

FRASER, WILLIAM: Apprenticed to Samuel Parke, Philadelphia, 1814–1821; removed to New Holland, Lancaster County, working for Esterlie and then, 1834, set up his own shop at New Ephrata

FRAZER, ALEXANDER: Menallen Township, Adams County, Pa., 1850s

FRAZER, JAMES: Logansport, Ind., 1830s–1840s

FRAZER, ROBERT: Lexington and Paris, Ky., 1790s–1800s

FRAZIER, SAMUEL: Baltimore, 1820s

FREEMAN BROTHERS: Augusta, Ga., 1850s–1860s

FRENCH, CHARLES: Brattleboro, or Rutland, Vt., migrated to Ohio *c.* 1825

FRENCH, JAMES O.: Baltimore, 1770s

FRENCH, LEMUEL: Boston, 1790s–1820

FRIEND, EDGELL: New York City, 1820s–1830s. Also a brass founder of clock parts

FRIEND, GEORGE: New York City, 1820s

FRINK, URBAN: Brattleboro, Vt., 1870s–1880s

FRONT, DANIEL: Reading (Pa., or Mass.?), working in 1780s–1790s Doubtful only as to exact locale; clocks bearing name and "Reading" without state designation are reported from Pennsylvania *and* Massachusetts

FROST & MUMFORD: Providence, R.I., 1810s

FROST, JONATHAN: Reading, Mass. *See* Pratt & Frost

FROST, OLIVER: Providence, R.I., 1800s

FRYE, JAMES: Haverhill, Mass., n.d.

FURNIVALL, JAMES: Marblehead, Mass., 1770s–1780s

FYLER, ORASMUS: Burke, Vt., *c.* 1830s

GAILLARD, PETER: Reading, Pa., 1790s

GAINES, JOHN: Portsmouth, N.H., 1800s

GALBRAITH, PATRICK: Philadelphia, 1796–1811

GALE, DANIEL: Bristol, Conn.; inventor of calendar clock made by Welch, Spring & Co.

GALPIN, MOSES: Distributor who had clocks made with his name on dial. Jerome and other Bristol makers produced clocks for this man

GALT, PETER: Baltimore, 1810s–1812

GALT, SAMUEL: Williamsburg, Va., 1750s

GALT, WILLIAM: Washington, D.C., 1810s to 1840s

GARDINER, B.: N.Y. City dealer 1830s–1840s

GARDINER, J. B.: Ansonia, Conn., 1857

GARRET, PHILIP (and also PHILIP GARRET & SONS): Philadelphia, 1810s–1820s alone and as partnership in 1830s

GARRETT, BENJAMIN: Goshen, Chester County, Pa., 1800–1825

GARTNER, JACOB: York County, Pa., 1780s–1800s

GATES, ZACHEUS: Charlestown, Mass., 1800s–1820s

GAW, WILLIAM: Philadelphia, 1810s–1820s

GAYHART, S.: Camden, N.J., 1840s

GAYLORD, C. E.: Chicago, 1856

GAYLORD, HOMER: Norfolk, Conn., 1800s; Homer, N.Y., 1810s

GEBHARD, R. L.: Son of Christian Gebhard, maker of astronomical clocks in France and Germany, mid nineteenth century, who brought one of the most complicated to the United States where it has been exhibited and in 1946 was still in running order, at Louisville, Ky.

GEDDES, CHARLES: Boston, 1770; New York City, 1776

GEGYE, RENE: Charleston, S.C., 1740s–1760s

GEIGER, JACOB, and/or JONAH: Northampton, now Allentown, Pa., 1787–1790s. Working in Maryland after 1793

GELSTON, GEORGE S.: New York City, 1830s

GEMMILL, JOHN: York, Pa., 1756–1760

GERDING & SIEMON: New York City importers of French clocks, 1830s

GERRISH, OLIVER: Portland, Me., 1830s

GETZ, PETER: Lancaster, Pa., 1790s–1820. Goldsmith, silversmith, die-cutter, and clock and watchmaker. David Rittenhouse called him an ingenious workman. Made some dies for the United States Mint

GIBBONS, THOMAS: Philadelphia, n.d.

GILBERT, JESSE: Brooklyn, N.Y., 1840s

GILBERT, J. F.: Rochester, N.Y., 1830. Listed as manufacturer. Made a patented improved looking-glass clock; may have been with Connecticut movement

GILBERT, JORDAN & SMITH: New York City, 1830s

GILBERT MANUFACTURING CO.: Winsted, Conn., 1866–1871

GILBERT, RICHARDS & CO.: Chester, Conn., 1830s

GILBERT, MARSH & CO. (or GILBERT & MARSH): Winsted, Conn., 1820s. William L. Gilbert and George Marsh

GILBERT, WILLIAM L.: Winsted, Conn., second quarter nineteenth century

GILES, JOSEPH: Trenton, N.J., 1800s–1820s

GILL, CALEB: Hingham, Mass., 1780s

GILL, ISAAC: Charleston, S.C., *c.* 1780s–1790s

GILL, LEAVITT: Hingham, Mass., 1780s

GILLIAM, EDWARD: Pittsburgh, Pa., 1830s

GILLMAN, B. C.: Exeter, N.H., 1780s–1830s. Tall, wall, and shelf clocks

GILMORE, WILLIAM: Pittsburgh, Pa., 1830s

GIRAUD, VICTOR: New York City, 1840s

GLINGERMAN: *See* Klingerman

GLORE, S.: New Hampshire (n.p.) *c.* 1830s

GLOVER, HENRY: New York City and Brooklyn, 1840s

GLOVER, WILLIAM: Boston, 1820s

GNECH (GNECHT; KNECHT) CHARLES D.: Charleston, S.C., 1820s

GOBEL, HENRY: New York City, 1850s

GOBRECHT, DAVID: Hanover, Pa., 1795–1829. Born at Lancaster, Pa., son of David Gobrecht

GOBRECHT, ELI & JACOB: Two men operating independently and so signing thirty-hour type tall-case clocks, York County, Pa., in 1800s

GODDARD, GEORGE S.: Boston, 1820s

GODDARD, NICHOLS: Northampton, Mass., 1793–1797 and Rutland, Vt., 1797. After 1797 LORD & GODDARD

GODFREY, WILLIAM: Philadelphia, 1750s–1760s

GODSCHALK, JACOB: Towamencin, Pa., 1720s to 1763–4; then at Philadelphia to 1780

GODSOE, B. F.: New York City, 1850

GOFF, CHARLES: n.p., n.d.

GOLDER, JOHN: New York City, 1810s

GOODFELLOW & SONS: Philadelphia, 1790s

GOODFELLOW, WILLIAM: Philadelphia, 1790s

GOODFELLOW, WILLIAM: Philadelphia, 1790s: WILLIAM & SON, 1800s

GOODFELLOW, WILLIAM: (son of William) Philadelphia, 1810s–1820s

GOODHART, JACOB: Lebanon, Pa., 1790s–1810s

GOODHUE, D. T.: Providence, R.I., 1820s

GOODHUE, RICHARD: Portland, Me., 1830s

GOODING, ALANSON: New Bedford, Mass., 1800s–1840

GOODING, HENRY: Duxbury, Mass., 1800s; Boston, 1810s–1850s

GOODING, JOHN: Plymouth, Mass., late 1790s or early 1800s to *c.* 1848–50

GOODING, JOSEPH: Dighton, Mass., 1793–1826; Troy (now Fall River), Mass., to 1838; again at Dighton to 1850

GOODING, JOSEPHUS: Bristol, R.I., 1830s–1850s

GOODING, JOSIAH: Bristol, R.I., 1790s–1840s–1850s

GOODMAN, JOHN: Cleveland, Ohio, 1850s

GOODMAN, THOMAS: Charleston, S.C., 1730s–1750s

GOODRICH, CHAUNCEY: Bristol, Conn., prior to 1830; then Ingraham & Goodrich (1833), Smith & Goodrich, Brown & Goodrich (1845–47)

GOODSPEED, LOT: Middletown, Conn., 1820s. Cased and finished clocks but did not make movements. Used Samuel Terry movements

GOODWIN & FRISBIE: Unionville, Conn., 1830s–1850s

GOODWIN, E. O.: Bristol, Conn., casemaker who marketed clocks under his name in 1850s but did not make movements

GOODWIN, HORACE, JR.: Hartford, Conn., 1830s

GOODWIN, V. C.: Unionville, Conn. Finished and cased but did not make clock movements

GOODWIN, WALLACE: Attleboro, Mass., 1850s

GORDON, SMYLEY: Lowell, Mass., 1830s

GORDON, THOMAS: New York, 1750s; Boston, 1760s. Probably also a dealer

GORGAS, BENJAMIN: Son of John Gorgas. Worked with his brother Jacob, near Ephrata, Lancaster County, Pa., 1760s–1790s

GORGAS, JACOB: Near Ephrata, Lancaster County, Pa., 1762–1797. Master clockmaker who issued a catalogue of his engraved work on dials *c.* 1765. Jacob Gorgas made in all one hundred and fifty fine tall-case clocks. He cast, cut, and assembled all his own movements. He was a cousin of David Rittenhouse. His father, John Gorgas, emigrated from the Netherlands to Philadelphia where he married Sophia Rittenhouse

GORGAS, JOHN: Father of Jacob, Germantown, Pa., 1710s–1750s. Believed to have taught David Rittenhouse.

GORGAS, JOSEPH: Son of Jacob. Worked near Ephrata and at Elizabethtown, Lancaster County, Pa., 1795–1815

GORGAS, SOLOMON: Son of Jacob. Worked in his father's shop and then alone, to 1800, after which he removed to Cumberland County, Pa., and abandoned the craft

GOSLER, GEORGE A.: York, Pa., 1800s

GOULD, ABIJAH: Nashua, N.H., 1800s–1820s; Rochester, N.Y., 1830s

GOVETT, GEORGE: Norristown, Pa., 1810s–1830s

GOWAN, PETER D.: Charleston, S.C., 1820s

GRAFF, JOSEPH: Northampton, now Allentown, Pa., 1790s–1800s. Moved to Maryland *c.* 1803

GRANT, ALFRED: New Haven, Conn., 1840s–1850s

GRANT, ISRAEL: Saint Louis, Mo., 1810s

GRANT, JAMES: Hartford, Conn., 1790s; advertised 1794. Weathersfield, Conn., after 1796

GRANT, WILLIAM: Boston, 1810s–1840s
GRAVES, ALFRED: Willow Grove, Pa., n.d., but early nineteenth century
GRAY, JAMES: New York City, 1840s
GREEN, JOHN: Carlisle, Pa., n.d., but early nineteenth century
GREEN, JOHN: Philadelphia, 1790s–?
GREENLEAF, DAVID: Hartford, Conn., 1788–1796
GREENLEAF, STEPHEN: Sundial maker, Boston, 1740s
GREENOUGH, N. C.: Newburyport, Mass., 1840s
GREER, JOHN: Carlisle, Pa., 1770s
GREINER, CHARLES: Charleston, S.C., *c.* 1780s
GRIDLEY, L. P. & C. E.: Logansport, Ind., 1860s–1870s
GRIDLEY, MARTIN: Logansport, Ind., 1830s–1840s
GRIDLEY, TIMOTHY: Sanbornton, N.H., 1810s
GRIFFEN, PETER: New York City, 1810s
GRIFFIN, HENRY: New York City 1790s–1810s; Brooklyn, 1810s–1820s
GRIFFIN & HOYT: New York City, 1820s–1830s
GRIFFITH, EDWARD: Litchfield, Conn., advertised 1790; Charleston, S.C., *c.* 1794; Savannah, Ga., after 1796
GRIFFITH, OWEN: Philadelphia, n.d.
GRIFFT: Kutztown, Pa., 1800s
GRIGGS, EBENEZER: Bristol, Conn., 1810
GRIGGS, SOLOMON: Bristol, Conn., 1810
GRIM, GEORGE: Orwigsburg, Pa., 1810s–1830s
GRISWOLD, CHARLES: New Haven, Conn., 1840s–1850s
GRISWOLD, DANIEL W.: East Hartford, Conn., 1789–1840
GROFF, AMOS: Rawlinsville, Lancaster County, Pa., 1850s
GROPENGIESSER, J. L.: Philadelphia, 1840s
GROTZ, ISAAC: Bethlehem and Easton, Pa., 1810s–1830s
GROVE, CHRISTIAN: Heidelberg, York County, Pa., 1800s
GROVE, WILLIAM: Hanover, Pa., 1830s–1870s
GRUBY, EDWARD L.: Portland, Me., 1830s
GRUMBINE, DANIEL: East Berlin & Hanover, Pa., 1820s–1870s
GUILD, JEREMIAH: Cincinnati, 1830s
GUILE, JOHN: Philadelphia, 1810s–1820
GUIMARTIN (also GILMARTIN), JOHN: Augusta, Ga., 1820s
GUINARD, F. E.: Baltimore, Md., 1810s–1820
GUNKLE (KUNKLE), JOHN: Cocalico, Lancaster, Pa., 1830–1840
GURNEY, L. F.: N. Bridgewater, Mass., 1860s

HAAS & CO.: New York City, 1820s–1830. Musical clocks
HAAS & GOETZ: New York City, 1820s–1830s
HAAS, GOTTLEIB: Red Hook (Dutchess County), N.Y., 1830s

HAETTICH, ANDREW: Cleveland, Ohio, 1850s
HAGE: *See* Hege and Hagey
HAGEY, GEORGE: Trappe, Pa., 1810s–1850
HAGEY, JOHN: Philadelphia, *c.* 1830
HAGEY, JONAS: Springtown, Pa., *c.* 1830
HAGUE, B.: New York City, 1850s
HAHN, HENRY: Reading, Pa., 1790s. Numbered his clocks. Dials known made of brass, pewter, iron and tin—all used on one dial
HAHN, JACOB: Reading, Pa., 1790s
HAIGHT (or HAIGH), J.: Baltimore, 1820s–1830s
HALE, JOSHUA: Lowell, Mass., 1840s
HALL & WADE: Newfield, Conn., *c.* 1793–1797
HALL, ASAPH: Goshen, Conn., *c.* 1820s–1840. Made eight-day wooden-movement clocks
HALL, CHRISTIAN: Litiz (now Lititz), Lancaster County, Pa., 1803–1840
HALL, D. G.: Lewiston, Me., 1850s–1860
HALL, HENRY WILLIAM: Litiz (now Lititz), Lancaster County, Pa., *c.* 1830–1860
HALL, JOHN: Philadelphia, 1810s; West Chester, Pa., 1815–1850
HALL, JOHN H.: New Haven, Conn., 1780s–1800. His label, engraved by Amos Doolittle, reads "Clocks Made"
HALL, PETER: Philadelphia, 1820s
HALL, SEYMOUR & CO.: Unionville, Conn., 1820s
HALLIDAY, E. H.: Camden, N.J., 1790s–1820s
HALLIDAY, HIRAM: Albany, N.Y., 1830s–1840s
HAM, GEORGE: Portsmouth, N.H., 1810s
HAM, SUPPLY: Portsmouth, N.H., 1790s–1820s
HAMILEN, NATHANIEL: Augusta, Me., 1790s–1820s
HAMILTON, S. P.: Savannah, Ga., 1860s
HAMLIN, WILLIAM: Providence, R.I., 1790s
HAMMERER, JACOB: n.p., n.d.
HAMMOND, SAMUEL: New York City, 1840s–1860s
HAMPTON, SAMUEL: Chelsea, Mass., 1840s
HANKS, BENJAMIN: Mansfield, Conn., *c.* 1775; Windham, Conn., *c.* 1777; Litchfield, Conn., *c.* 1785. Advertised in that year. Invented a unique self-winding clock which was kept wound by a small set of wind vanes exposed outdoors and connected to the clock with gears. Only one example, and that incomplete, reported as still extant
HANNA, HUGH: Wabash, Ind., 1830s. Probably salesman only. Had exclusive rights to vend wooden clocks in Wabash County, 1834

HANSELL, JAMES: Philadelphia, 1810s–1840s. Made fine shelf clocks
HARDEN, JAMES: Philadelphia, 1810s
HARDER, W. A.: New York City, 1840s
HARDMAN, J.: Lebanon, Ohio, 1820s
HARDY, WILLIAM: Charleston, S.C., 1770s
HARLACHER, BENJAMIN: York County, Pa., 1799–1829
HARLAND, THOMAS: Norwich, Conn. Advertised 1773, 1780, 1787, 1794. Died, 1807. Had a manufactory; employed fine workmen, including Cleveland, Dodge, Tracy, and Burnap
HARMSON, ———: Newport, R.I., 1720s
HARPUR, WILLIAM: Philadelphia, 1850s
HARRIS, JOHN: Charleston, S.C., *c.* 1715–1738
HARRISON, JAMES: Waterbury, Conn., 1790–1810; Boston, 1814–15; New York City, 1820s–1830s
HARRISON, JOHN: Philadelphia, n.d.
HARRISON, JOHN MURRAY (probably same as John), n.d.
HARRISON, LEMUEL: Waterbury, Conn., 1790s–1810s
HARRISON, WOOSTER: (brother of James) Trumbull, Conn., from 1795; advertised in 1800
HART, ALPHA: Goshen, Conn., 1820s
HART & WILCOX: Norwich, Conn., n.d.
HART, ELIPHAZ: Norwich, Conn., 1810s
HART, G.: Bridgeport, Pa., 1850s
HART, HENRY: Goshen, Conn., 1820s
HART, JUDAH: Norwich, Conn., 1810s–1820s
HART, ORRIN: Bristol, Conn., 1824–1833. Manufacturer
HARTLEY, JOHN: York, Pa., *c.* 1800–1820s
HARTMAN, A.: New York City, 1840s
HARTH, H. C.: Manufacturer, New York City, 1850s
HARTZLER, JOSEPH: Millwright and clockmaker of Beartown, Lancaster County, Pa., 1850s
HARWOOD, GEORGE: Rochester, N.Y., 1830s. Probably a dealer only
HASELTON & WENTWORTH: Lowell, Mass., 1830s
HASTINGS, B. B.: Cleveland, Ohio, 1830s, advertised in 1837
HATCH, GEORGE D.: Attleboro, Mass., 1810s–1850s
HATCH, JOHN B.: Attleboro, Mass., 1870s
HATCH, JONATHAN: Westtown, Pa., 1810s
HAUPT, H.: Cairo, Ill., 1860s
HAWXHURST & DEMILT: New York City, 1790s
HAWXHURST, NATHANIEL: New York City, 1780s–1790s
HAYES, PETER: Poughkeepsie, N.Y., 1830s
HAZEN, N. S.: Cincinnati, Ohio, 1830s–1840s

HEAGY, JACOB: Franconia, N.H., 1790s–1810s. Not yet authenticated as to date and place

HEALY, CHARLES: Syracuse, N.Y., 1840–1850s

HEALY, JOHN W.: Worcester, Mass., manufacturer, 1850s

HEATH, REUBEN: Scottsville, N.Y., 1790s–1810s

HEATH, WILLARD B.: Bangor, Me., 1830s–1870s

HEDGES, GEORGE: Waterford, N.Y., 1820s–1830; Buffalo, 1830s

HEFFLEY, ANNANIAS: Berlin, Pa., *c.* 1825–1865

HEFFLEY, DANIEL: Berlin, Pa., *c.* 1825–1865

HEFFORDS, M.: Middleboro, Mass., n.d.

HEGE, JACOB: Lower Salford, Pa., late eighteenth and early nineteenth century. Made over one hundred thirty-hour tall clocks; had a small factory, probably before the now-famed Eli Terry hang-up clock factory at Plymouth, Conn.

HEGE, SAMUEL: Franconia, Pa., early to mid eighteenth century. Made many thirty-hour and eight-day brass tall clocks. Over one hundred credited to him

HEILIG, HERMAN: Germantown, Pa., 1850s

HEILIG, JACOB: Lancaster and Philadelphia, Pa., 1770s–1820s

HEILIG, JOHN: Germantown, Pa., 1820s

HEINTZELMAN, HIERONYMOUS: Lampeter Square and Willow Street, Lancaster, Pa., from *c.* 1750. A Swiss clockmaker associated with C. & D. Forrer, (which see). Any tall clocks of *c.* 1750–1770 marked Heintzelman only, or "H.H." only, are by this maker. Some are found in Bachman cases

HEINTZELMAN, JOHN CONRAD: Manheim, Lancaster, Pa., son of Hieronymous, working *c.* 1786–1804. This maker was grandfather of General Samuel P. Heintzelman.

HEINTZELMAN, PETER: Lancaster County, Pa. (various locales), 1806–1816

HEINY, CLEMENTS: New York City, 1840s

HEISLEY, FREDERICK: Lancaster, Pa., b.1759–d.1839. Partner of John Hoff, 1794–1802. Frederick, Md., 1783–1793; Harrisburg, Pa., *c.* 1805; and finally at Pittsburgh, Pa., from 1820s to 1839

HEISLELY (or HEISLEY), F. A.: Pittsburgh, Pa., 1820s–1830s. Probably same as Heisley, Frederick, above. Listed in Pittsburgh as clock, watch, and mathematical instrument maker

HEMINGWAY, A.: Chicago, 1856. Factor and agent

HEMPSON, ROBERT: New York City, 1820s–1830s

HENDERSON, WILLIAM: New Castle, Del., 1770s

HENDRICK, BARNES & CO.: Forestville, Conn., 1849–1852

HENDRICKS, URIAH: New York City, 1750–1770. Probably also a dealer

HENDRIE, W. A.: Chicago, 1856
HENEBERGER, P.: Harrisburg, Pa., 1790–1830
HEPTON, F.: Philadelphia, 1780s
HEQUEMBOURG, C.: New Haven, Conn., 1810s–1830s. Dealer
HERANCOURT (G.) & DRESBACHE (C. F.): Columbus, Ohio, 1830s
HERON, E.: Charleston, S.C., 1780s–1790s
HERON, ISAAC: Boundbrook, N.J., advertised, 1764; New York City, 1768–1776
HERON, JAMES: Newtown, Pa., *c.* 1760–1780
HERR, WILLIAM, JR.: Providence, R.I., 1848
HERTZ, JACOB: Lancaster and Berks counties, Pa., *c.* 1780–1810. One tall-case clock known. Case of pine, painted, with vine-carved quarter columns on both body and base. Dial is painted
HERWICK (also HARDWICK), JACOB: Carlisle, Pa., 1780s
HEWITT, E. A.: N. Bridgewater, Mass., 1860s
HEYDORN & IMLAY: Successors to Isaac Doolittle, Conn., 1808–1811
HIBBARD, CALEB: Chester County, Pa., 1800–1818
HIBBEN, ANDREW: Charleston, S.C., 1760–1770
HICKS, WILLET: New York City, 1790s
HILDEBURN & WATSON: Philadelphia, 1830s
HILDEBURN & WOODWORTH: Philadelphia, 1810s
HILDEBURN, S.: Philadelphia, 1810s
HILDEBURN, W.: Philadelphia, 1810s–1820
HILDRETH, JONAS: Salisbury, Vt., 1800s
HILL & ROSS: Zanesville, Ohio, 1830s
HILL, BENJAMIN: Berks County (Richmond Township), Pa., 1800s
HILL, D.: Reading, Pa., 1820–1840
HILL, D.: Harrisburg, Pa., 1810–1840
HILL, E. J.: Albion, N.Y., 1850s–1860s
HILL, HENRY: New York City, 1740s–1760s
HILL, JOACHIM: Flemington, N.J., 1810s–1850s
HILL, JOHN B.: Beverly, Mass., 1850s–1860s
HILL, PETER: Burlington, N.J., eighteenth century. According to George De Cou, Esq., of Moorestown, N.J., Peter Hill was a clockmaker of color—a Negro who had learned the trade and mastered it. This is a clockmaker whose history should be studied further for its social significance
HILL, SAMUEL: Harrisburg, Pa., 1786–1809. Came direct from England
HILL, WILLIAM: New York City, 1810s
HILLER, JOSEPH: Salem, Mass., after 1770; Boston, 1760s–1770

HILLERD (OR HILLIARD) CHRISTOPHER: Hagerstown, Md., 1800s–1840s

HILLIARD, JAMES: Charleston, S.C., 1730s

HILLMAN, F.: New York City, 1850s

HILLS, AMARIAH: New York City, 1840s

HILLS, BROWN & Co.: Bristol, Conn., 1840–41

HILLS, CHARLES C.: Haverhill, Mass., n.d.

HILLS, D. B.: Plainville, Conn., 1870–1880

HILLS, GOODRICH & Co.: Plainville, Conn., 1840s–1850s

HIMELY (HIMPLY: HIMILY) JOHN: Charleston, S.C., 1780s

HINMAN, ALONZO: New Haven, Conn., 1840s–1850s

HINSHON, J. P.: Terre Haute, Ind., 1850s

HITCHCOCK, H.: Lodi, N.Y., 1800s

HITCHCOCK, S. R.: Humphreysville, N.Y., 1810s

HOADLEY, LUTHER: Winchester and Winsted, Conn., 1800s–1813

HOADLEY, S. & L.: Samuel and Luther Hoadley, Winchester, and/or Winsted, Conn., 1800s–1813

HOADLEY, SILAS: Plymouth, Conn., late 1790s to 1840s. With Seth Thomas took over the Eli Terry hang-up clock factory which he operated with Thomas to 1813 and thereafter alone

HOADLEYS' & WHITING: Winchester, Conn., 1810s–1820s

HOBBS, JAMES: Baltimore, 1790s–1800s

HOCKER, G.: Ephrata, Lancaster County, Pa., 1760s. Reported as being a clockmaker affiliated with the Seventh Day Baptists monastery

HODGES, ERASTUS: Torrington, Conn., 1830s

HODGES & NORTH: Wolcottville, Conn., 1830s

HODGSON, WILLIAM: Philadelphia, 1780s

HOFER, CHARLES: Macon, Miss., 1850s

HOFF & HEISELY: Lancaster, Pa., 1796–1800s

HOFF, GEORGE: Lancaster, Pa., 1766–1816. Tall-case, hour, quarter-hour, and chiming clocks. Made many clocks over a long period

HOFF, JOHN: Lancaster, Pa. (son of George), 1785–1819

HOFFARD, SAMUEL: Berlin, Pa., 1825–1850

HOFFMAN, C. M.: Lebanon, N.H., 1850s–1860s

HOFFNER, HENRY: Philadelphia, 1790s

HOKE, GEORGE: Hanover, Pa., 1810s–1820s

HOLBROOK, GEORGE H.: Brookfield and Medway, Mass., 1800s

HOLBROOK, H.: Medway, Mass., 1830s

HOLDEN, ELY: Philadelphia, 1840s–1850. Manufacturer. Made banjo-style clocks

HOLDEN, HENRY: New Haven, Conn., 1840s–1850. Named as a "clocksmith"

HOLDEN, JOSEPH: Dayton, Ohio, 1830s

HOLLINSHEAD, HUGH: Mt. Holly & Moorestown, N.J., last half eighteenth century

HOLLINSHEAD, GEORGE: Woodstown, N.J., last half eighteenth century

HOLLINSHEAD, JACOB: Salem, N.J., 1770s

HOLLINSHEAD, JOHN: Burlington, N.J., 1770s–1780s

HOLLINSHEAD, JOSEPH: Burlington, N.J., *c.* 1740s

HOLLINSHEAD, JOSEPH, JR.: Burlington, N.J., 1770s

HOLLINSHEAD, MORGAN: Moorestown, formerly Chester, N.J., 1770s–1830s

HOLLIS, JOSEPH: West Chester, Pa., 1820s

HOLLISTER, J. H.: Greenfield, Mass., 1850s–1860s

HOLLOWAY, ROBERT: Baltimore, 1820s; partner of Benjamin Chandlee

HOLMAN, D.: Baltimore, 1800s–1820s. Made banjo clocks, as fine as any examples produced by any of the Willards. This man's clocks are worthy of special study and a monograph of some scope

HOLMAN, S.: Hartford, Conn., 1810s

HOLMES, J.: Philadelphia, 1840s

HOLMGREEN, CHARLES: Hamilton, N.Y., 1850s–1860s

HOLTON, HARRY: Wells River, Vt., 1850s–1860s

HOLWAY, PHILIP: Falmouth, Mass., 1800s

HOMER, W.: Moreland, Pa., 1840s

HOOD, FRANCIS: New York City, 1810s

HOOD, JOHN: Philadelphia, n.d.

HOOK, MICHAEL: Lancaster, Pa., 1780s–1800s

HOOKER & GOODENOUGH: Bristol, Conn., 1840s

HOOKER & MORGAN: Pine Plains, N.Y., 1810s–1820

HOOLEY, RICHARD: Flemington, N.J., 1810–1830. Information supplied by Hiram E. Deats, Esq., Flemington, N.J., 1946

HOOVER, JOHN: Emmitsburg, Md., 1754

HOPKINS & ALFRED: Harwinton, Conn., 1820–1825; Hartford, 1825–1845

HOPKINS & LEWIS: Litchfield, Conn., 1820s. Asa Hopkins, partner, was a maker of clockmakers' engines, 1810

HOPKINS, ASA: Litchfield, Conn., 1810s–1820s

HOPKINS, H. P.: Philadelphia, 1830s

HOPKINS, JASON: Lincoln, Me., 1840s–1850s; Bangor, Me., to 1862. Inventor of the Auburndale watch. Also manufactured pianos and clock cases

HOPPER, JOSEPH: Philadelphia, 1810s–1820s

HOQUET, AUGUSTUS: Philadelphia, 1820s

HORGAS, JOSEPH: Myerstown, Pa., 1800s–1810s. Clock so marked or reported so marked, in George Horace Lorimer sale March 31, 1944. This is probably a clock by Joseph Gorgas, who worked at Myerstown, and is mentioned in this list. (The capital letter "G" in Old English can quite readily be mistaken for an "H.")

HORN, E.: Lowell, Mass., 1830s

HORN, E. B.: Boston, 1840s

HORTON, ALFRED: New Haven, Conn. 1840s–1850s

HORTON & PECK: Litchfield, Conn., 1800s

HORTON, H. B.: Patentee (1865) of the calendar clock made by Ithaca Clock Co. Was clockmaker at Cincinnati, 1830s–1840s

HORWOOD, CHARLES: Bristol, Conn., *c.* 1750–1780

HOSTETTER, JACOB, SR.: Hanover, Pa., 1788–1825; thereafter at New Lisbon, Ohio, to 1831

HOSTETTER, JACOB, JR.: Hanover, Pa., 1806–1818; thereafter at New Lisbon, Ohio, to the 1830s. May have had shops in other settlements in Columbiana County, Ohio

HOTCHKISS, ALVA: Poughkeepsie, N.Y., 1820s–1830s; New York City from 1830s to 1840s

HOTCHKISS & BENEDICT: Auburn, N.Y., 1830s

HOTCHKISS & FIELD: Burlington, Conn., 1820s

HOTCHKISS & PIERPONT: Plymouth, Conn., 1800s–1810s

HOTCHKISS, ELISHA: Burlington, Conn., 1810s

HOTCHKISS, HEZEKIAH: New Haven, Conn., 1748–1761

HOTCHKISS, ROBERT & HENRY: Plymouth, Conn., 1830s–1840s

HOTCHKISS, SPENCER & CO.: Salem Bridge, Conn., 1830s

HOUGH, J. H.: Bridgeport (no state), *c.* 1800s–1820s. Name appears on eight-day striking tall clock in cherry case, grandmother size, found in Ohio. May be Conn., Mass., Ohio, or Penna. as all these states have a Bridgeport. Further data are not available

HOUSE, GEORGE: Hanover, Pa., *c.* 1790s–1830

HOUSE, G. V. & CO.: New York City, 1840s. Manufacturers

HOUSTON, WILLIAM: Philadelphia, n.d.

HOVEY, CYRUS: Lowell, Mass., 1860s

HOWARD & DAVIS: Boston, 1847–1856

HOWARD, E.: Roxbury, Mass. Made clocks and watches of superior grade 1840 to 1882. In 1880s he was making exceptionally fine tall-case clocks in Sheraton-style cases!

HOWARD BANJO CLOCKS: More properly a glossary item, reference is to Howard Watch & Clock Co., banjo-cased timepieces for the steamboat, railroad, and commercial office trade. These banjos have either circular bottoms or rectangular bottoms with rounded sides

HOWARD, THOMAS: Philadelphia, 1770s–1780s
HOWARD, WILLIAM: Boston, 1815
HOWE, JUBAL: Boston, 1830s
HOWELL & HALL: Albany, N.Y., 1800s
HOWELL, NATHAN: New Haven, Conn., *c.* 1762–1784
HOWELL, SILAS W.: New Brunswick, N.J., n.d.
HOYT, FREEMAN: Sumter, S.C., 1830s–1860s
HOYT, GEORGE: Albany, N.Y., 1830s
HOYT, HENRY: New York City, 1810s; Albany, 1820s–1830s
HOYT, JAMES: Troy, N.Y., 1830s
HOYT, S. & CO.: New York City, early 1800s
HOYT, SEYMOUR: Brooklyn, N.Y., 1840s
HUBBARD & HITCHCOCK: Buckland, Mass., *c.* 1800–1820s
HUBBARD, C. K.: Hartford, Conn., 1860s
HUBBARD, DANIEL: Medfield, Mass., 1820s
HUBBELL & BEACH: Bristol, Conn., 1859–1863
HUBBELL, LA PORTE: Bristol, Conn., 1849–1880
HUBBELL, LA PORTE & SON: Bristol, Conn., 1874–1880s
HUBER, CHRISTIAN: Cocalico, Lancaster County, Pa., 1765–1789
HUCKEL, SAMUEL: Philadelphia, 1810s–1820s
HUDSON, EDWARD: Mount Holly, N.J., n.d. Tall clocks, probably last half eighteenth and/or early nineteenth century
HUDSON, WILLIAM: Mount Holly, N.J. Same dates as Edward Hudson
HUGUENIN, CHARLES FREDERICK: Philadelphia, 1790s
HUGUENIN, J. C.: San Francisco, Cal., 1860s–1870s.
HUGUS (also HUGO), MICHAEL: Berlin, Somerset County, Pa., 1794–1825
HUMBERT, CHARLES: New York City, 1810s
HUMBERT & DROZ: Philadelphia, 1790s
HUMPHREY (also HUMPHRIES), DAVID: Lexington, Ky., 1780s–1790s
HUMPHREY, NORMAN: Casemaker of New York City, 1840s. May have sold but did not make clocks, only cases
HUMPHREYS (or HUMPHRYS), JOSHUA: Charlestown and East Whiteland, Chester County, Pa., 1768–1773
HUNT, E.: New York City, 1780s
HUNT, JOHN: Plainville, Farmington, Conn., 1830s–1840s
HUNTINGTON & PLATTO: Ithaca, N.Y., 1854; Plymouth Hollow, Conn., 1855–1868. Ithaca after 1868. Became the Ithaca Calendar Clock Co.
HUNTINGTON, GURDON: Windham, Conn., 1784–1789: Walpole, N.H., 1790–1804
HURLBUT, HORACE: New Haven, Conn., 1850s

Hurst, David: Sporting Hill, Lancaster, Pa., 1850s
Hurtin & Burgi: Boundbrook, N.J., 1766
Huston, James: Trenton, N.J., *c.* 1760s; Philadelphia, 1770s
Huston, Joseph: Albany, N.Y., 1850s
Huston, William: Philadelphia, 1770s–1800s
Hutchins, Abel: Concord, N.H., 1788–1819. Apprentice of Simon Willard
Hutchins, Levi: Concord, N.H., 1786–1819. Apprentice of Simon Willard. Both Abel and Levi Hutchins made tall clocks and mantel clocks of fine quality
Hutchins, Nicholas: Baltimore, 1810s
Hutchinson, Thomas: Philadelphia, 1820s
Huygens: Huyghens: Huijghens, Christian: Inventor of the pendulum clock. Robert Hooke of London is also credited with this use of the pendulum principle in clock escapement
Hyland, William C.: New York City, 1840s
Hyman, Henry: Lexington, Ky., 1800s–1810s
Hyman, Samuel: Philadelphia, 1790s; Baltimore, 1800s
Hyums, Isaac: n.d., n.p.

Ihrie (sometimes Uri), Edward: Easton, Pa., 1790s–1810s
Imay, K. K.: n.p., n.d. Further research needed to identify
Imbery, John: New York City, 1820s–1830s
Inch, John: Annapolis, Md., 1740s
Ingersoll, Daniel: Boston, 1800s
Ingraham & Co., The E.: Bristol, Conn., 1880–1884
Ingraham & Goodrich: Bristol, Conn., 1833
Ingraham & Stedman: New York City and Connecticut, 1850s
Ingraham, E. & A.: Bristol, Conn., 1852–1856
Ingraham, E. & Co.: Bristol, Conn., 1857–1880
Ingraham, Elias: Bristol, Conn., casemaker, producing cases for George Mitchell and C. and L. C. Ives. Formed partnership, 1831, with William Bartholomew, having case factory selling to many movement makers. Withdrew 1832, became partner of Chauncey Goodrich, and in 1835 was making fancy chairs, mirrors, and clock cases. Brother Andrew purchased assets of business, 1840, took in a partner, Benjamin Ray, and began making brass clocks. Combined, 1844, with E. C. Brewster & Co., forming Brewster & Ingraham Co., 1852, E. & A. Ingraham, 1856, Elias Ingraham & Co., 1861, and thence to now as E. Ingraham Company. Elias Ingraham was one of the really important men in Connecticut clockmaking. The company he founded has survived for more than

a century. Only *c.* 1856–1859 was the factory out of Bristol; during those years it was at Ansonia

INGRAHAM, REUBEN: Plainfield and Preston, Conn., 1760s–1800

IRISH, CHARLES: New York City, 1810s

ITHACA CALENDAR CLOCK CO.: Ithaca, N.Y., 1868–1919. Made clocks under Hawes, Atkins and Horton patents. *See* Huntington & Platto

ITNYER, JOHN: Hagerstown, Md., *c.* 1750s–1770s

IVES, AMASA & CHAUNCEY: Bristol, Conn., 1811–1812

IVES, AMASA, JR., & CO.: Bristol, Conn., 1811–1812

IVES, AMASA, SR.: Bristol, Conn., *c.* 1770s–1790s. Father of the famous Ives brothers

IVES & CO.: Bristol, Conn., 1839–1843

IVES & LEWIS: Bristol, Conn., 1819–1823

IVES BROTHERS: Bristol, various dates between 1808–1862. Brothers were as follows, dates are those of birth and death: Ira, 1775–1848; Amasa, 1777–1817; Philo, 1780–1822; Joseph, 1782–1862; Shaylor, 1785–1840; Chauncey, 1787–1857

IVES, CHARLES G.: Bristol, Conn., 1816–1824

IVES, CHAUNCEY: Bristol, Conn., 1816–1829

IVES, CHAUNCEY & LAWSON: Bristol, Conn., 1830–1838

IVES, GEORGE: Lebanon, Pa., n.d.

IVES, IRA: Bristol, Conn., 1810s–1820s

IVES, JOSEPH: Bristol, Conn. Made tall clocks from 1810 and fine brass clocks from 1820. First to use rolled brass. Invented the thirty-day wagon-spring clock and variants thereof. Invented the bronzed looking-glass clock, 1822, and the Ives Patent Accelerating or lever-spring clocks (wagon spring) and also the "elliptical" spring which means the same thing. Moved to Brooklyn, N.Y., 1826, and made wagon-spring clocks, some of which are found in cases looking like the work of Duncan Phyfe. In 1833 assigned his patents to John Birge, Erastus Case, Harvey Case, Sylvester Willard, and P. R. Chauncey and Lawson Ives. Firm he headed was Joseph Ives & Co., Bristol, 1818–1819, and factor in all other Ives firms to 1860

IVES, LAWSON: Bristol, Conn., 1820s–1830s

IVES, ROLLIN I.: Bristol, Conn., 1861–1865

JACKS & GIBSON: Charleston, S.C., 1780–1790s

JACKS, JAMES: Charleston, S.C., 1780s–1790s and 1800s to 1820s. Worked at Philadelphia *c.* 1797–1799

JACKSON, GEORGE, JR.: East Marlborough, Chester County, Pa., 1798–1812

JACKSON, ISAAC: New Garden & London Grove, Chester County, Pa., 1762–1807

JACKSON, JOHN: Marlborough, Chester County, Pa., 1730–1770

JACKSON, JOHN: Charleston, S.C., late eighteenth century

JACKSON, JOSEPH: Mill Creek, Del., *c.* 1805–1825

JACKSON, R.: Springfield, Ohio, 1800s–1810s

JACKSON, THOMAS: Portsmouth, N.H., Boston, and Preston, Conn., during the years 1750 to 1790s and perhaps later

JACQUES, CHARLES: New York City, 1880s. Agent for V. Blanpain, Paris

JAMES, EDWARD: Cabinetmaker of Philadelphia who cased clocks and labeled them with his name. Working after Revolution, 1780s–1800s. A clock cased and labeled by this man is reported as having sold in 1930 for $9,000

JAMES, JOSHUA: Boston, 1820s

JAMES, J. J.: Augusta, Ga., 1820s

JAMES, WILLIAM: Portsmouth, R.I., 1717

JAMESON, JACOB: Columbia, Lancaster County, Pa., 1818–1823, then to Dayton, Ohio, where he made some thirty-day tall clocks and later, it is believed, worked with Marsh, Williams & Hayden. Later data are not verified

JAMIN, JEAN BAPTISTE: Baltimore, 1790s–1800s

JARRETT, SEBASTIAN: n.d., n.p.

JENNERER, CHARLES E.: Saint Louis, Mo., 1810s

JEANES, THOMAS: Philadelphia, n.d.

JEFFERIES, ———: Glasgow, Ky., *c.* 1825–1840. *See* Eubank & Jefferies. The Glasgow here mentioned is not to be confused with Port Glasgow, a village in New York State no longer on the map, eliminated by the simple device of changing the name

JEFFERIES, CURTIS: West Chester, Pa., 1810s–1830s

JEFFREYS, SAMUEL: Philadelphia, 1760s–1770s

JENCKS, JOHN E.: Providence, R.I., 1800s

JENKINS, HARMAN: Albany, N.Y., 1810s

JENKINS, IRA: Albany, N.Y., 1810s

JENKINS, W.: Richmond, Ind., 1800s–1820s

JENNE & ANDERSONS: Big Rapids, Mich., 1860s

JEROME & CO.: New Haven, 1845–1850s

JEROME & DARROW: Bristol, Conn., 1824–1833. This factory had the largest production in its time of operation

JEROME, ANDREW: New Haven, Conn., 1840s–1850s

JEROME, CHARLES: New Haven, Conn., 1840s–1850s

JEROME, CHAUNCEY: Plymouth, Conn., and other points, to 1818–1822. Bristol, Conn., 1822–1845. New Haven, after 1845. *See* Chapter VII

JEROME, C. & N. (Chauncey & Noble): Bristol, Conn., 1834–1839. Branches at Richmond, Va., and Hamburg, S.C., in 1835 and 1836. Assembly and casing done at two last named points to avoid the Yankee peddlers' tax levied on all who sold products made out of states. Putting branch in the state avoided the tax

JEROME & GRANT: Bristol, Conn., 1842–1843

JEROME, GILBERT & GRANT: Bristol, 1839–1840

JEROME, JEWELL & CO.: Bristol, Conn., 1847–1849

JEROME MANUFACTURING CO.: New Haven, Conn., 1850s

JEROME, NOBLE: Bristol, Conn., in various ventures, alone or with partners, including brother Chauncey, 1820s–1840s

JEROMES & DARROW: Firm name when spelled "Jeromes" instead of Jerome and Darrow indicates that the two Jeromes, Chauncey & Noble, were in the firm

JEROME, THOMPSON & CO.: Bristol, Conn., n.d.

JESSOP, JONATHAN: York, Pa., late 1780s (as apprentice) to 1850. Apprentice to Elisha Kirk and succeeded to Kirk's business 1791. Kirk's tall-case clock numbered 67 is further identified as Jonathan Jessop No. 1—a very handsome thing for the master to permit, and done probably to mark Jessop as having turned journeyman. This clock is dated 1784. Jessop befriended Phineas Davis and taught him watchmaking. Davis built early locomotives for the Baltimore & Ohio Railroad

JESSOP, JOSEPH U.: York, Pa. (son of Jonathan), 1823–1850

JEWELL, JEROME & CO.: Bristol, Conn., 1840s

JOB, JOHN: Philadelphia, 1810s

JOCELIN (JOCELYN) SIMEON: New Haven, Conn., 1770s–1800. In latter year he built a factory and produced tall-case, shelf, and banjo clocks to 1820. There is some evidence that Jocelyn made banjo clocks at the same time Willard began to use the case for his patented timepiece. Further study is indicated as highly desirable

JOCELYN, NATHANIEL: New Haven, Conn., 1790s

JOHNSON, ADDISON: Wolcottville, Conn., 1820s

JOHNSON, CHAUNCEY: Albany, N.Y., 1820s

JOHNSON, JABEZ: Charleston, S.C., 1780s–1790s

JOHNSON, MILES: Wallingford, Conn. Tall-case clocks, n.d.

JOHNSON, SIMON: Sanbornton, N.H., 1830s–1860

JOHNSON, WILLIAM: New York City, 1830s–1840s. Listed as manufacturer

JOHNSON, W. S.: New York City., 1850s. Listed as manufacturer

JOHNSTON, ARTHUR: Hagerstown, Md., 1785–1815. Other records show he worked to 1840

JOHNSTON, A. & W.: Hagerstown, Md., 1785–1815. Arthur & William Johnston

JOHNSTON & FISHER: Frederick, Md. Probably only George Fisher, brother-in-law of Arthur Johnston, Hagerstown, Md.

JOHNSTON, J. H. & CO.: New York City, 1800s–1820s

JOHNSTON, JOHN: Charleston, S.C., 1790s

JOHNSTON & MELHORN: Boonsboro and Hagerstown, Md., 1785–1818

JOHNSTON, ROBERT: Philadelphia, 1825

JONCKHEER, FRANCIS: Baltimore, 1810s

JONES, ABNER: Weare, N.H., 1780s

JONES & FRISBIE: New Hartford, Conn., n.d.

JONES, BALL & POOR: Boston, 1840s

JONES, EDWARD K.: Bristol, Conn., 1820s

JONES, EZEKIEL: Boston, *c.* 1790–1820. Made banjo-type clocks at same time Willard was perfecting this style now associated with his name. The banjo seems now to have been made almost simultaneously at Boston, Baltimore, and by one maker in Connecticut. A monograph on the subject need not be planned to discredit Willard but to point out that, even though Willard is credited with its development, other clockmakers were doing the same thing and not copying his "exclusive" idea. There is an opportunity for some patient researcher in this banjo-clock story

JONES, GEORGE: Clockmaker of Wilmington, Del., who was also a dealer. Made tall clocks and mantel clocks. *c.* 1803–1850

JONES, GEORGE, JR.: Wilmington, Del., 1818–1840s

JONES, GEORGE A.: Bristol, Conn., to 1870s. Factory

JONES, GRIFFITH: Baltimore, 1820s

JONES, JACOB: Baltimore, 1810s

JONES, JACOB: Pittsfield, N.H., n.d. Authenticity of entry not yet clear

JONES, SAMUEL: Baltimore, 1810s

JOSEPH, ISAAC: Boston, 1820s

JOSLYN (also JOCELYN), JAMES: New Haven, Conn., 1790s–1820s

JOYCE, ROBERT: New York City, 1790s

JOYCE, THOMAS F.: Philadelphia, 1820s

KEARN, FELIX: New Haven, Conn., 1840s–1850s

KEDZIE, J.: Rochester, N.Y., 1840s

KEE, JOHN M.: Chester, S.C. n.d., but probably last half eighteenth century. Data not complete. Reported as Kay, and as Kayquay. Clocks bearing name as Kee said to be extant but not seen by compiler or researcher reporting name

KEELER, JOSEPH: Norwalk, Conn., latter half eighteenth century

KEIM, JOHN: Reading, Pa., after 1779

KELLEY, DAVID: Philadelphia, 1810

KELLOGG, DANIEL: Hebron, Conn., *c.* 1787–1800

KELLY, ALLEN: Sandwich, Mass., 1810–1830

KELLY, EZRA: New Bedford, Mass., early nineteenth century. Finally became proprietor of the famed Kelly watch oil

KELLY, JOHN: New Bedford, Mass., 1830s

KELLY, MICHAEL: New York City, 1850s

KEMBLE, WILLIAM: New York City, 1780s

KEMLO, FRANCIS: Chelsea, Mass., 1840s

KENDRICK: KENDRICK & CHURCHILL: KENDRICK, HUBBELL & CO.: KENDRICK, BARNES & CO.: KENDRICK, HUBBELL & BEACH: All Bristol, Conn., various partnerships and companies making marine clocks and thirty-hour and eight-day house clocks, 1847–1854

KENNARD, JOHN: Newfields, N.H., *c.* 1825

KENNEDY, ELISHA: Easton, Pa., 1780s; Middletown, Conn., after 1788

KENNEDY, PATRICK: Philadelphia, 1797

KENNEDY ELECTRIC CLOCK CO., New York City, 1860s

KENNEDY, S. A.: New York City, 1860s. Inventor of electric clock. Associate of Samuel F. B. Morse in development of telegraph

KENNEY, ASA: West Millbury, Mass., 1790–1800s

KEPLINGER, WILLIAM: Baltimore, 1820s–1830s. A son, Frederick, removed to Lancaster, Pa., where he worked as case- and cabinetmaker. Family finally had a furniture factory and store in last-named place

KEPPLINGER, JOHN: Baltimore, *c.* 1800–1810. Son of Samuel. *See also* William Keplinger, a brother of this man

KEPPLINGER (KEPLINGER), SAMUEL: Gettysburg, Pa., *c.* 1785; Baltimore, after 1800

KERN, HERMAN: Mount Joy, Lancaster County, Pa., 1850s

KERNER & PAFF: New York City, 1790s. Importers

KERNER, NICHOLAS: Marietta, Lancaster County, Pa., 1850s

KERR, WILLIAM, JR.: Providence, R.I., 1850s. Manufacturer

KERSEY, ROBERT: Easton, Md., 1790s. A son, Robert, settled in Lancaster County, Pa.

KETCHAM & HITCHCOCK: New York City, 1810s

KEYWORTH, ROBERT: Washington, D.C., 1822

KEYWORTH, T.: York, Pa., 1850s

KILBORN, HENRY: New Haven, Conn., 1840s–1850

KIMBALL, JAMES: Montpelier, Vt., *c.* 1800–1810

KIMBALL, JOHN, JR.: Boston, 1820s

KIMBERLY, R.: Ansonia, Conn., n.d.

KING, HENRY N.: New York City, 1810s

KING, HENRY: *See* Roi, Henry

KING, THOMAS: Baltimore, Md., 1820s

KING, W. B.: Questionable; may be Ring, W. B., n.p., n.d., but a tall clock with Massachusetts history is known; the first letter of name King or Ring may be a "K" or a broken "R." Hence the doubt

KINKAID, GEORGE: Cincinnati, 1830s

KINKAID, JAMES: Christiana, Del., advertised in 1774

KINKAID, JOSEPH & ALEXANDER: Newark & Christiana, Del., *c.* 1780–1800

KINKAID, JAMES: Sadsbury, Pa., and Philadelphia, *c.* 1760s

KINKAIRD, THOMAS: Christiana, Del., 1770s. Probably an error; should be Kinkaid

KINKEAD, JAMES: Churchtown, Lancaster County, Pa., and Morgantown, now in Berks County, Pa., 1790s–1800s

KIPPEN, GEORGE: Bridgeport, Conn. Known to have been a dealer only

KIRCHOFF, E. H.: Philadelphia, 1800s

KIRCHOFF, J. H.: Philadelphia, 1800s

KIRK, AQUILLA: York, Pa., 1790s; Baltimore after 1800

KIRK (also KIRKE), CHARLES: Bristol, Conn., 1828–36; New Haven to 1840s. Made marine clocks

KIRK, ELISHA: York, Pa., 1780–1790. Apprenticed to Isaac Jackson of Chester County *c.* 1773. Said to have made one hundred and twenty clocks, 1780–1790

KIRK, JOHN: Bristol, Conn., 1831

KIRK, TIMOTHY: York, Pa., 1780s

KIRKWOOD, ALEXANDER: Charleston, S.C., advertised in 1768

KIRKWOOD, JOHN: Charleston, S.C., advertised 1761; Wilmington, N.C., 1770s–1780s

KLECKNER, SOLOMON: Mifflinburg, Pa., 1818–1860

KLEIN, JOHN: Amityville, Pa., 1800s

KLEISER, J.: Philadelphia, 1820s

KLINE, B.: Philadelphia, 1820s

KLINE & CO.: New York City, 1860s

KLINE, JOHN: Lancaster, Pa., 1790–1810; Philadelphia, 1812–1820; Reading, Pa., 1820s–1830s

KLING (or KLINGMAN), JACOB: Reading, Pa., 1790s–1800s. York, Pa., 1810s–1820

KLINGMAN, DANIEL: York, Pa., 1800s–1830

KLINGERMAN, A.: Reading, Pa., *c.* 1780s. Questionable; legend only thus far

KLINGLE, JOSEPH: Philadelphia, 1820s

KNEEDLER, JACOB: Horsham, Pa., 1790s

KNEELAND & ADAMS: Cabinetmakers, Hartford, Conn., 1792–1795; believed to have employed clockmakers to supply movements for cases they made. Tall-cased jobs only. Firm was not clockmaking company but cabinet company having a line of clocks

KNIGHT, LEVI: Salem, Ind., 1840s–1850s. Wooden-movement clocks

KNOWLES, JOHN: Philadelphia, advertised in 1784

KNOWLES, ROBERT: Bangor, Me., 1830s

KOCH, JACOB: Casemaker of York Springs, Pa., making cases for John Albert. Any clocks signed Koch by this man are Albert movements in Koch cases

KOCK, RICHARD: York, Pa., 1800s–1836

KOHL, M.: Columbia, Lancaster County, Pa., 1840s–1850s

KOHL, NICHOLAS: Willow Grove, Pa., 1830s

KOPLIN (KOPLINE), WASHINGTON: Norristown, Pa., 1850

KOPLINE, T.: Norristown, Pa., 1850s

KRAEMER, F.: New York City, 1840s

KRAFT, JACOB: Shepherdstown, West Virginia, 1790–1820

KROEBER, F.: Yorkville district, New York City, 1850s–1880s. Casemaker who purchased movements stamped with his name from Seth Thomas, Ingraham, and other Connecticut makers

KROUSE, JOHN J.: Northampton (now Allentown), Pa., n.d.

KROUSE, JOHN S.: Bethlehem, Pa., n.d.

KROUT, JACOB: Plumstead, Pa., 1830s

KRUEGER, A.: Camden, N.J., 1850s

KRUGER, L.: Cleveland, Ohio, 1850s–1860s

KULP, WILLIAM: Lower Salford, Pa., n.d.

KUMBEL, WILLIAM: New York City, 1770s–1780s

KUNTZ, M. S.: South Whitehall Township (no state), n.d. Name appears on a tall clock with simulated (painted on and non-operable) moon phase, *c.* 1825

LABHART, W.: New York City, 1810s

LACEY, JOHN: Philadelphia, 1820

LACKEY, HENRY: Philadelphia, 1800s–1810s

LADOMUS, CHARLES ALEXANDER: Chester, Pa., 1825–1854

LADOMUS, JOSEPH: Chester, Pa., 1850s

LADOMUS, LEWIS: Philadelphia, 1840s

LA FOY, THEODORE: Newark, N.J., 1850s

LAMB, ANTHONY: New York City, 1740–1750s

LA MOINE, A.: Philadelphia, 1810s

LAMPE, JOHN: Annapolis, Md., 1770s–1780; Baltimore after 1780
LAMSON, CHARLES: Salem, Mass., 1850s
LANE, AARON: Elizabethtown, N.J., *c.* 1785–1800. Some musical clocks
LANE, JAMES: Philadelphia, 1810s
LANE, J.: Southington, Conn., n.d. Probably 1830s
LANE, LYMAN J.: New Haven, Conn., 1840s–1850s
LANE, MARK: Southington, Conn., 1830s
LANGDON & JONES: Bristol, Conn., 1845–55
LANGDON & ROOT: Bristol, Conn., 1851–1854
LANGMACK, H.: Davenport, Iowa, 1850s
LANNY, D. F.: Boston, 1780s
LANSHE, JOHN: "Canonvaga" is place reported on dial; may be Conestoga, Conewago, or other Indian place name from either Lancaster or York County, Pa. Not authenticated
LA PIERRE, BENNET: Baltimore, 1800s
LA PLACE, M.: Wilmington, N.C., 1790s
LA QUAINE, M.: Philadelphia, n.d.
LARKIN, JOSEPH: Boston to 1840
LATIMER, J.: Philadelphia, 1810s–1820
LATHAM, JAMES: Albany, N.Y., 1790s
LATHAM, ———: Marple (originally Marpool), Delaware County, Pa. This is the first clockmaker ever investigated by the writer. Homer Eaton Keyes in 1927 asked me to seek data on this man. "No progress" was the report in 1928. "No progress" is the report almost twenty years later. One clock bearing the name and place is recorded
LATOURNAU (also LE TOURNAY), J. B.: Baltimore, 1820s–1840s
LATSHAW (also LATSHAR), JOHN: York, Pa., 1779–1780. Thence to Reading Township (Adams County)
LAUGHLIN, A. S.: Barnett, Vt., 1850s–1860s
LAUNAY, D.: Boston, *c.* 1790; New York City, 1791–1800s
LAUNDRY, A.: Philadelphia, n.d.
LAWRENCE, GEORGE: Lowell, Mass., 1830s
LAWRENCE, SILAS H.: New York City, 1840s
LAWSE (or LAWSHE), JOHN: Amwell, N.J., 1780s–1810s
LAWSON, W. H.: Waterbury, Conn., n.d.
LEACH, CALEB: Plymouth, Mass., 1770s–1790s
LEACH & BRADLEY: Utica, N.Y., 1830s
LEAVENWORTH & SON: Waterbury, Conn., 1807
LEAVENWORTH & SON: Albany, N.Y., 1810s
LEAVENWORTH, MARK: Waterbury, Conn., and perhaps other places, 1810–1830s. He marketed an improved pillar-and-scroll, *c.* 1830

LEAVENWORTH, WILLIAM: Waterbury, Conn., 1800s–1810s. Albany, N.Y., 1810s

LEAVIT, M. F.: Kalamazoo, Mich., 1860s

LEAVITT, JOSIAH: Hingham, Mass., 1770s

LEE & GODDARD: Rutland, Vt., *c.* 1810–1820

LEE, STEPHEN: Charleston, S.C., *c.* 1780s

LEE, WILLIAM: Charleston, S.C., *c.* 1710–1730

LEFFERTS & HALL: Philadelphia, 1820s

LEFFERTS, CHARLES: Philadelphia, 1810s

LE GRAS (LE GROS: LE GROZE), JOHN: Baltimore, 1790s

LE GOUX, J. F.: Charleston, S.C., 1780s–1790s

LE HURAY, NICHOLAS, SR. & JR.: The elder, from Isle of Guernsey, working at Philadelphia, 1810; the son at Ogletown, Del., *c.* 1810, and at Philadelphia from *c.* 1812 to 1830

LEIBERT, HENRY: Norristown, Pa., 1850s

LEIGH, DAVID: Pottstown, Pa., 1840s

LEINBACH, ELIAS & JOHN: Reamstown, Lancaster County, Pa., *c.* 1788–1810. Mostly thirty-hour tall clocks, but in considerable quantities

LEMIST & TAPPAN: Philadelphia, *c.* 1815–1820

LEMIST, W. K.: Dorchester, Mass., 1810–1820

LEMON, J. J.: Louisville, Ky., 1840s

LENHART, CHRISTIAN: Carlisle, Pa., 1780s

LENHART, GODFREY: York, Pa., 1775–1819

LEONI & CO.: New York City, 1840s

LE ROY, ABRAHAM: Lancaster, Pa., *c.* 1738–1770. Fine brass-dialed tall-case clocks

LE ROY, ANNA MARIA: Daughter of Abraham, Lancaster, Pa. Actually a clockmaker, married Wilmer Atkinson, and made clocks bearing his name, 1750–1760

LESCOIT, LAMBERT: Providence, R.I., *c.* 1760–1780. Also, apparently, working at Hartford, Conn., 1770s

LESCOIET, LANBIER: Same as Lescoit, Lambert

LESLIE & PRICE: Philadelphia, 1790s–1800s

LESLIE & WILLIAMS: New Brunswick, N.J., 1780s–1790; Trenton, N.J., 1799–1805

LESLIE, ROBERT: Baltimore (agent for Leslie & Price), 1790s

LESLIE, ROBERT (SR.?): Philadelphia, 1740s–1790

LESLIE, WILLIAM J.: Trenton, New Jersey, 1799–1830

LESTER, ROBERT: Philadelphia, 1790s

LETELIER, J.: Philadelphia, n.d.

LEUPP (or LUPP), HENRY: New Brunswick, N.J., n.d. Tall-case clocks

LEVELY, GEORGE: Philadelphia, 1770s–1774; Baltimore, to *c.* 1800
LEVI (or LEVY), ISAAC: Philadelphia, advertised 1780
LEVIN & FERGUSON: Alexandria, La., 1850s–1860
LEVY, MICHAEL & ISAAC: Baltimore, advertised 1785
LEVY, MICHAEL: Philadelphia, 1813
LEWIS & CO.: Bristol, Conn., 1875
LEWIS & IVES: Bristol, Conn., 1819–1823
LEWIS, BENJAMIN: Bristol, Conn., 1864–1870
LEWIS, CURTIS: Reading, Pa., 1790s–1820s
LEWIS, ERASTUS: Waterbury, Conn., 1800s
LEWIS, JACKSON: San Jose, Cal., 1860s
LEWIS, JOHN: Philadelphia, 1840s
LEWIS, LEVI: Bristol, Conn., 1809–1823
LIDDELL, THOMAS: Frederick, Ind., 1760
LIEBERT, H.: Norristown, Pa., 1840s–1850s
LIMEBURNER, JOHN: Philadelphia, 1790s
LIND, JOHN: Philadelphia, 1775
LINDER, CHARLES: Geneva, N.Y., 1810s
LINDSAY, THOMAS: Frankford (Philadelphia), n.d.
LINDSAY, W. K.: Pittsburgh, Pa., 1820s–1830s
LINDSAY, WILLIAM: Portsmouth, Ohio, 1830s–1840s
LINDSEY, W. R.: Davenport, Iowa, 1850s
LISNEY, WILLIAM: New York City, 1840s
LITCHFIELD MANUFACTURING CO: Litchfield, Conn., 1850–1860
LITTLE, PETER: Baltimore, 1790s–1820s
LITTLEJOHN, JAMES: Charleston, S.C., advertised 1761
LOCKWOOD & SCRIBNER: New York City, 1840s
LOCKWOOD, JOSHUA: Charleston, S.C., 1756–1781
LOCKWOOD, WILLIAM: Charlestown, Mass., n.d. Tall-case clocks
LOGAN, ROBERT: Saint Louis, Mo., 1819
LOHSE & KEYSER: Philadelphia, 1830s
LOMAD (or LOMAS), JOHN (or JOHNS): Chambersburg, Pa., n.d. Tall clocks. Name is not quite settled; we have a report of a clockmaker named Lomas Johns, which may be this man. Hence this might be better listed under Johns but is not because complete data are lacking
LOMES, WILLIAM: New York City, 1840s
LONG, GEORGE: Hanover, Pa., late 1790s–1800s
LONG, JOHN: Hanover, Pa., 1800s–1820s
LOOMIS, HENRY K.: Frankfort (N.Y.?), n.d.
LORD & GODDARD: Rutland, Vt., 1790s–1830
LORD, JAMES: Woodbury, N.J. Tall clocks, n.d.

LORING, HENRY W.: Boston, 1810s–1840s. Made banjo clocks
LORNBY, C.: Connecticut; no place, n.d. May be "Clornby." Data are not complete on this maker
LORTON, WILLIAM: New York City, 1810s–1850. Claimed to be a manufacturer as well as a dealer
LOSS, AUGUSTUS: Pittsburgh, Pa., 1830s
LOSS, P.: Germantown, Pa., 1850s
LOVELL & SMITH: Philadelphia, early 1840s. G. Lovell & Co. to 1880s
LOVELL, A. E.: Philadelphia, 1840s
LOVELL MFG. CO.: Erie, Pa., 1850s–1880s. The Lovell Company were makers of clothes washers and wringers but produced a luminous-dial clock in the 1880s. This clock had a bronze front case, alarm, and some clocks had exposed escapement
LOVIS, JOSEPH: Hingham, Mass., 1770s–1800
LOWENS, DAVID: Philadelphia, 1780s
LOWNES, HYATT: Hagerstown, Md., 1790s
LOWREY, DAVID: Newington, Conn., 1760s–1819
LUCY, D. E.: Houlton, Me., 1850s
LUDWIG, JOHN: Philadelphia, 1790s
LUFKIN & JOHNSON: Boston, 1800s–1810s
LUKENS, ISAIAH: Philadelphia, *c.* 1800–1840. Listed as town clock-maker in 1823 directory
LUKENS, J.: Philadelphia, 1830s
LUKENS, SENECA: Horsham, Pa., 1780s–1820s
LUSCOMB, SAMUEL: Salem, Mass., 1770s–1780
LYMAN, G. E.: Providence, R.I., 1848
LYMAN, ROLAND: Lowell, Mass., 1830s
LYMAN, THOMAS: Windsor, Conn., 1790s
LYNCH, ABRAHAM: Baltimore, 1790s–1800s
LYNCH, JOHN: Baltimore, 1790s–1840s
LYONS, JOHN, JR.: New Haven, Conn., 1840s–1850s

MCCABE, JOHN: Baltimore, advertised 1774
MCCLARY, SAMUEL: Wilmington, Del., 1803–1815
MCCLARY, SAMUEL: Wilmington, Del., 1810–1850
MCCLARY, SAMUEL & THOMAS: Wilmington, Del., 1840s
MCCLURE (or MCCLURG), JOHN: Boston, 1820s
M'COLLINS, THOMAS: Philadelphia, 1820s
MCCONNELL, J. C.: Waynesburg, now Honeybrook, Pa., 1830s–1840s
MCCORMICK, ROBERT: Philadelphia, n.d.
MCDANIEL, W. H.: Philadelphia, 1820s
MCDOWELL, JAMES: Philadelphia, 1790s–1820s

McDowell, John: Philadelphia, 1810s
McElwain, David & George: Rochester, N.Y., 1840s–1850s
McElwee, James: Philadelphia, 1813
M'Fadden, J. B.: Pittsburgh, 1830s
McGann, Patrick: Charleston, S.C., 1780s–1790s
McGraw, Donald: Annapolis, Md., advertised 1767
M'Harg, Alexander: Albany, N.Y., 1810s to 1850s
McHugh, James: Lowell, Mass., 1860s
McIlhenny, Joseph E.: Philadelphia, 1810s
McIlhenny & West: Philadelphia, 1810s–1820
McKay, William P. & Co.: Boston, n.d.
McKee, John: *See* Kee, John M.
M'Keen, Henry: Philadelphia, 1830s
McMillian, J. W.: Greenville, Ala., 1860s
M'Mullen, Edward: Philadelphia, 1840s
McMyers, John: Baltimore, 1790s
M'Niesh, John: New York City, 1810s
McQuillan, B.: New York City, 1850s
Maag, Henry: Philadelphia, n.d.
Mac Farlane, John: Boston, 1800s–1810s
Mackay, Crafts: Boston, 1780s; Charleston, S.C., 1790s–1800s
Macomb Company: Macomb, Ill., 1880s. Calendar clocks
Magnin, David: New York City, 1810s
Maire, Charles: Louisville, Ky., 1840s
Maker, Matthew: Charleston, S.C., 1760s–1770s
Malloy, George: Lowell, Mass., 1850s
Manchester, G. D.: Plainfield, Conn., 1850s–1860s
Manning, Richard: Ipswich, Mass., 1760s–1770s
Manross, A.: Forestville, Conn., 1849–50
Manross & Norton: Bristol, Conn., 1838–1840
Manross, Elisha: Bristol, Conn., 1825–1854
Manross, Elisha, Jr.: Bristol, Conn., 1862–1869
Manross, E. & C. H.: Bristol, Conn., 1854–56
Manross Brothers: Bristol, Conn., 1856–1861
Manross, Prichard & Co.: Bristol, Conn., 1841–1842
Mans, John: Columbia, Lancaster County, Pa., 1800–1820
Marache, Solomon: New York City, 1750s–1760s
Marand, Joseph: Baltimore, 1800s
Marble, Simeon: New Haven, Conn., 1810s
Marien, John: New York City, 1840s
Marine Clock Mfg Co.: New Haven, Conn., 1840s

MARKHAM & CASE: Columbia, S.C., 1790s or 1800s to 1820s. Tall-case and Grandmother clocks. Also mantel clocks to 1840s

MARKS, ISAAC: Philadelphia, 1790s

MARQUAND, ISAAC: Fairfield, Conn., 1780s–1790s

MARRIAN, JOHN H.: New York City, 1840s

MARSH, B. B.: Paris, Ky., 1810s–1840s

MARSH, GEORGE: Bristol, Conn., 1828–1830; Walcottville, 1830s

MARSH, GILBERT & CO.: Farmington, Conn., 1820s

MARSH, WILLIAMS & CO.: Dayton, Ohio, 1830s. The first clock factory beyond the Allegheny Mountains

MARSH, WILLIAMS & HAYDEN; MARSH, WILLIAMS, HAYDEN & CO.: Dayton, Ohio, 1833–1840. Water-power factory on the Miami Hydraulic; the power of the Miami Canal. In 1833 this factory had a production of twenty-five hundred clocks a year. Walnut wheels with ivory bushings mark these all-wood clocks. An example is pictured in Chapter X

MARSHALL & ADAMS: Seneca Falls, N.Y., *c.* 1820–1830. It is believed the Marshall of this firm was also connected with Franklin & Marshall, mentioned in this list

MARSHALL & WHITE: Petersburg, Va., 1820s

MARSH, T. K.: Paris, Ky., 1800s

MARTIN & MULLAN: Baltimore, advertised in 1764. Thomas Martin and Robert Mullan

MARTIN, GEORGE A.: Bethel, Me., 1850–1860s

MARTIN, J.: Philadelphia, 1840s–1850

MARTIN, PETER: New York City, 1810s

MARTIN, SAMUEL: New York City, 1800s–1810s

MARTIN, THOMAS: Baltimore, 1860s

MASON, GEORGE: Waseca, Minn., 1860s–1870s. This man made cases and clocks. He cased Swedish and Norwegian hang-up clocks (wag-on-wall) brought in by immigrants and made complete clocks. It is believed he worked earlier than the 1860s but data are not complete except for the date bracket here given

MASON, G. H.: Boston, 1840s

MASON, SAMUEL: Philadelphia, 1825

MASON, WILLIAM H.: Mt. Holly, N.J., n.d. Tall clocks

MASSEY, JOHN: Charleston, S.C., 1710s–1738

MASSEY, JOSEPH and/or JOHN: Charleston, S.C., *c.* 1710s–1736

MASSOT, HORACE: Charleston, S.C., 1780s

MASTERS, JOHN: Boston, and Bath, Me., 1820s–1840s

MASTERS, WILLIAM: Bath, Me., 1820s–1850s

MATHEY, LEWIS: Philadelphia, 1797

MATHIEU, GASTON: New York City, 1840s

MATLACK, WHITE & WILLIAM: New York City, 1760s–1770s; Philadelphia, 1777–1780s. In 1780 the firm embraced the William Matlack who is recorded as working in Charleston, S.C., in 1780s. He may have acted as agent in the Carolina metropolis

MATLACK, WILLIAM: Charleston, S.C., 1780s

MATTHEWS, JEWELL & CO.: Bristol, Conn., 1851–1853

MAUREPAS, M.: Bristol, Conn., 1850s. Not definitely established

MAUS, FREDERICK: Philadelphia, 1780s–1790s

MAUS (MAAS), JACOB: Trenton, N.J., 1770s or 80s–*c.* 1790s

MAUS, WILLIAM: Quakertown and Hilltown, Pa., *c.* 1810

MAXWELL, A.: Philadelphia, 1800s–1810s

MAXWELL, JAMES: "Hourglass maker" of Boston, working to 1710s

MAYNARD, GEORGE: New York City, 1700s–1730. Tradition puts this maker in the seventeenth century, *c.* 1690s, but documented records of the period are lacking

MEACHAM, W. J.: Holyoke, Mass., 1850s–1860s

MEAD, BENJAMIN: Castine, Me., 1800–1810

MECHLIN, JACOB: Alsace, Berks County, Pa., 1759–1760. Mechlin was a French Huguenot

MEDLEY, A. G.: Louisville, Ky., 1840s

MEEKS, EDWARD, JR.: New York City, 1790s–1820s. Tradition holds this maker was also a casemaker and that his son Edward Meeks, III, established a large furniture factory in New York City operating from the 1820s. It would seem that tradition is at fault. Edward Meeks and Sons (*c.* 1825) was the name of the furniture factory, probably founded by the clockmaker

MEGARY, ALEXANDER: New York City, 1820s–1830s

MEGEAR, THOMAS J.: Philadelphia, *c.* late 1790s–1820s. This maker produced fine banjo-cased movements contemporaneously with S. Willard

MEILY, EMANUEL: Lebanon, Pa., 1800s–1820

MELCHER, ——: Plymouth Hollow, Conn., 1790s. Data are not clear

MELHOM, MICHAEL: Boonsboro, Ind., 1820s–1830s

MELLY BROTHERS: New York City, 1820s. Probably dealers

MENDENHALL, THOMAS: Lancaster, Pa., 1770s–1780s; Philadelphia after 1785

MENDS, BENJAMIN: Philadelphia, Pa., *c.* 1790s–1810s

MENDS, JAMES: Philadelphia, 1790s

MENZIES, JAMES: Philadelphia, 1800–1820s

MERCHANT, WILLIAM: Philadelphia, n.d. Data not complete

MEREDITH, J. P.: Baltimore, 1820s

MERRIMAN & BRADLEY: New Haven, 1810s–1820s

MERRIMAN, BIRGE & CO.: Bristol, Conn., 1820s–1830s. Made clocks invented by Joseph Ives

MERRIMAN, SILAS: New Haven, Conn., 1760–1805

MERRIMAN, DR. TITUS: Physician of Bristol, Conn., who entered clock business and had a shop of his own, *c.* 1809–1812. Became member of a firm composed of Seth Richards, Butler Dunbar, and himself. Clocks bearing the name Titus Merriman are known, or reported. He was active from the 1800s to 1830s. *See also* text of this book

MERRY, F.: Philadelphia, 1790s

METCALF, LUTHER: Medway, Mass. Casemaker; clocks bearing his name are cased, possibly "finished," but not made complete by him. No record of his producing movements found in this research undertaking

METTEN, LAURENS: Saint Louis, Mo., 1845–1850s

MEYER, DAVID: Myerstown, Lebanon County, Pa., n.d. Tall clocks reported

MEYER, J. A.: New York City, 1830s to late 1840s; Canton, Ohio, 1850s–1860s

MEYERS, JOHN: Frederick, Md., 1790s–1820s

MICHAEL, LEWIS: York, Pa., 1788–1790s

MIETY, EMANUEL: Lebanon, Pa., n.d. Data are not clear

MILLAR, THOMAS: Philadelphia, 1820s–1830s; a dealer

MILLARD, SQUIRE: Warwick, R.I., 1750s or 1760s to 1780s

MILLER & WILLIAMS: Cincinnati, 1830–1840s. Firm of Miller & Williams made clocks and edge tools. Employed Warren Warner, a clockmaker

MILLER, AARON: Elizabeth, N.J. Recorded as instrument and clockmaker; brass and bell founder. Maker of clock parts, 1740–1770. His shop was of considerable importance in colonial period noted

MILLER, ABRAHAM: Easton, Pa., 1810s–1830

MILLER, EDWARD F.: Providence, R.I., 1820s

MILLER, GEORGE: Germantown, Pa., 1760s–1790s; Lancaster, Pa., after 1797. Often called Gorg. Miller. Said to have been a pupil of Christopher Witt

MILLER, HENRY A.: Southington, Conn., *c.* 1830s–1840s

MILLER, JOHAN: Germantown, Pa., 1780s–1800

MILLER, J. B.: Portland, Ore., 1860s. (Yes, Oregon is correct!)

MILLER, KENNEDY: Elizabeth, N.J., *c.* 1780s–1810

MILLER, PARDON: Newport, R.I., 1820s–1850

MILLER, PETER: Lynn Township, Lehigh County, Pa., 1790s–1840s
MILLER, S. W.: Philadelphia, 1840s
MILLER, WILLIAM S.: Philadelphia, 1840s
MILLINGTON, ISAAC: The Buck, Lancaster County, Pa., 1850s (Note: "The Buck" is a place name deriving from the Buck Tavern; it is a scattered village of workmen's homes)
MILLS & CHASE: New York City, 1850s
MILLS, JOSEPH: Philadelphia, 1720s–1759
MILLS, J. R. & CO.: New York City, 1840s
MILLS, WILLIAM: New York City, 1840s
MILNE, ROBERT: New York City, 1790s–1800s; Philadelphia, 1810s
MINOR, E. C.: Jonesville, Mich., 1860s
MINOR, RICHARDSON: Stratford, Conn., 1760–1797
MINOT, J.: Boston, 1790s–1810s. Not a clockmaker. He was a dial painter
MITCHELL & ATKINS: Bristol, Conn., 1820s–1835
MITCHELL & HINMAN: Bristol, Conn., 1828–1830
MITCHELL & MOTT: New York City, 1790–1810
MITCHELL, GEORGE: Bristol, Conn., 1827–1840
MITCHELL, HENRY: New York City, 1780s–1800s
MITCHELL, PHINEAS: Boston, 1820s
MITCHELL, WILLIAM, JR.: Richmond, Va., 1820s
MITCHELSON, DAVID: Boston, 1774. Maker and/or dealer
MIX, ELISHA: New Haven, Conn., 1840s–1850s
MOHLER, JACOB: Baltimore, 1760s–1770s, advertised in 1773
MOLL, JOHN: New Sweden (Pennsylvania, 1670s), retired to Labadist Monastery on Elk River, Maryland, *c.* 1684. A son, John, was also a member of this religious (Protestant) monastery in 1698. Very early American clockmaker of Dutch training
MOLLOY, GEORGE: Lowell, Mass., 1840s–1850s
MONGIN, DAVID: Charleston, S.C., advertised in 1740 and 1744
MONNIER (MONYER), DANIEL: Philadelphia, *c.* 1825
MONROE & CO., E. & C. H.: Bristol, Conn., 1850s
MONROE, CHARLES: Bangor, Me., 1830s
MONROE, JOHN: Barnstable, Mass., n.d.
MONROE & WHITING: Concord, Mass., 1800–1810
MONTANDEN (Hannah) & ROBERTS (Oliver): Lancaster, Pa., 1800s, advertised in 1802–1803
MONTANDEN, HANNAH: Lancaster, Pa., 1802–1810. She was the second lady clockmaker of this clockmaking center (*See* LeRoy, Anna Maria) and conducted her husband's business after his death as a partnership with Oliver Roberts and alone

MONTANDEN, HENRY LEWIS: Lancaster, Pa., 1778–1802. He made fine clocks
MONTEITH & Co.: Philadelphia, early 1840s
MONTEITH, CHARLES: Philadelphia, late 1840s
MONTGOMERY, A.: Baltimore, 1820s
MONTGOMERY, ROBERT: New York City, 1780s
MOOAR, LOT: Nashua, N.H., 1830s. May have been repairman only
MOOLINGER, HENRY: Philadelphia, 1790s
MOORE, FREDERICK: New Haven, Conn., 1840s–1850s
MOORE, GEORGE H.: Lynn, Mass., 1850s–1860s
MORGAN, THEODORE: Salem, Mass., 1830s
MORGAN, THOMAS: Philadelphia, 1760s to 1780 with the years 1772–1779 spent working in Baltimore
MORGUE, PETER: Charleston, S.C., *c.* 1720s–1739
MORPHY, JOHAN: Allentown, Pa., n.d. Data not complete
MORRELL & MITCHELL: New York City, 1800s–1820s
MORRELL, BENJAMIN: Boscawen, N.H., 1810s–1840s
MORRELL, JOHN: Baltimore, 1820s
MORRIS, A.: Reading, Pa., 1770s
MORRIS & CORNELL: Waterloo, Iowa, 1860s
MORRIS & WILLARD: Grafton, Mass., *c.* 1769–1770. Simon Willard, with his master, for a year of partnership. Morris (William or John; data are not clear) was an English clockmaker who, settling at Grafton, taught Willard. These data from Daniel J. Steele, Boston, specialist on Willard banjo clocks in 1910s–1920s
MORRIS, BENJAMIN: Hilltown, Pa., 1760s–1780. Tradition says he made more than three hundred tall-case clocks
MORRIS, ENOS: Hilltown, Pa., 1770s–1780s
MORRIS, JOHN: *See* Morris, William
MORRIS, WILLIAM (and/or JOHN): Grafton, Mass., 1760s–1770s
MORSE & Co.: Plymouth Hollow, Conn., 1840s
MORSE, ELIJAH: Canton, Mass., 1810s
MORSE, HENRY: Canton, Mass., *c.* 1810s
MORSE, MILES: Plymouth Hollow, Conn., 1845–1850; with a store in New York City
MOSELY, R. E.: Newburyport, Mass., 1840s
MOTT & MORREL: New York City, 1800s
MOTT, JAMES: New York City, 1820s–1840s
MOTT, JORDAN: New York City, 1800s–1820s
MOULTON, E. G.: Saco, Me., 1810s–1820s
MOULTON, EDWARD S.: Rochester, N.H., 1810s. Data not clear; may be Rochester, N.Y., but early date makes this doubtful

MOULTON, FRANCIS: Lowell, Mass., 1830s

MOULTON, THOMAS: Dunbarton, N.H., early 1800s; said also to have worked at Rochester, N.Y.

MOURGUE, PETER: Same as Peter Morgue

MOWROUE, FRANCIS: New York City, 1810s

MOYER, JACOB: Montgomery County, Pa., n.d.

MOYER, JACOB: Montgomery County, Pa., n.d. Skippack is mentioned as place

MULLAN, ROBERT: *See* Martin & Mullan

MULLER, N.: New York City, 1850s

MULLIKEN, JONATHAN: Newbury, Mass. (Newburyport section), 1770s–1780s

MULLIKEN, JOSEPH: Newburyport, Mass., 1790s–1804

MULLIKEN, NATHANIEL: Lexington, Mass., 1751–1767

MULLIKEN, NATHANIEL, II: Lexington, Mass., 1767–1775

MULLIKEN, SAMUEL: Newbury, Mass., 1740s–1756

MULLIKEN, SAMUEL, JR.: Newbury, Mass., 1781–1786; Salem, Mass., 1786–1790; Lynn, Mass., 1790–1807

MULTER, PETER A.: New York City, 1850s

MUNGER, ASA: Auburn, N.Y., 1820s

MUNGER & BENEDICT: Auburn, N.Y., 1830s

MUNGER & PRATT: Ithaca, N.Y., 1830s

MUNROE & WHITING: Concord, Mass., 1800s–1810s. Manufacturers

MUNROE, DANIEL: Concord, Mass., 1790s–1800s. Boston after 1808

MUNROE, DANIEL, JR.: Boston, 1820s

MUNROE, DANIEL & NATHANIEL: Concord, Mass. Brass founders and clockmakers *c.* 1796–1816. Reputedly manufacturers

MUNROE, JOHN: Charleston, S.C., advertised in 1785–1790s

MUNROE (also MONROE), NATHANIEL: Concord, Mass., 1800–1817; Baltimore, 1817–1825

MUNYAN BROTHERS: Pittsfield, Mass., 1850s–1860s

MURDOCK & CO., J.: Utica, N.Y., 1820s

MURPHY, JOHN: Northampton (now Allentown), Pa., and at Pikeland and Charlestown, Chester County, Pa., working 1770s–1790s

MURRAY & SON: Fredericksburg, Va., 1880s. Reported as making clocks; may have been jeweler dealers only

MYERS, MOSES: Poughkeepsie, N.Y., 1840s

MYGATT, COMFORT: Danbury, Conn., 1763–1807; Canfield, Ohio, after 1808 to 1820s. Note: Comfort Mygatt must have lived to a great age to cover the span here attributed to him by seemingly sound data. It is not an impossibility that the man was working until in his eighties. Also it is quite logical that this Connecticut clockmaker emigrated to the Ohio country much of which was considered a part of Connecticut's grant.

NARNEY, JOHN: Charleston, S.C., 1780s–1790s

NASH, THOMAS: First clockmaker of authentic record in the American colonies; clockmaker and gunsmith of New Haven, 1638–1658. No recorded clockmaker of New England, New Amsterdam, or New Sweden predates this maker. No records of Virginia artisans this early are known

NEAL, DANIEL: Philadelphia, 1820s

NEAL, ELISHA: New Hartford, Conn., 1820s–1830s. He cased movements made by Samuel (brother of Eli) Terry. Not a clockmaker himself

NEISSER, AUGUSTINE: Germantown, Pa., 1730s–1770s or 1780s

NELSON, JOHN A.: Boston, to 1830s

NELSON, R. & J.: Davenport, Iowa, 1850s

NETTLETON, HEATH & CO.: Scottsville, N.Y., 1800s–1810s

NETTLETON, W. K.: Rochester, N.Y., 1830s

NEWBERRY, JAMES: Annapolis, Md., advertised in 1748

NEWBERRY, JAMES, JR.: Philadelphia, 1810s

NEWELL, A.: Boston, 1780s

NEWELL, SEXTUS: Bristol, Conn., 1809

NEWELL, THOMAS: Sheffield, Mass., n.d.

NEW ENGLAND CLOCK CO.: Bristol, Conn., 1851

NEW HAVEN CLOCK CO.: New Haven, Conn., 1850s to date

NEWMAN, JOHN: Boston, advertised in 1764

NEWTON, J.: Trenton, N.J., 1800s–1820

NEYSER, AUGUSTINE: Philadelphia, 1750s–1760s

NEYSER, WILLIAM: Germantown, Pa., n.d., but probably 1790s–1810s

NICHOLET, JULIAN: Pittsburgh, 1830s

NICHOLL, JOHN: Belvidere, N.J., 1790s or 1800s–1820s

NICHOLLS, GEORGE: New York City, 1720s–1750s

NICHOLS, C. R.: Fulton, N.Y., 1850s–1860s

NICHOLS, WALTER: Newport, R.I., 1848

NICOLET, JOSEPH: Philadelphia, 1790s

NICOLETTE, JULIAN: Baltimore, 1820s

NICOLETTE, MARIE: Philadelphia, 1790s. Not yet documented as correct

NINDE, J.: Baltimore, 1790s

NIXON, JOHN: New York City, advertised 1773

NOBLE, PHILANDER: Pittsfield, Mass., 1810s–1840s

NOLEN & CURTIS: Boston, 1816–1818

NOLEN, SPENCER: Boston, 1813; Philadelphia, 1819. Latter place lists and identifies man as maker of clock and watch dials. Data are not complete

NORRIS, BENJAMIN: New Britain, Pa., n.d. Tall clocks

NORTH, ETHEL: Torrington, Conn., 1820. "Ethel" North was a man, a brother of Norris North

NORTH, NORRIS: Walcottville, Conn., 1820s; also at Torrington

NORTH, PHINEAS: Torrington, Conn., 1790s–1800s

NORTHROP, R. E.: New Haven, Conn., 1820s

NORTHRUP & SMITH: Goshen, Conn., 1820s

NORTON, ELIJAH: Utica, N.Y., 1820s

NORTON, JOHN (also NORTON, JOHN & SONS): Yorktown, Va., 1750s–1800. Dealers and traders supplying the plantation trade. Their history as merchants published by Deitz Press, Richmond, Va., 1937

NORTON, JOHN: York County, Pa. Manchester Township. Data incomplete

NORTON, NATHANIEL: New Haven, Conn., 1840s–1850s

NORTON, SAMUEL: Hingham, Mass., 1780s

NORTON, THOMAS: Rising Sun, Pa., 1790s–1810; Germantown, Pa., 1812–1820

NOWLENS MANUFACTURING CO.: Boston, n.d.

NOWLIN, L.: Chicago, 1840s

NOYES, L.: Nashua, N.H., 1830s–1840s. *See also* Wyman, Rogers & Cox

NUSZ, FREDERICK: Frederick, Md., advertised, 1819

NUTTER, E. H.: Dover, N.H., 1820s–1830s

NUTTER, JOHN D.: Mt. Vernon, N.H., *c.* 1820s–1830s

NUTZ, L. N.: Cincinnati, Ohio, 1830s

OBER, HENRY: Elizabethtown, Lancaster County, Pa., *c.* 1820

O'HARA, CHARLES: Philadelphia, 1790s

OLIVER, G.: Philadelphia, 1780s–1790s

OLIVER, JOHN: Charleston, S.C., 1780s–1790s

OLIVER, W.: Bristol, Conn., 1820s

OLMSTEAD, NATHANIEL: New Haven, Conn., 1820s

OLWINE, HENRY: Yellow Springs and Pikeland, Chester County, Pa., 1812–1835

OLWINE, ABRAHAM: Pikeland, Chester County, Pa., 1820s

OLWINE (also ALWINE), HENRY: Philadelphia, 1840s

OOSTERHOUT, DIRK: Yonkers, N.Y., mid eighteenth century

OOSTERHOUDT, PETER E.: Kingston, N.Y., 1785–1810

ORNE, R. S.: Boston, 1840s

ORR, THOMAS: Philadelphia, 1810s
ORRICK, M.: Baltimore, 1780s
ORTON, PRESTON & CO.: Farmington, Conn., 1810s
OSGOOD, JOHN: Haverhill, Mass., 1800s
OSGOOD, JOHN: Boston, 1820s
OTIS, FREDERICK S.: Bristol, Conn., 1853–1854
OTTO, A. F.: Chicago, 1856
OWEN & CLARK: New York City, 1850s
OWEN & READ: Cincinnati, 1830s–1840s
OWEN & SILE: Chester, Pa., eighteenth century
OWEN, GEORGE B.: Winsted, Conn., *c.* 1810s–1820s
OWEN, G. B. & CO.: New York City, 1850s
OWEN, GRIFFITH: Philadelphia, 1780–1810
OWEN, JOHN: Philadelphia, 1810s
OWEN, M. T.: Abbeville, S.C., 1840s–1860s
OYSTER, DANIEL: Reading, Pa., *c.* 1799 to 1825–1830

PACKARD, ISAAC: N. Bridgewater, Mass., 1800s; with Rodney Brace
PACKARD & SCOFIELD: Rochester, N.Y., 1810s–1820s
PACKARD, J.: Rochester, N.Y., 1810s–1820s
PAINE & LE ROY: Albany, N.Y., 1810s–1820s
PALMER, J.: Philadelphia, 1790s
PARDEE, ENOCH: Poughkeepsie, N.Y., 1840s
PARK & ELLS: Troy, N.Y., 1850s
PARK, SETH: Newtown, Pa., 1790s
PARKE, AUGUSTUS: Philadelphia, 1820
PARKE, SOLOMON: Newtown, Bucks County, Pa., 1760s
PARKE, SOLOMON & CO.: Philadelphia, 1797–1820; at Newtown, 1770–1797
PARKER, DANIEL: Boston, 1750s–1770s. Jeweler, goldsmith, and silversmith who also had for sale clock parts, fusees, gravers, and tools
PARKER, GARDINER: Westborough, Mass., 1760s–1770s
PARKER, GEORGE: Utica, N.Y., 1820s
PARKER, ISAAC: Deerfield, Mass., 1780s
PARKER, ISAAC: Philadelphia, 1820
PARKER, THOMAS: Philadelphia, 1780s–1830s
PARKER, THOMAS (JR.?): Philadelphia, 1810s–1820s
PARKER, T. H.: Philadelphia, 1830s
PARKER, WILLIAM: Philadelphia, 1825
PARKINS, JOSEPH: Philadelphia, 1830s
PARKS, HUGH: New York City, 1840s
PARKS, JONAS: Bennington, Vt., *c.* 1760s–1770s; brass-dialed tall clocks

PARLIN, A. S.: Norwich, Conn., 1850s–1860s
PARMELE, ABEL: New Haven, Conn., 1720s–1730s; Branford, Conn., 1730s–1760s
PARMELE, EBENEZER: Guilford, Conn., 1710–1770
PARMIER, JOHN: Philadelphia, 1790s
PARRY, JOHN J.: Philadelphia, 1790s–1810s
PARRY, JOHN: Trenton, N.J., 1790s–1800s; Philadelphia, *c.* 1796
PARSONS, SILAS: Connecticut; n.p., n.d. Probably mid to late eighteenth century
PARTRIDGE, HORACE: Bristol, Conn., 1868–1879
PASS & STOW: Philadelphia brass founders reputed to have cast parts and blanks for clocks
PATTEN & FERRIS: New York City, 1820s–1830
PATTEN, RICHARD: New York City, 1820s
PATTEN, ZEBULON: Bangor, Me., 1830s–1870
PATTON, ABRAHAM & DAVID: Philadelphia and Baltimore, 1790s–1820s
PATTON & JONES: Baltimore, 1790s–1810s
PAYNE, L.: New York City, 1730s–1750s
PEALE, CHARLES WILSON: Annapolis, Md., 1760s. This great American artist started his career as a clockmaker
PEARCE, WILLIAM: Charleston, S.C., *c.* 1780s
PEARSALL & EMBREE: New York City, 1780s
PEARSALL, JOSEPH & THOMAS: New York City, 1760s–1773
PEARSON & GREY: Georgetown, S.C., advertised in 1768
PEARSON & HOLLINSHEAD: Burlington, N.J. Tall clocks, n.d., but *c.* 1750–1760
PEARSON, ISAAC: Burlington, N.J., 1720s–1760s
PEARSON, WILLIAM: New York City, advertised in 1768–1769 and 1774
PEASE, ISAAC: Enfield, Conn., 1810s
PECK & CO.: Litchfield, Conn., 1820s
PECK & HOLCOMB: Sanbornton, N.H., 1810s–1820s; managers of Timothy Gridley's Manufactory
PECK, BENJAMIN: Providence, R.I., 1820s
PECK, EDSON C.: Derby, Conn., 1820s
PECK, ELIJAH: Boston, 1780s
PECK, HAYDEN & CO.: Saint Louis, Mo., 1838–1839. "Manufacturers, located at 148 N. 3rd Street"
PECK, MOSES: Boston, 1753–1780s
PECK, TIMOTHY: Litchfield, Conn., after 1791, to 1808; prior to that at Middletown, Conn., 1787–1791
PENFIELD, JOSIAH: Savannah, Ga., 1820s
PENFIELD, SYLVESTER: New York City, 1840s

PEPPER, H. J.: Philadelphia, 1840s
PERKINS & CO., THOMAS: Pittsburgh, *c.* 1836–1840
PERKINS, R.: Jeffrey, N.H., 1820s
PERKINS, THOMAS: Philadelphia, advertised 1785; Pittsburgh, 1810–1820
PERRET, P. H.: Cincinnati, Ohio, 1820s
PERRIGO, JAMES: Wrentham, Mass., and perhaps at Dedham, 1760–1800. James Perrigo was born 1737 and died 1808. According to Dedham Historical Society, this Perrigo was a Huguenot
PERRIGO, JAMES, JR.: Wrentham, Mass., 1790s–1830s. There is a Perrigo clock pictured in Chapter X which could have been made by either of the Perrigos, father or son
PERRY, ALBERT: Salem, Mass., 1850s–1860s
PERRY, MARVIN: New York City, advertised in 1768 and 1776
PERRY, THOMAS: New York City, advertised in 1749, 1756, and 1774
PETERS, A. R.: Marietta, Lancaster County, Pa., 1850s
PETERS, EDWARD: New York City, 1840s
PETERS, J.: Philadelphia, 1830s
PETTIBONE, LYNDES: Brooklyn, N. Y., 1830s–1840s
PFAFF, A.: Philadelphia, *c.* 1790s–1820s
PFALTZ, J. M.: Baltimore, 1810s
PHELPS & BARTHOLOMEW: Ansonia, Conn., 1880s
PHELPS, SILAS: Lebanon, Conn., 1740s–1780s
PHILIP, JOHN: Bell and brass founder of New York City, 1717, who is recorded as making clock parts and blanks
PHILLIPE & LE GRAS: Baltimore, 1790s–1800s
PHILLIPS, JAMES: Charleston, S.C., *c.* 1780s–1790s
PHILLIPS, JOSEPH: New York City, 1710s–1730s
PICARD, J. C.: Cincinnati, 1830s
PICKERING, JOHN: Cincinnati, 1830s–1840s
PICKERING, JOSEPH: Philadelphia, 1820s
PIERCE, PRESERVED: Swanzey (Swansea), Mass., 1770s–1780s
PIERRET, MATTHEW: Philadelphia, 1790s
PIERSON, H. S.: Portland, Me., 1830s
PINE, DAVID: Strasburg, Lancaster County, Pa., 1770s
PINK, OSBORNE & CONRAD: Philadelphia, 1840s
PIPER, JAMES: Chester, Md., 1770s–1790s
PITKIN, LEVI: East Hartford, Conn., 1795–1805; Rochester, N.Y., 1810–1830; Ogdensburg, N.Y., 1835–1850
PITMAN & DORRANCE: Providence, R.I., 1800s–1810s
PITMAN, SAUNDERS: Providence, R.I., 1780s–1790s
PLACE, W. S.: Charleston, Me., 1850s

Platt, A. S.: Bristol, Conn., before 1849
Platt, A. S. & Co.: Bristol (factory), 1849–1856
Platt & Blood: Bristol, Conn., 1840s
Platt, Ebenezer: New York City, 1775–1800
Platt, John: Philadelphia, 1840s
Platt, Samuel: Boston, 1825
Polack, Francis C.: York, Pa. Married widow of Frederick Cook of Columbia, Lancaster County, Pa., succeeded to the clockmaking and silversmithing trade of the former, at York, after 1846
Polhans, Henry: Saint Louis, Mo., 1860s
Polhans, Philip: Saint Louis, Mo., 1864–1878. Town clockmaker. Name variously spelled Bolhanz, Polhans, Pollhaus. Made tower clocks
Pollhans, Adam: Saint Louis, Mo., 1879–1890; manufacturer of clocks
Polsey, J.: Boston, Mass., 1820s–1840s. Believed a factory hand of Howard's who did after-hours work on his own
Pomeroy & Parker: Bristol, Conn., 1852–1857
Pomeroy & Robbins: Bristol, Conn., 1847
Pomeroy, Chauncey: Bristol, Conn., 1830s
Pomeroy, Eltweed: Clockmaker and gunsmith of Massachusetts Bay colony, 1640s. It is safe to assume that every gunsmith of the seventeenth century knew enough about clockmaking to produce a clock; the two crafts were very much allied in England and also in the Colonies. Any clockmaker could make a gun; any gunsmith could make a clock
Pomeroy, H.: Elmira, N.Y., 1830s
Pomeroy, John & Co.: Bristol, Conn., 1840s
Pomeroy, M. & Co.: Bristol, Conn., 1849–1850
Pomeroy, Noah: Bristol, 1847–1878
Pomeroy, Noah & Co.: Bristol, Conn., 1849–1851
Pond & Barnes: Boston, advertised in 1847. Manufacturers
Pond, L. A.: Boston, Mass.; and Chelsea, 1840s
Pond, Philip: Bristol, Conn., 1840s
Pool, Thomas: Cincinnati, Ohio, 1830s
Pope, Joseph & Robert: Boston, 1780–1790s
Porter, Daniel: Williamstown, Mass., 1790s
Porter, George: Boston, 1830s–1840s
Porter, William: Williamstown, Mass., to 1799–1800, then at Waterbury, Conn.
Post, Samuel: New London, Conn., 1780s–1785
Potter, Ephraim: Concord, N.H., 1770s–1790s
Potter, H. J.: Bristol, Conn., 1840s

POTTER, J. O. & J. R.: Providence, R.I., 1848

POTTER, JOHN: Farmington, Conn., 1770s–1780s

POUND, ISAAC: Charleston, S.C., advertised in 1746

POWELL, JOHN: Baltimore, *c.* 1745. A bound servant; an English clockmaker who served years of time to pay for his passage to the Colonies

PRAESELF (or PRAEFELT), JOHN: Philadelphia, 1797

PRATT & FROST: Daniel Pratt, Jr., and Jonathan Frost, Reading, Mass., factory for production of wooden shelf clocks complete. Established 1832 and in operation to *c.* 1845 or later. Made many clocks sold by Massachusetts clock peddlers of that day

PRATT, DANIEL: Reading, Mass. In 1832 established a factory with Jonathan Frost (*See* Pratt & Frost), and in 1846 established a store at Boston, continued by Daniel Pratt and B. M. Boyce to 1895

PRATT, DANIEL'S SON: Boston; clock store, so named in 1880s

PRATT, PHINEAS: Saybrook, Conn., 1760s–*c.* 1810

PRATT W. & BROTHER: Boston, *c.* 1850

PRESNOT, HENRI: New York City, 1800s

PRESTON, PAUL: Buckingham, Bucks County, Pa., 1750s. Clock and sundial maker

PREYLE, J.: Charleston, S.C., *c.* 1780s

PRICE, ISAAC: Philadelphia, 1779

PRICE, JOSEPH: Baltimore, 1790s

PRICE, PHILIP: Philadelphia, 1810–1820; Cincinnati, Ohio, 1820–1823; Lebanon, Ohio, 1823–1830s

PRICE, ROBERT: New York City, 1820s–1830s

PRICE, WILLIAM H.: West Chester, Pa., 1820s

PRICHARD & MUNSON: Bristol, Conn., 1844

PRINCE, ISAAC: Philadelphia, 1790s

PRIOR, DANIEL: New Haven, Conn., 1840s–1850s

PRITCHARD & HOLDEN: Dayton, Ohio, 1838

PROBOSCO, JOHN: Trenton, N.J., 1800–1823; removed to Lebanon, Ohio, 1823, in which year he advertised himself at that place as clock and watchmaker, silversmith, et cetera, lately from Trenton, in New Jersey

PROCTOR, CARDEN: New York City, advertised in 1747 and also in 1775

PROCTOR, WILLIAM: New York City, 1730s–1760s

PRONTAUT, ANTHONY: New York City, 1840s

PROUD, JOHN: Newport, R.I., 1720s–1730s

PROUD, ROBERT: Newport, R.I., 1770s–1780s

PROUD, WILLIAM: Newsport, R.I., 1750s–1760s
PUDNEY, G.: New York City, 1820s
PULSIFER, F.: Boston, 1850s
PURSE, THOMAS: Baltimore, 1790s–1810s
PURSE, W.: Charleston, S.C., *c.* 1790s

QUANDALE, L.: Philadelphia, 1810s
QUARE, DANIEL: English clockmaker who invented the one-year clock and the repeating watch. He worked 1680–1710. Clocks marked Daniel Quare, without place, are to be attributed to him. Boston, Philadelphia, New York, and Charleston, S.C., makers are reported as importing, or remodeling imported clocks by Quare
QUEST, HENRY: Lancaster County, Pa., at Waterford (now Marietta), 1810–1820
QUEST, SAMUEL: Lancaster County, Pa., at Maytown, *c.* 1810–1830; brother of Henry Quest
QUESTED, I.: n.d., n.p.
QUIMBY, PHINEAS: Belfast, Me., 1830s–1850s
QUIMBY, WILLIAM: Belfast, Me., 1820s–1850s
QUIN, THOMAS: New York, 1760s; Philadelphia, 1770s–1780s
QUINCY, HENRY: Portland, Me., 1830s

RACINE, DANIEL: Baltimore, 1790–1800s
RAHMER, G.: New York City, 1840s
RAMSDEN, WRIGHT: Brooklyn, N.Y., 1830s–1840s
RANKIN, ALEXANDER: Philadelphia, 1820s–1830s
RANLET, NOAH: Gilmanton, N.H., 1790s–1820s
RANLET, SAMUEL: Maine, n.d., n.p. (doubtful). *See* Raulet, Samuel
RANSINGER, M.: Elizabethtown, Lancaster County, Pa., 1850s
RAPP, WILLIAM: Philadelphia, 1830s–1840s
RAULET (variant of Ranlet?), SAMUEL: Monmouth, Me., 1800s
RAUS, EMANUEL: Philadelphia, n.d. Tall clocks
RAWSON, JASON R.: Holden, Mass., and Saxton, Vt., 1830s–1840s
RAY & INGRAHAM: Bristol, Conn., 1841–1843
REA, A.: Salem, Mass., 1780s
REA, GEORGE: Flemington, N.J., 1795–1815. Data are not complete; assurance of activity of man given by Hiram Deats, Esq.
READ, WILLIAM H.: Philadelphia, 1830s
REED, E.: N. Bridgewater, Mass., 1780s–1790s
REED, FREDERICK: Philadelphia, 1820s
REED, ISAAC: Stamford, Conn., 1760s–1776. There is a record of work resumption after Revolution, from 1784–1799

REED, ISAAC: Frankford, Pa., n.d. Tall clocks. May have been the Isaac Reed of Stamford who resumed work near Philadelphia
REED, JOHN: Philadelphia, 1840s
REED, SILAS: New Brunswick, N.J., n.d. Tall clocks
REED, SIMEON: Cummington, Mass., 1770s
REED, STEPHEN: New York City, 1810s
REED, Z.: Goshen, Mass., 1790s
REEVE, BENJAMIN: Greenwich, N.J., n.d. Tall clocks
REEVE, R.: Philadelphia, 1800s
REEVES, DAVID: Philadelphia, 1830s
REGENSBURG, MOSES A.: West Chester, Pa., 1830s–1840s
REILLY, JOHN: Philadelphia, 1797
REILLY & CO., J. C.: Louisville, Ky., 1810s–1830s
REMINGTON, O. H.: Akron, Ohio, 1860s
RENTZELHEIMER, A.: Allentown, Pa., n.d.
REYMOND, M.: Charleston, S.C., advertised in 1785. From Paris, France
REYNOLDS (E. J.) & BENTON (J.): Rochester, N.Y., 1850s
REYNOLDS, JOHN: Hagerstown, Md., 1790s–1830s
REYNOLDS, JOHN: Hagerstown, Md. Brass founder and clockmaker, 1800s–1820s
RICE, CHARLES: Lewiston, Minnesota, last half nineteenth century
RICE, GIDEON: New York City, 1840s
RICE (JOSEPH) & BARRY (STANDISH): Baltimore, advertised in 1785
RICE, J. T.: Albany, N.Y., 1810–1830s
RICE, JOSEPH: Baltimore, advertised in 1784
RICH & WILLARD: Boston, 1840s
RICH, ALEX: Charleston, S.C., 1790s
RICH, JOHN: Bristol, Conn., *c.* 1775–1812
RICHARDS, ALANSON: Bristol, Conn., *c.* 1820–1840
RICHARDS & MORRELL: New York City, 1820s–1830s
RICHARDS, B. & A.: Bristol, Conn., 1825–1835
RICHARDS, BRYAN: Bristol, Conn., 1823
RICHARDS, SAMUEL: Paris, Me., 1850s–1860s
RICHARDS, SETH & SON: Bristol, Conn., 1815
RICHARDS, THOMAS: New York City, 1800s
RICHARDS, W. & S. R.: Philadelphia, 1820
RICHARDSON, FRANCIS: Philadelphia, from 1736. Made fine tall clocks. Working to *c.* 1755–1760
RICHARDSON, WILLIAM: Norfolk, Va., 1790s
RICHMOND, F.: Providence, R.I., 1824–1850
RICKSECKER, ISRAEL: Dover, Ohio, 1830s–1870s
RIDER, ARTHUR: Baltimore, 1820s

RIESLE, EGIDIUS: New York City, 1840s

RIGGS, WILLIAM H.: Philadelphia, 1820s–1850s; made many banjo-style clocks for steamship lines, Pennsylvania and Reading railroads, banks and commercial houses; also chronometers and nautical instruments. All Riggs clocks are fine timekeepers. The banjo clocks usually have curved side pieces on the rectangular bottom boxes and the tablets are simple gold-lined glass panels. Several hundred Riggs banjo clocks were still in Pennsylvania Railroad service in 1930

RILEY, JOHN: Philadelphia, advertised in 1783

RING, W. B.: *See* King, W. B.

RITTENHOUSE, BENJAMIN: Worcester, Montgomery County, Pa. Worked 1760s–1770s. Brother of David

RITTENHOUSE, DAVID: America's first truly great clockmaker and scientist; pupil of John Gorgas (who married Sophia Rittenhouse). David Rittenhouse was born 1732, grandson of first Mennonite bishop in America. Original name Rittenhuijsen, and Dutch. Family migrated from Netherlands to Rhineland during Spanish occupation of Netherlands and from Rhineland to Pennsylvania. David, raised on a farm near Norriton (Norristown), constructed a clock at the age of seventeen. Studied astronomy and surveying; laid first stone of Mason-Dixon line. Removed to Philadelphia 1770, where he built fine clocks and instruments. During Revolution was chairman of committee on substitution of iron weights for lead weights in clocks. Constructed orreries and mathematical instruments, astronomical clocks, and machines. Said to have made six clocks in the year 1769. Died 1796. Cousin of Jacob Gorgas of "near Ephrata," Lancaster County, with whom he had constant traffic in relation to clockmaking. Enthusiastic researchers, on finding records of transactions between Rittenhouse and English clock and parts makers have been somewhat confused. These data, already known, have been assumed to mean Rittenhouse imported the clocks he signed as made by him. This importing of parts, as a practice, is mentioned in the text of this present volume, Chapters II, III, and IIII. Also, in this list, we mention parts importers

ROBERTS & LEE: Boston, 1772, advertised "time-telling night lamps (lamp clocks) that could be used in the nicest chamber without giving offense." Clock lamps, while actually a form of timekeeper, are seldom considered in the category of clocks

ROBERTS, CANDACE: Lady clock-dial and tablet decorator; daughter of Gideon Roberts. She worked for perhaps half a score of clockmakers

ROBERTS, ELIAS: Bristol, Conn., *c.* 1760. Reputed to have taught his sons, Elias and Gideon, clockmaking before his death in the Wyoming massacre, near Wilkes-Barre, Pa., 1778

ROBERTS, ELIAS & CO.: Bristol, Conn., *c.* 1808–1810; a "memorial" company in honor of the father Elias, conducted by his sons

ROBERTS, F.: Philadelphia, 1820s

ROBERTS, GIDEON: Bristol, Conn., *c.* 1780–1812. First Bristol clock factory established by this man, sold many clocks (hang-up type and tall-case) in Pennsylvania, Virginia, and Carolinas. In 1800 he began using printed paper dials. His thirty-hour wooden-movement tall clocks, made in lots of ten or more at a time, mark the real beginning of repetitive production in clocks and well may have given Eli Terry his idea. Roberts died in 1813, after having proved that clocks could be made at a low price and sold readily in many parts of the country

ROBERTS, JOHN: Philadelphia, 1797

ROBERTS, OLIVER: Lancaster, Pa., 1790s–1810. *See* Montanden & Roberts

ROBERTS, S.: Trenton, N.J., 1790s–1820s

ROBINSON, OBED: Attleboro, Mass., 1780s–1790s

ROBINSON, ——: Chillicothe, Ohio, *c.* 1810–1820. Clocks bearing the name Robinson and the place name Chillicothe are known

ROBINSON, SAMUEL: Pittsburgh, *c.* 1810s–1830s. Since many Pittsburgh artisans were in the habit of selling in the Ohio country, this Robinson of Pittsburgh may have been the maker producing the clocks marked Chillicothe, Ohio. Data are not complete on this but the possibility should be considered

ROBJOHN, THOMAS: New York City, 1840s

ROCKWELL, HENRY: New York City, 1840s

ROCKWELL, SAMUEL: Providence, R.I., *c.* 1745–1760; then at Middletown, Conn., from *c.* 1760 to 1770s

RODE, WILLIAM: Philadelphia, 1780s–1790s

RODMAN, ISAAC PEARSON: Burlington, N.J., n.d. Tall clocks

ROGERS, ABNER: Berwick, Me., 1820s

ROGERS, ISAAC: Marshfield, Mass., 1800s–1820s

ROGERS, JAMES: New York City, 1820s–1860s

ROGERS, JOHN: Billerica, Mass., prior to 1765; Newton, Mass., 1765–1800s. Worked also at Boston prior to 1765

ROGERS, NATHANIEL: Windham, Me., 1792–1810

ROGERS, PAUL: Berwick, Me., n.d.

ROGERS, PETER: New York City, 1820s–1830s

ROGERS, SAMUEL: Plymouth, Mass., n.d.

ROGERS, THOMAS: New York City, 1820s–1830s
ROGERS, WILLIAM: Boston, 1860s
ROHR, JOHN: Philadelphia, 1806–1812
ROI, HENRY: Hamburg, Pa., 1800s–1820s
ROORBACK, M.: New York City, 1760s–1770s
ROOT, LA FAYETTE: New Haven, Conn., 1850s
ROOT, SAMUEL E.: Bristol, Conn., 1850s–1890s. Made clocks and paper dials
ROOT, SYLVESTER: Bristol, Conn., 1842–44
ROSE, DANIEL: Reading, Pa., 1780–1820
ROSE, DANIEL, JR.: Reading, Pa., 1820–1840
ROSETT & MULFORD: Elizabeth, N.J., cabinetmakers who made cases and cased some clocks with their name. Not clockmakers
ROSS, ROBERT: New York City, 1850s
ROSSELOT, P. A.: New York City, 1840s. Dealer in clock materials
ROTH, N.: Utica, N.Y., 1840s
ROTHROCK, JOSEPH: York, Pa., 1780s–1790s
ROULSTONE, JOHN: Boston, advertised in 1768
RUDISILL, GEORGE: Manheim, Lancaster County, Pa., 1810s–1820s
RUSSEL, J.: Geneva, N.Y., 1800s
RUSSEL, SAMUEL: Middleton, Mass., 1840s
RUSSELL, GEORGE: Philadelphia, 1830s
RUSSELL, JOHN: Deerfield, Mass., 1760s
RUSSELL, WILLIAM: Augusta, Ga., 1820s
RUTTER, M.: Baltimore, 1800s

SABER, GEORGE: Reading, Pa., *c.* 1800s
SADD, HARVEY: New Hartford, Conn., 1798–1829; Austinburgh, Ohio, 1829–1840
SADD, THOMAS: East Windsor, Conn., 1750s
SADTLER, P. B.: Baltimore, 1800s
SAGE, A. & CO.: Savannah, Georgia, n.d. Tall-case clocks
SAGEY (or SAYEY), JOHN: Germantown, Pa., n.d. Tall clocks
SALADE: *See* Solliday
SALMON, ALFRED: Cincinnati, Ohio, 1820s
SALYBACKER, I.: Columbia, S.C., 1850s–1860s
SAMPSON, ALEXANDER: Hagerstown, Md., 1799–1805
SAMUELS & DUNN: Clock racketeers who cased cheap movements in New York City and used faked Jerome labels, 1840s
SANDELL, EDWARD: Baltimore, 1810s
SANDOZ, FREDERICK: Charleston, S.C., 1790s–1800s
SANDS, STEPHEN: New York City, advertised in 1772 and 1774

SANFORD, EATON: Plymouth, Conn., 1760s–1780s
SANFORD, ISAAC: Hartford, Conn., 1780s–1790s
SANFORD, SAMUEL: Plymouth, Conn., 1840s–1870s
SANSON, JOHN: New York City, 1840s. Casemaker. Did not make movements he used
SARGEANT, JACOB: Mansfield, Conn., 1784–1787; Springfield, Mass., 1787–1795; Hartford, Conn., 1795–1840
SARGEANT, JOSEPH: Springfield, Mass., 1800s
SAUTER, RICHARD: Hanover, Pa., 1770s
SAVAGE, T. Y.: Raleigh, N.C., 1820s
SAVAGE, WILLIAM: Glasgow, Ky., 1810–1819. Later at Horsewell and Green River, but data do not divulge if he made clocks at latter spots
SAVOY, N.: Boston, 1830s
SAW, WILLIAM: New Haven, Conn., 1840s–1850s
SAWIN & DYAR (sometimes spelled Dyer): Boston, *c.* 1810–1840s. This firm made excellent banjo clocks, superbly cased
SAWIN, JOHN: Boston. Apprentice of Aaron Willard, 1823–1860. Lived at Chelsea, Mass., where he maintained a "night shop" at corner of Fourth and Chestnut streets; Boston shop at 66 Court St. Member of firm Sawin & Dyar
SAWIN, SILAS W.: New York City, 1820s–1830s
SAWYER, C. & H. S.: Colebrook, Conn., 1840s
SAXTON & LUKENS: Philadelphia, 1820s–1840s
SAYRE & RICHARDS: New York City, 1805–1810
SAYRE, JOHN: New York City, 1790s–1805
SCHEID, DANIEL: Summeytown, Montgomery County, Pa., n.d.
SCHEM & FALCONNET: Charleston, S.C., 1790s
SCHEM, J. F.: Charleston, S.C., 1785–1790s
SCHERR, LEWIS: Philadelphia, 1840s–1850s
SCHMALZE, F.: Freytown, York County, Pa., 1858
SCHOMO (also SHUMO and SCUMO) THOMAS: Philadelphia, 1820s
SCHREINER, C. W.: Philadelphia, 1810s
SCHULLER, J.: Philadelphia, 1840s
SCHUYLER, P. C.: New York City, 1800s
SCHWARTZ, GEORGE & PETER: George enlisted in Revolutionary Army from York, Pa., 1777; no record of his return to York but record of, or as in business of, clockmaking prior to enlistment. Peter recorded as working in York, 1770s–1790s
SCOTT, J.: Charleston, S.C., 1790s–1800s
SCOTT, JOHN: Chambersburg, Pa., 1790s–1820s
SCOTT, ROBERT: Richmond, Va., *c.* 1780

SCOTT, THOMAS: Downingtown, Pa., 1834–1850
SCOTT, W. D.: Louisville, Ky., 1840s
SCUDDER, JOHN: Westfield, N.J., 1760s–1770s. Not a clockmaker; casemaker who traded cases for movements by clockmakers, casing movements and selling clocks with his name on dials and in cases
SEAMAN, THOMAS: New York City, 1840s
SEARSON, JOHN: New York City, 1750s
SEDGWICK & BOTSFORD: Watertown, Conn., *c.* 1820s
SEIP, DAVID: Northampton, now Allentown, Pa., n.d.
SELKIRK, SAMUEL: Kalamazoo, Mich., 1850s–1860s
SENG & HESS: New York City, 1850s
SENNERT, F. L.: Lititz, Lancaster County, Pa., 1850s. Tall clocks
SERVOSS, CHARLES: Philadelphia, 1840s
SERVOSS, JOSEPH: Philadelphia, 1850s
SEVERBERG, CHRISTIAN: New York City, 1750s
SEYMOUR & CHURCHILL: Bristol, Conn., 1846–1852
SEYMOUR, ROBERT: Waterbury, Conn., 1810s
SEYMOUR, WILLIAMS & PORTER: Farmington, Conn., 1835–1836
SHADE, DANIEL: Summeytown, Montgomery County, Pa., n.d. Tall clocks
SHADFORTH, WHITTAKER: Richmond, Va., 1790s
SHAEFFER, BENJAMIN: Elizabethtown, Lancaster County, Pa., 1850s. Tall clocks
SHAFFER, PHILIP: Lancaster, Pa., 1788–1802. Tall clocks
SHARF, JOHN: Mifflinburg, Pa., 1820–1860. Tall clocks
SHAW, B. E.: Newport, Vt., 1850s–1860s
SHAW, JOSEPH KERNBERG: Philadelphia, *c.* 1760–1780
SHAW, P.: Olney, Ill., 1860s. Dealer who advertised he made clocks
SHAW, SETH: Providence, R.I., 1850s. Manufacturer
SHEARMAN, ROBERT: Wilmington, Del., *c.* 1760–1780; Philadelphia, 1790s–1800s
SHEPHERD & BOYD: Albany, N.Y., 1810s
SHEPHERD, MATTHEW: New York City, 1760s; Charleston, S.C., 1770s–1790s
SHEPHERD, NATHANIEL: New Bedford, Mass.; early nineteenth century; became partner of Ezra Kelly in watch and clock oil business
SHERMAN, ROBERT: Philadelphia, 1790s
SHERMER, JOHN: Philadelphia, 1810s
SHERRY & BYRAM: Sag Harbor, L.I., N.Y. Made regulators and fine timepieces, 1840s–1850s
SHERWIN, WILLIAM: Buckland, Mass., 1820s–*c.* 1840s
SHIDET, V.: Shreveport, La., 1850s–1860s
SHIELDS, THOMAS: Philadelphia, n.d.

SHIPMAN & SON, N.: Norwich, Conn., 1870s. Research fails to justify obvious conclusion that either this date is in error, or that of the Nathaniel Shipman above listed

SHIPMAN, NATHANIEL: Norwich, Conn., *c.* 1785–1800

SHIPP & COLLINS: Cincinnati, Ohio, 1820s–1830s

SHIPP, S. A.: Cincinnati, Ohio, 1820s

SHOEMAKER, DAVID: Mt. Holly, N.J., n.d. Tall clocks

SHOURDS, SAMUEL: Bordentown, N.J., 1740s–1760s

SHREINER, HENRY: Lancaster, Pa., 1850s–1860s. Made tall clocks

SHREINER, MARTIN: Lancaster, Pa., 1790–1830. Made tall clocks and numbered them. Highest number recorded is 356; strike, chime, thirty-hour, and eight-day clocks; also made fire engines and pumps

SHREINER, MARTIN & PHILIP: Sons of Martin above listed; Lancaster, Pa., 1830–1860. Martin of this firm lived well into twentieth century and recorded much of family clockmaking history

SHREINER, P. & SON: Columbia, Lancaster County, Pa., 1850s

SHROEDER, CHARLES: Baltimore, 1800s–1820s

SHULER, JOHN: Philadelphia, 1840s–1850s

SHUMAN, JOHN: Easton, Pa., 1780s

SHUTZ, GUSTAVE: Philadelphia, 1820s

SHUTZ, PETER: York, Pa., 1758–1790. Recorded as "Schweitzer Uhrmacher"; i.e., "Swiss Clockmaker." Name variously spelled Sheetz, Sheitz, Sheitzen, and Schutzi. Emigrated to colonies from Switzerland

SIBLEY & MARBLE: New Haven, Conn., 1800s

SIBLEY, ASA: Woodstock, Conn., 1784–1810; Rochester, N.Y., 1815–1825

SIBLEY, GIBBS: Canandaigua, N.Y., 1780s–1810s

SIBLEY, S.: Great Barrington, Mass., 1790s

SIGOURNEY, CHARLES, JR.: Hartford, Conn., 1790s–1800s; importer of brass parts and blanks, hardware and tools for clockmakers

SILL, M. & F.: New York City, 1840s

SILVER & WAY: Bristol, Conn., 1864–1866

SIMONS, ELIJAH: Massachusetts, n.p., *c.* 1800s

SIMONTON, GILBERT: New York City, 1820s

SIMPLEX COMPANY: Gardner, Mass., making time recorders, using Seth Thomas movements. Late nineteenth century

SIMPSON, ALEXANDER: Hagerstown, Md., 1799–1805

SINDLER, ANDREW: Newchurch, Va., n.d.

SINNET, JOHN: Boston, advertised, 1769; New York City, advertised 1770s. Maker and dealer in imported clocks

SINNOT, PATRICK: Philadelphia, 1750s; Baltimore, 1760s

SLICER, WILLIAM: Annapolis, Md., casemaker; doubtful if clocks bearing his name were made by him. Working 1760s–1770s

SLIGH, SAMUEL: West Caln, Chester County, Pa., 1790s

SMART, GEORGE: Lexington, Ky., 1790s–1810s

SMITH, AARON: Ipswich, Mass., 1820s

SMITH (L.) & BLAKESLY (A.): New York City, *c.* 1830s

SMITH & BROTHER: Philadelphia, 1840s

SMITH & GOODRICH: Forestville, Bristol, and other points in Connecticut; had four factories operating between 1847 and 1852

SMITH & SILL: Waterbury, Conn., 1830s

SMITH & TAYLOR: New York City, 1840s

SMITH, B.: New York City, advertised as manufacturer and dealer; had large store at corner Division Street and Bowery where he sold clocks of every description: town, regulator, railroad, steamboat, mantel, and wall, barometers and combinations

SMITH, CHARLES A.: Late amateur maker working in 1890s–1930s at Brattleboro, Vt. Made and sold hundreds of clocks

SMITH, CHARLES: Reading, Pa., 1810s–1820s

SMITH, E.: New Haven, Conn., casemaker; early nineteenth century

SMITH, ELIAS: Philadelphia, 1840s–1850s

SMITH, ELISHA: Sanbornton, N.H., 1800s

SMITH, GEORGE: Carlisle, Pa., 1780s. Validity of name, place and date not as yet established

SMITH, HENRY A.: Rochester, N.Y., 1830s

SMITH, HENRY C.: Waterbury, Conn., 1810s; Plymouth Hollow, Conn., 1840s

SMITH, JESSE, JR.: Salem, Mass., 1830s–1840s

SMITH, J.: Concord, Mass., 1790s–1800s

SMITH, JOHN: Charleston, S.C., advertised in 1754

SMITH, JOHN: Lancaster, Pa., 1799–1801

SMITH, JOHN W.: Stowe, Vt., 1870s–1890s

SMITH, JOSEPH: Brooklyn, N.Y., 1830s–1840s

SMITH, JOSEPH: Chester, Pa., *c.* 1750s

SMITH, JOSIAH: Reading, Pa., 1800s; New York City, *c.* 1830s and 1840s. Data are not clear

SMITH, L.: Keene, N.H., 1790s–1830s

SMITH, LEVI: Bristol, Conn., 1842–1845

SMITH, LUTHER: Keene, N.H., n.d. but probably 1790s–1810s

SMITH, LYMAN: Stratford, Conn., 1800s–1820

SMITH, ———: Sudbury, Mass., 1640s. Mentioned in one existing document

SMITH, N. W.: Columbus, Ohio, 1810

SMITH, PHILIP: Marcellus, N.Y., 1825–1846. Specially cased Connecticut movements. This man evidently cased but did not make movements

SMITH, R.: Hartford, Conn., 1830s

SMITH, RANSOM: New York City, 1840s

SMITH, R. & Co.: Waterbury, Conn., 1830s

SMITH, SEARS: Rochester, N.Y., 1830s

SMITH CLOCKS: Made *c.* 1810; Columbus, Ohio. Research thus far fails to reveal names of individuals, or full name of Smith engaged in this production

SMITH, WILLIAM: New York City, 1810s

SMITH, WILLIAM & ROBERT: Philadelphia, 1820s; may have worked independently

SMITH, ZEBULON: Bangor, Me., 1830s–1840s

SNOW, WILLIAM: Kalamazoo, Mich., 1850s–1860s

SNYDER, PETER: Exeter, Berks County, Pa., after 1779

SOLLIDAY, BENJAMIN: Rock Hill, Pa., 1790s. Brother of Jacob

SOLLIDAY, DANIEL: Montgomery County, probably Evansburg, Pa., n.d. Tall clocks

SOLLIDAY, FREDERICK: Penna., n.d., n.p. Tall clocks

SOLLIDAY, GEORGE: Montgomery County, Pa., early nineteenth century. Tall clocks

SOLLIDAY, JACOB: Bedminster, Pa., 1783–1807. Also at Northampton, now Allentown, Pa. Sollidays were working "all over the map" in Bucks, Northampton, and Berks counties from *c.* 1780s to 1830s

SOLLIDAY, JOHN: Bucks, and Northampton counties, Pa., 1830s–1870s

SOLLIDAY, JOHN: Reading, Pa., in 1800s (Not yet established.)

SOLLIDAY, PETER: (Son of Jacob). Bedminster, Pa., 1790s–1800s

SOLLIDAY, SAMUEL: (Son of Benjamin) Doylestown, Pa., 1830s

SOLOMON, PARKE & Co.: Philadelphia, advertised 1796

SOUER (SOWER) CHRISTOPHER: Pupil of Dr. Christopher Witt, Germantown, Pa., apparently working at clockmaking *c.* 1740–1760

SOUTH, JAMES: Charlestown, Mass., 1800s–1810s

SOUTHERN CLOCK CO.: Saint Louis, Mo., 1880s. Calendar clocks

SOUTHWORTH, ELIJAH: New York City, 1790s–1830s

SOUZA (or SUIZA) SAMUEL: Philadelphia, *c.* 1820

SOWER, DANIEL: Phoenixville, Pa., 1820s–1840s

SPANGLER, JACOB: York, Pa., 1788–1840. Son of Rudi Spangler. Jacob Spangler cut his clock hands with a letter "S" in them

SPANGLER, JACOB: York, Pa., 1810s–1820s

SPANGLER, RUDOLPH: York, Pa., 1770s

SPANGLER, RUDI: York, Pa., 1760s–1800. Son of Baltzer Spangler, Swiss clockmaker believed to have worked 1740s in Lancaster and Chester counties but not yet authenticated

SPALDING, EDWARD: Providence, R.I., 1750s–1780s

SPALDING, EDWARD, JR.: Providence, R.I., 1780s–1810s

SPARCK, PETER: Philadelphia, 1790s

SPAULDING, ABIRAM: Brooklyn, N.Y., 1830s–1840s

SPENCE, GAVIN: New York City, 1810s

SPENCE, JOHN: Boston, 1820s

SPENCER, HOTCHKISS & CO.: Salem Bridge, now Naugatuck, Conn., nineteenth century

SPENCER, JULIUS: Utica, N.Y., 1820s

SPENCER, NOBLE: Wallingford, Conn., prior to 1796; Stratford, Conn., after 1797

SPENCER, WOOSTER & CO.: Salem, Conn., 1820s–1830s

SPERRY & BRYANT: New York City, 1850s

SPERRY & SHAW: New York City, 1840s. Apparently clock racketeers; in 1846 they advertised manufacture of 100,000 clocks annually more than 50,000 of which were exported to Great Britain. They sold clocks with faked labels of Chauncey Jerome

SPERRY, ANSON: Waterbury, Conn., *c.* 1810s

SPERRY, C. S.: New York City, 1840s. Manufacturer

SPERRY, ELIJAH M.: New York City, 1840s

SPERRY, F. S.: New York City, 1850s

SPERRY, HENRY & CO.: New York City, 1840s

SPERRY, HENRY: New York City, 1850s

SPERRY, J. T.: New York City, 1810s–1820s

SPERRY, SILAS: New Haven, Conn., 1840s–1850s; listed as a "clocksmith"

SPERRY, T. S.: New York, 1840s

SPERRY, WILLIAM: Philadelphia, 1840s–1850s

SPERRY, W. S.: New York City, 1840s. Listed as a case manufacturer

SPIES (SPICE) WILLIAM: Hanover, Pa., early 1800s

SPILLER, JOHN: New York City, 1820s–1830s

SPOTWOOD & CO.: Baltimore, 1780s

SPRING, SOLOMON C. & CO.: Bristol, Conn., 1864–1868

SPROGELL, JOHN: (also SPROGLE), Annapolis, Md., advertised in 1760s and 1770s. Working in Philadelphia, 1790s–1800s

SPURCK, PETER: Philadelphia, 1790s

SQUIRE & BROTHERS: SQUIRE & LANE: New York City after 1856. Extensive dealers under both names. Clocks are marked with these names but were not made by them. Also sold coin silverware with their mark but they did not produce it

STANLEY, J.: Chillicothe and Zanesville, Ohio, 1800s–1810s
STANTON, JOB: New York City, 1810s
STANTON, W.: Providence, R.I., 1810s
STANTON, W. P.: Rochester, N.Y., 1830s; firm was Henry & William Stanton in 1850s, same place
STAPLES & DOBBS: New York City to 1780s
STAPLES, JOHN R.: New York City, 1788–1790
STARR, FREDERICK: Rochester, N.Y., 1830s
STARRETT, JAMES: Chester County, Pa., at East Nantmeal Township in 1790s–1800s
STAUFFER, SAMUEL: Manheim, Lancaster County, Pa., 1790–1820. Made some clocks in a partnership with Christian Eby, 1820–1830. These are marked Stauffer & Eby
STEBBINS, L.: Waterbury, Conn., 1810s
STECHELL, VALENTINE: Frederick, Md., advertised in 1793
STEEL, R. F.: Adams, N.Y., 1850s–1860s
STEEL, SAMUEL: New Haven, Conn., 1840s–1850s
STEEL, WILLIAM: Albion, Mich., 1860s
STEICKLEADER, JOHN: Hagerstown, Md., 1791–1793
STEIN, ABRAHAM: Philadelphia, 1790s
STEIN, DANIEL: Norristown, Pa., 1830s–1850s
STEIN, JACOB: Allentown, Pa., 1790s–1840s Jacob & Son: 1820–1840
STEINMAN, GEORGE: Lancaster, Pa. Casemaker only; any clocks signed by him have movements by others, and probably Lancaster County (not city) clockmakers. Steinman made cases and purchased movements for them; no record of case-movement trading
STEINSEIFFER, JOHN: Hagerstown and Williamsport, Md., 1770s–1780s
STEKMAN (STECKMAN), H.: Middletown, Pa., working 1858. Tall clocks
STEVENS, BRYANT & CO.: Bristol, Conn., *c.* 1820s–1840s
STEVENS, CHARLES G.: New York City, 1840s
STEVENS, E.: West Springfield, Mass.; 1790s–1820s; wood-movement tall clocks in primitive-type pine cases
STEVENS, GEORGE: Boston, 1880s; manufacturer
STEVENS, JOHN: Bangor, Me., 1830s–1850s
STEVENS, JOHN: New Haven, Conn., 1840s–1850s
STEVENS, M.: Chillicothe, Ohio, 1810s
STEVENS; STEVENS & HEATH: Chillicothe, Ohio, *c.* 1820s
STEVENSON, HOWARD, and DAVIS: Boston, 1840s
STEVER & HILL: Bristol, Conn., 1852–1856
STEVER & PRINDLE: Whigville and Burlington, Conn., producing clocks with labels indicating Bristol, not Whigville or Burlington make. Date is *c.* 1852–1856

STEVER, BRYANT & CO.: Bristol, Conn., 1830s; STEVER & BRYANT, 1852–56

STEVER, JEREMIAH: Bristol, Conn., 1851–1866

STEWART, ARTHUR: New York City, 1820s–1840s

STEWART, JAMES: Baltimore, 1790s

STICHLER, JOHN: Marietta, Lancaster County, Pa., 1850s

STICKNEY, MOSES: Boston, 1820s

STILLAS, JOHN: Philadelphia, advertised in 1783; Baltimore after 1790

STILLMAN, IRA: Newport, R.I., 1850s

STILLMAN, W.: Burlington, Conn., 1780s–1790s

STILLSON, D.: Rochester, N.Y., 1830s

STOCKTON, SAMUEL: Philadelphia, 1820s

STODDARD & KENNEDY: New York City, 1790s

STOKEL, JOHN: New York City, 1820s–1850s

STOLLENWORK, P. M.: Philadelphia, 1800s–1810; New York City, 1810s–1820s; then as P. M. Stollenwork and Brothers, after *c.* 1825

STONER, RUDI: Lancaster, Pa., 1750–1769. A Swiss clockmaker

STORRS, N.: Utica, N.Y., 1800s–1820s

STORRS, S.: Utica, N.Y., 1820s

STOW, P. M.: Philadelphia, 1810s

STOW, SOLOMON: New York City, 1810s–1820s; Southington, Conn., 1828–1836: Shelf clocks

STOWELL, A.: Worcester, Mass., 1790s–1800s; Boston, 1800s–1820

STOWELL, ABEL: Boston, 1820s–1850s

STOWELL, JOHN: Boston, 1820s–1830s

STOWELL, JOHN: Medford, Mass., 1810s–1820s

STOWELL, J. J.: Charlestown, Mass., 1830s–1840s

STOY, GUSTAVUS: Lancaster, Pa., 1790s–1800s; Lebanon, Pa., 1810s; Schnitz Creek, Pa., 1820s

STRAEDE, CHARLES: Lititz, Lancaster County, Pa., 1850s. Tall clocks

STRATTON, CHARLES: Worcester, Mass., 1820s–1830s; Holden, Mass., from 1836 to 1839

STREIBY, MICHAEL: *See* Streipy

STREIPY, MICHAEL: Also STREIBY; Greersburgh, Pa., 1800s–1830s

STRETCH, PETER: Philadelphia, 1690s to 1740s. Peter Stretch was born 1670 and died 1746

STRETCH, THOMAS: Philadelphia, *c.* 1720–1760

STUDLEY, DANIEL: Hanover, Mass., 1800s

STUDLEY, DAVID: Hanover, Mass., 1800s–1830s; Bridgewater, Mass., 1830s–1840s

STUDLEY, LUTHER: Bridgewater, Mass., 1840s

STURGEON, SAMUEL: Shippensburg, Pa., 1800s–1820
SULLIVAN, C. D. & Co.: Saint Louis, Mo., 1847–1854
SULLIVAN, J. T.: Saint Louis, Mo., 1850s
SUMMERHAYS, JOHN: New York City, 1810s
SUTTON, ROBERT: New Haven, Conn., 1820s
SWAN, BENJAMIN: Haverhill, Mass., 1810s–1830s: Augusta, Me., 1830s–1840s
SWAN, MOSES: Augusta, Me., 1850s
SWARTZ, ABRAHAM: Lower Salford, Pa., n.d.
SWARTZ, PETER: York, Pa., 1780s–1790s
SWENEY, THOMAS: Philadelphia, 1850s. Fine regulators, some in late-style banjo cases
SYBERBERG (or SYBERBERGER), CHRISTIAN: New York City, 1750s; Charleston, S.C., 1757–1760
SYDERMAN, PHILIP: Philadelphia, 1780s–1790s

TABER, ELNATHAN: Roxbury, Mass., 1780s–1840s
TABER, H.: Boston, 1850s
TABER, J.: Saco, Me., *c.* 1810s–1820s
TABER, S. M.: Providence, R.I., 1820s
TABER, S. & Co.: Providence, R.I., 1840s
TABER, STEPHEN: New Bedford, Mass., 1790s–1850; also reported working in Providence, R.I.
TABER, THOMAS: Boston, 1850s
TABOR, L. A.: Holyoke, Mass., 1850s–1860s
TAF, JOHN: Philadelphia, 1790s
TALBOT, SYLVESTER: Dedham, Mass., 1813–1847. Maker and manufacturer
TAPPAN, W. B.: Philadelphia, 1810s–1820s
TAYLOR, CHARLES: Sedalia, Mo., 1860s
TAYLOR, JOSEPH: York, Pa., 1780s–1800s. Clocks (tall-case type) numbered in the high nineties signed by this man are extant. It is to be doubted not that he made so many clocks but that he made *any* clocks; it would seem, from data thus far accumulated, that he was a dealer casing the movements of any other makers and vending them over the vast area of western Pennsylvania
TAYLOR, LUTHER: Philadelphia, 1820s
TAYLOR, P. L. & Co.: Brooklyn, N.Y., 1820s–1830s
TAYLOR, SAMUEL: Philadelphia, 1790s–1800s
TAYLOR, SAMUEL E.: Bristol, Conn., 1858–60; recorded as working at Worcester, Mass., in early to middle 1850s
TAZEWELL, S. O.: Bridgeton, N.J., n.d. Tall clocks

TEMPLETON, ROBERT: Newport, R.I., 1770s

TENNEY, WILLIAM: Dutchess County, N.Y., 1790s–1800s. Data not conclusive

TERHUNE & EDWARDS: New York City, 1859

TERHUNE, H.: New York City, 1850s

TERNBACH, M.: Saint Louis, Mo., 1820s

TERRY & ANDREWS: Bristol, Conn., 1842–50; Ralph and Theodore Terry and C. F. Andrews

TERRY & BARNUM: Bridgeport, Conn., 1850s; merged with Jerome, at New Haven; Jerome later claimed this firm was insolvent when the merger took place

TERRY & DOWNS: Bristol, Conn., 1853–55

TERRY CLOCK CO.: Winsted, Conn., 1852–76; Silas B. Terry and his sons. Also at Pittsfield, Mass., 1880s, by sons of Silas Terry and George Bliss

TERRY, DOWNS & BURWELL: Bristol, Conn., 1851–52

TERRY, ELI: East Windsor, Conn., 1792–94; Plymouth, Conn., 1794–1833. In spite of much researching, the entire story of Eli Terry is not yet fully told. As recently as 1946 there were conflicting opinions as to his purchase of the Heman Clark factory at Plymouth Hollow, or purchase of same factory by Seth Thomas. Also, there is no known legal document covering the sale of his hang-up clock factory to his workmen, Thomas and Hoadley. Heman Clark definitely is known to have made pillar-and-scroll eight-day brass movement clocks several years before Eli Terry used the same case for his thirty-hour, patented wooden-movement shelf clock. Seth Thomas purchasing the Heman Clark factory in 1813, may have used the pillar-and-scroll case, as used by Clark, to case the Terry-type movement before Terry himself used the case. Terry was awarded, in all, nine patents on clocks. His first, 1797, was for a special time-telling dial and hands; the second for his thirty-hour shelf clock (1816), and from then on seven other patents were granted on wooden-wheel clocks, 1822 to 1845. Terry was born in 1772 and died in 1852. His brother, Samuel, also a clockmaker, was born in 1774 and died in 1853. Eli's sons, Eli, Jr., Henry, and Silas, are all herein listed

TERRY, ELI, JR.: Plymouth, Conn., 1824–1830; Terryville, Conn., as ELI TERRY JR. & CO.: After 1830

TERRY, ELI JR., & HENRY: Plymouth, Conn., 1822–1824

TERRY, ELI & SONS: Plymouth, Conn., 1818–1824

TERRY, E. & SONS: The immediately above listed partnership under sole control of Henry Terry, 1824–1830

TERRY, ELI & SAMUEL (Eli, Sr., and brother Samuel): Plymouth, Conn., 1824–1827
TERRY, ELI, III: Plymouth, Conn., 1860s
TERRY, HENRY: Plymouth, Conn., 1824–1830
TERRY, L. B.: Albany, N.Y., 1830s
TERRY, RALPH & JOHN B.: Bristol, Conn., 1835–36
TERRY, SAMUEL (Brother of Eli, Sr.): East Windsor, Conn., to 1818; Plymouth, Conn., 1818–1825; Bristol, Conn., 1825–1830. Samuel Terry's sons, Ralph, John, Theodore, and Samuel, were all involved in clockmaking and were in various partnerships and companies
TERRY, SILAS B.: Plymouth and Terryville, Conn., 1824–1850
TERRY, THEODORE: Ansonia, Conn., 1850–1852
TERRY, T.: Boston, 1810s–1820s
TERRY, THOMAS, & HOADLEY: A "partnership" of legend if not fact, at Plymouth, Conn., 1809–1810
TERRY, WILLIAM A.: Bristol, 1857
TERRY, WILLIAM: Nine Partners, N.Y., 1790s
TERRYVILLE MANUFACTURING CO.: Silas and other Terrys, 1840s–1850s, at Terryville, Conn. This entry ends the Terry story in this list
TEUFEL, H.: Chicago, Ill., 1856
THATCHER, GEORGE: Lowell, Mass., 1850s–1870s
THAYER, E. & CO.: Williamsburg, Mass., 1830s
THOMAS & HOADLEY: Plymouth, Conn., *c.* 1810–1813
THOMAS, ISAAC: Williamstown, Pa., 1775–1802
THOMAS, ISAIAH: Philadelphia and Lancaster, Pa., 1860s–1880s
THOMAS, JOSEPH: Penn Square and Philadelphia, 1830s
THOMAS, MORDECAI: Willistown, Chester County, Pa., 1795–1820
THOMAS, SETH: Plymouth Hollow and Thomaston, Conn., from 1813, when he dissolved arrangement with Hoadley and began production on his own account, purchasing the factory of Heman Clark. In operation continuously since 1813 as Seth Thomas, Seth Thomas Sons & Co., Seth Thomas Company, Seth Thomas Clock Company, and perhaps other designations for specific purposes. In 1866 a branch department manufactured and sold bronze- and marble-cased clocks that were better than the French ones. Seth Thomas factory is now a branch or division of General Time Instruments Corporation. They have assembled an imposing collection of old Seth Thomas clocks and clocks of other makers. Seth Thomas is perhaps the best-known and most widely known name in American clockmaking

THOMSON (or THOMPSON), JAMES: Pittsburgh, Pa., 1810s
THOMPSON & RANGER: Brattleboro, Vt., 1850s–1860s
THOMPSON, HIRAM: Bristol, Conn., 1878–1900; successor to Noah Pomeroy
THOMPSON, JAMES: Baltimore, 1790s–1800s; Pittsburgh, Pa., 1810s–1820s
THOMPSON, JOHN: Boonsboro, Md., 1820s–1830s. Believed to have been the John Thompson earlier of Philadelphia
THOMPSON, JOHN: Philadelphia, 1820s
THOMPSON, SILAS G.: New Haven, Conn., 1840s–1850s
THOMPSON, WILLIAM: New York City, advertised, 1775; also made instruments of various kinds
THOMPSON, WILLIAM: Port Tobacco and Upper Marlborough, Md., 1760s; Baltimore, 1790s
THOMPSON, WILLIAM: Carlisle, Pa., 1790s–1800. Not authenticated
THORNTON, JOSEPH: Philadelphia, 1810s–1820
THORPE, E. & CO.: Upper Alton, Ill., *c.* 1850
THORP, H. W.: Beaver Dam, Wis., 1860s
THREADCRAFT, B.: Charleston, S.C., 1790s–1800
THUM, CHARLES: Philadelphia, late eighteenth and early nineteenth century. Tall clocks
TIEBOUT, ALEXANDER: New York City, 1790s
TIFFT, HORACE: North Attleboro, Mass., *c.* 1790–1840
TIMBY SOLAR CLOCK: *See* Whiting, S.E.
TINGES, CHARLES: Baltimore, 1780s–1810s
TISDALE, E. D.: Taunton, Mass., 1860s
TITCOMB, ALBERT: Bangor, Me., 1840s–1880s
TOBIAS & CO., M. I.: New York City, 1820s–1830s
TODD, M. L.: Beaver, Pa., 1830s
TODD, RICHARD: New York City, 1830s
TODD, TRACY: Louisville, Ky., 1840s
TOLFORD, J.: Kennebunk, Me., 1800s; Portland, Me., 1810s
TOMKINS, G. S.: Providence, R.I., 1820s
TONCKHURE, FRANCIS: Baltimore, last quarter nineteenth century
TOWER, REUBEN: Hingham and Hanover, Mass., 1800s–1820s
TOWNE, I. S.: Montpelier, Vt., 1850s–1860s
TOWNSEND, CHARLES: Philadelphia, 1810s
TOWNSEND, CHRISTOPHER: Newport, R.I., 1770s–1810s
TOWNSEND, DAVID: Philadelphia, 1780s
TOWNSEND, ISAAC: Boston, 1790s
TOWNSEND, JOHN: Philadelphia, 1810s
TOWNSEND, H.: Conway, Mass., 1850s–1860s

TRACY, ERASTUS: Norwich, Conn., 1790–1793; New London, Conn., 1793–1795
TRACY, GURDON: New London, Conn., 1787–1792
TRAHN, CO., PETER: Philadelphia, 1840s–1850
TRAMPLEASURE, J.: Jersey City, N.J., 1850s
TREADWELL, OREN: Philadelphia, 1840s
TREAT, GEORGE: Newark, N.J., 1850s
TREAT, ORRIN: New Haven, Conn., 1840s–1850s
TREAT, SHERMAN: Bristol, Conn., 1825–35
TRIBE, G.: Newark, N.J., 1850s
TRONE, PETER: Philadelphia, 1840s
TROTH, JAMES: Pittsburgh, Pa., 1810–1820
TROTT, ANDREW: Boston, 1800s–1810s
TROTT & CLEVELAND: New London, Conn., 1792–1796: John Proctor Trott and William Cleveland
TROTT, JOHN PROCTOR: New London, Conn., 1790s
TROTT, JONATHAN: New London, Conn., 1791–1812
TROTT, PETER: Boston, 1800s
TROTTER, JEREMIAH: New York City, 1820s–1830s; Cincinnati, Ohio, 1830s–1840s
TRUMAN, JEFFERY: Waynesville, Warren County, Ohio, 1820s
TRUMBULL, & HASKELL: Lowell, Mass., 1860s
TULLER, WILLIAM: New York City, 1830s
TURELL, SAMUEL: Boston, 1780s
TURNBULL, JOHN: Baltimore, 1780s
TURNER, JOHN: New York City, 1840s
TUTHILL, DANIEL: Saxton's River, Vt., 1840s
TWISS, B. & H.: Meriden, Conn., 1820s–1830s
TWOMBLEY & CLEAVES: Biddeford, Me., 1850s–1860s
TYSON, L.: Philadelphia, 1820s

ULRICH, VALENTINE: Reading, Pa., 1760s
UNION MANUFACTURING CO.: Bristol, Conn., 1843–45
UNDERHILL, DANIEL: New York City, 1810s
UNDERWOOD, DAVID: West Chester, Pa., 1790s
UPSON, MERRIMAN & CO.: Bristol, Conn., 1831–1838
URTELIG, VALENTINE: Reading, Pa., 1760–1770s

VAN ALLYN (VANALLEIJN): Clockmaker of Dutch trading post on Connecticut River near Hartford, 1630s. May be legendary figure
VAIL, EDWARD: LaPorte, Ind., 1840s–1870s; founder of the Watch Making and Horological Institute

VALENTINE, ——: Womelsdorf, Pa., n.d. Tall clocks

VAN DER SLICE, JOHN: Womelsdorf, Pa., 1800s

VAN EPS, GEORGE K.: New York City, 1840s. Importer of Dutch goods and some clocks

VAN VLIET, B. C.: Poughkeepsie, N.Y., 1830s

VAN STEENBERGH, P.: Kingston, N.Y., 1780s

VAN WYK, VAN WYCK (VAN WIJCK), STEPHEN: New York City, 1800s-1810s

VEAZIE, JOSEPH: Providence, R.I., 1805

VERMONT CLOCK COMPANY: Fairhaven, Vt., n.d.

VIBBER (VIBERT?), RUSSEL: Westtown, Chester County, Pa., 1810s

VINTON, DAVID: Providence, R.I., 1790s

VOGEL, FREDERICK: Schoharie, or Schoharie County, N.Y., 1820s–1840

VOGHT, HENRY: Reading, Pa., 1790s

VOGT, JOHN: New York City, 1750s

VOIGHT, H.: Philadelphia, 1770s–1790s

VOIGHT, SEBASTIEN: Philadelphia, 1770s–1790s

VOIGHT, THOMAS: Philadelphia, 1810s–1830s

VUILLE, ALEXANDER: Baltimore, 1760s

WADE, NATHANIEL: Stratford, Conn., 1797–1800s

WADSWORTH, JEREMIAH: Georgetown, S.C., 1820s

WADSWORTH, J. C. & A.: Litchfield, Conn., 1830s

WADSWORTH & TURNER: Litchfield, Conn., 1830s

WADY, JAMES: Newport, R.I., 1740s–1750s

WAIT, DEWEY & CO.: Ravenna, Ohio., 1850s–1860s

WALES, SAMUEL H.: Providence, R.I. Manufacturer, 1849–1856

WALKER, A.: Lockport, N.Y., 1830s

WALKER, ISAAC: Long Plain, Mass., 1800s

WALKER, THOMAS: Fredericksburg, Va., *c.* 1760s–1780s

WALL & ALMY: New Bedford, Mass., 1820s. *See* Wall, William A.

WALL, WILLIAM A.: Hanover, Mass., and with Almy at New Bedford, Mass. This is the William A. Wall now famed as an artist of the American scene. Worked as clockmaker early in nineteenth century

WALLACE, JOHN: Pittsburgh, Pa., 1830s

WALLACE, ROBERT: Philadelphia, last half eighteenth century. Tall clocks

WALTER, JACOB: Baltimore, 1810s–1840s

WALTER, M. F.: Hartford, Conn., 1850s–1860s

WALTERS, HENRY: Charleston, S.C., advertised in 1757

WALTON, HIRAM: Cincinnati, Ohio, 1820s

WARD & GOVETT: Philadelphia, 1810s
WARD, ANTHONY: Philadelphia, 1710s; New York, 1720s–1740s
WARD, ANTHONY: Philadelphia, 1800s
WARD, ISAAC: Philadelphia, 1810s
WARD, JAMES: Hartford, Conn., 1790s–1800s. Dealer in clocks, importer of dials, blanks, tools, and materials for clockmakers
WARD, JEHU: Philadelphia, 1810s–1820s
WARD, JOSEPH: New York City, 1730s–1760s
WARD, LAUREN: Salem Bridge, Conn., 1820s–1840s
WARD, MADOCK: New Haven, Conn., 1800s
WARD, MADOCK: Wallingford, Conn., 1724–1780
WARD, NATHAN: Fryeburg, Me., 1800s
WARD, RICHARD: Salem Bridge, Conn., 1830s–1840s
WARD, THOMAS: Baltimore, advertised 1777
WARD, WILLIAM: Salem Bridge, Conn., 1830s–1840s
WARE, BACON: Salem, N.J., 1790s–1820s
WARE, BASCOMB: Southern New Jersey, 1800s. n.p.
WARE, GEORGE: Camden, N.J., 1820s
WARFE, JOSEPH: Frederick, Md., advertised in 1819
WARING, GEORGE: New York City, 1840s
WARNER, ALBERT: Bristol, Conn., 1857–1888
WARNER & REED: New York City, 1800s
WARNER & SCHUYLER: New York City, 1790s
WARNER, CUTHBERT: Baltimore, 1790s–1800s
WARNER, E.: Lexington, Ky., 1810s–1820s
WARNER, GEORGE: New York City, 1790s–1800s
WARNER, JOHN: New York City, 1790s–1810s
WARNER, THOMAS: Cincinnati, Ohio, 1820s
WARNER, WARREN: Cincinnati, Ohio, 1830s–1840s. (*See* Miller & Williams.)
WARRINGTON, JOHN: Philadelphia, 1810s
WARRINGTON, J. & S. R.: Philadelphia, 1820s
WASBROUGH & SON: Bristol, Conn., *c.* 1760–1780. Tall clocks, brass dialed, by this firm are known; all are fine clocks
WATERBURY CLOCK CO.: Waterbury, Conn., 1857
WATERBURY, M.: Amber, N.Y., clock factory, operating 1830s–*c.* 1850
WATERMAN, HENRY: Millbury, Mass., 1810s–1830s
WATERS, THOMAS: Frederick, Md., eighteenth century. Tall clocks
WATSON, G.: Cincinnati (dealer), 1820s. Agent for Ephraim Downs
WATSON, J.: Chelsea, Mass., 1840s
WATSON, JAMES: New London, Conn., 1796–1800; Philadelphia, 1800s–1820s

WATSON, LUMAN: Cincinnati, Ohio, 1800s–1826. Made many tall clocks, mantel clocks, and timepieces; advertised a factory-manufacturing clock equal to any made in the East. Was also agent for Ephraim Downs of Bristol, Conn.

WATSON, LUMAN & SON: Cincinnati, Ohio, after 1830

WATT, JOHN I.: Pennsylvania, n.d., n.p.

WAY, JOHN: Waggontown, Chester County, Pa., 1796–1800

WEATHERLY, DAVID: Philadelphia, 1810s. Also Weatherby

WEAVER, CHRISTIAN: New Castle, Del., 1790s–1820s

WEAVER, N.: Utica, N.Y., 1840s

WEAVER, WILLIAM: Wilmington, Del., *c.* 1800s–1820s

WEBB, ISAAC: Boston, *c.* 1690s–1720s. In 1708 he advertised removal from old shop to new location

WEBSTER, R.: Bristol and Farmington, Conn., n.d.

WEEKS, JASON: Bangor, Me., 1830s–1860s

WEIDEMEYER (WIDMYER), JOHN: Fredericksburg, Va., 1790s–1820s

WEIGEL, HENRY: Bottstown (York), Pa., 1827

WEISS, JEDEDIAH: Bethlehem, Pa., n.d. Tall clocks

WEISSER, MARTIN: Allentown, Pa., n.d. Probably after 1825

WELCH, E. N.: Bristol and Forestville, Conn., 1856–1887

WELCH, E. N. MANUFACTURING CO.: Forestville, Conn., 1864–

WELCH, SPRING & CO.: Forestville, Conn., 1869–1884

WELCH, GEORGE: Gettysburg, Pa., early nineteenth century

WELCH, WILLIAM: New York City, 1810s

WELDON, OLIVER: Bristol, Conn., 1841–1842

WELLER, FRANCIS: Philadelphia, n.d.

WELLS, A.: Bristol, Conn., *c.* 1825–1840. Unusually good thirty-hour and eight-day movements manufactured by this seldom-noted maker

WELLS, HENDRICK & CO.: Bristol, Conn., 1845

WELLS, JOSEPH A.: Bristol, Conn., 1832–1847

WELSH, GEORGE: New York City, 1850s–1870s

WELTON, H. & CO.: Terryville, Conn., n.d. Brass one-day O-G

WELTON, H. & H.: Plymouth, Conn., 1840s

WELTON, HERMAN: New York City, 1840–1844

WELTON, MERIT: New York City, 1844–1846. Apparently read law and entered legal profession in 1846, in which he continued to *c.* 1850

WENTZ, HILARY: Philadelphia, 1820s

WENZEL COMPANY: Washington, D.C., 1880s. Pneumatic clocks

WEST, BENJAMIN: Southbridge, Mass., 1820s–1830s

WEST, EDWARD: Lexington, Ky., 1780s–1820s

WEST, THOMAS: Philadelphia, 1810s–1820s

WESTGATE, BALDWIN & CO.: Fall River, Mass., 1867
WESTON, J.: Boston, 1840s–1850s
WESTON, JAMES & SON: Boston, 1860s
WETHERELL, N.: Philadelphia, 1830s–1840s
WHEATON, CALEB: Providence, R.I., 1770s–1790s
WHEATON, CALEB & SON: Providence, R.I., 1800s–1820s
WHEATON, CALVIN: Providence, R.I., 1790s
WHEATON, GODFREY: Providence, R.I., 1820s
WHEELER, CHARLES: New Brunswick, N.J., n.d.
WHERRIT, SAMUEL H.: Richmond, Ky., 1820s
WHETCROFT, WILLIAM: Annapolis, Md., 1773; Baltimore, 1778. Importer of parts, blanks, plates, et cetera
WHIPPLE, ARNOLD: Providence, R.I., 1810s
WHITAKER, GEORGE: Providence, R.I., 1800s
WHITAKER, JOSIAH & CO.: Providence, R.I., 1820s
WHITAKER, THOMAS: Providence, R.I., 1820s
WHITE, D. C.: Newark, N.J., 1830s
WHITE, F.: Brooklyn, N.Y., 1800s–1830s
WHITE, JOHN: New York City, 1810s
WHITE, JOSEPH: Philadelphia, 1800s
WHITE, L. W.: North Adams, Mass., 1850s–1860s
WHITE, MATLOCK: New York City, 1770s
WHITE, PEREGRINE: Woodstock, Conn., 1774–1830
WHITE, SEBASTIAN: Philadelphia, 1790s
WHITEAR, JOHN: Fairfield, Conn., 1730s–1760s. Brass founder presumed to have cast blank wheels and parts for clockmakers and is also listed as a working clockmaker
WHITEAR, JOHN, JR.: Fairfield, Conn., 1762–1770s
WHITEHEAD, JOHN: Norristown, Pa.; Haddonfield, N.J.; and Philadelphia. Working at these three places, perhaps not in order named, early nineteenth century
WHITING, K.: Winchester, Conn. Also reported from Woodstock, Vt., n.d. but probably 1800s–1810s. Tall clocks with wooden movements
WHITEHEAD, WILLIAM: Philadelphia, 1850s
WHITING & MARQUAND: Fairfield, Conn., 1790s
WHITING & MUNROE: Concord, Mass., 1800s–1817
WHITING, RILEY: Winsted and Winchester, 1800s–1830s
WHITING, SAMUEL: Concord, Mass., 1810s–1820s
WHITING, S. E.: Saratoga Springs, N.Y., in 1850s–1860s. Made the Timby patented solar timepiece and the Timby solar clock
WHITMAN, EZRA: Bridgewater, Mass., 1790s–1840s

Whitney, Asa: New York City, 1800s
Whitney, Ebenezer: New York City, 1810s–1820s
Whitney, Moses: Boston, 1820s
Whittaker & Dana: Providence, R.I., 1820s–1830s
Whittaker, Thomas: n.d., n.p.
Whittaker, William: New York City, 1730s–1750s
Whittemore, J.: Boston, 1850s
Wickens, Obed: New York City, 1840s
Widdefield, William: Philadelphia, 1810s
Wiggins, Thomas & Co.: Philadelphia, 1830s
Wiland (or Wieland), John G.: Salem, Mass., *c.* 1780
Wilbour, Job B.: Newport, R.I., 1815–1850. Manufacturer
Wilbur, Charles: New York City, 1840s. Probably a dealer
Wilcox, A.: New Haven, Conn., 1820s
Wilcox, Cyprian: New Haven, Conn., 1820s
Wildbahn, Thomas: Reading, Pa., 1790–1796
Wilder, Charles: New York City, 1840s
Wilder, Ezra: Hingham, Mass., *c.* 1825–1860
Wilder, Joshua: Hingham, Mass., 1770s–1810s
Wilder, T.: Hingham, Mass., eighteenth century
Wilkins, Asa: Wiscasset, R.I., 1800s–1810s
Wilkinson, Charles: Canton, N.Y., *c.* 1815–1835. Tall clocks, mantel clocks, and banjo clocks known by this maker
Wilkinson, W. S. & J. B.: Chicago, 1880s
Willard, Aaron: Roxbury, Mass., 1780–1790; Boston, 1795–1823. Had factory in Boston where he produced many banjo clocks. There is evidence that Aaron Willard was actually the first Willard to put a timepiece in a banjo-shaped case
Willard, Aaron, Jr.: Boston, 1806–1850
Willard, Alexander: Ashby, Mass., 1801–1820. Cheap wooden and fine brass movements; made some musical organ clocks
Willard, Benjamin: East Hartford, Conn., early 1760s; Grafton, Mass., 1765; "Roxbury Street" and other points with brother Simon; Lancaster, Pa., and York, Pa., during Revolution. Married Margaret Moore of York, Pa. Returned to Grafton in 1783; remained there to early 1800s; died at Baltimore, 1803
Willard, Benjamin F.: (Son of Simon) b.1803–d.1847; worked at Boston. In 1846 with Rich & Willard
Willard, B.: New York City; listed in 1818 Directory as having shop at 80 Broadway
Willard, Ephraim: Medford, Mass., 1770s; Roxbury, 1800s; New York City, early 1800s

WILLARD, HENRY: Boston, 1820s
WILLARD, JACOB P.: Ashby, Mass., 1801–1820 (brother of Alexander)
WILLARD, PHILANDER: Ashburnham, Mass., 1790s–1820s; Ashby, Mass., 1820s–1830s
WILLARD, SIMON: Roxbury, Mass., 1780s–1830s
WILLARD, SIMON, JR.: Boston, 1830s–1840s
WILLARD, ZABDIEL: Boston, late 1840s. With this Willard ends the Willard listing—a family of clockmakers with Christian names beginning with A and running through the alphabet to Z
WILLIAMS & HATCH: North Attleboro, Mass., at the Whiting factory, operating in 1840s–*c.* 1870, making wall and shelf clocks
WILLIAMS & VICTOR: Lynchburg, Va., 1790s–1810s
WILLIAMS, DAVID: East Caln, Chester County, Pa., 1790s
WILLIAMS, DAVIS: Newport, R.I., 1800s–1820s
WILLIAMS, GEORGE R.: Charleston, S.C., 1780s
WILLIAMS, ICHABOD: Elizabeth, N.J., 1830s; amateur maker
WILLIAMS, NICHOLAS: Liberty Town, Frederick County, Md., advertised in 1792
WILLIAMS, ORTON, PRESTONS & CO.: Farmington, Conn., 1820s
WILLIAMS, STEPHEN: Providence, R.I., 1800s
WILLIAMS, THOMAS: Flemington, N.J., 1792–1808
WILLIS, JOHN: Burlington, N.J., n.d. Tall clocks
WILMURT, JOHN J.: New York City, 1790s
WILMURT, STEPHEN: New York City, 1800s
WILLS, JOSEPH: Philadelphia, 1740s–1759
WILLS, JOSEPH: Reading, Pa., 1760s–1770s
WILMOT & RICHMOND: Savannah, Ga., 1840s–1860s
WILMOT, SAMUEL: Georgetown, S.C., 1820s–1830s; Charleston, S.C., 1830s
WILSON & DUNN: New York City manufacturers, 1840s
WILSON, HOSEA: Baltimore, 1810s
WILSON, ROBERT: Philadelphia, 1830s
WILTBERGER, CHARLES H.: Washington, D.C., *c.* 1822
WING, MOSES: Windsor, Conn., 1781–1809
WINGATE, FREDERICK: Augusta, Me., 1800s
WINGATE, PAINE: Boston, 1780s; Newburyport, Mass., 1800s; Augusta, Me., 1810s
WINSHIP, DAVID: Litchfield, Conn. Believed to have been case and dial maker only, and a dealer. Clocks are known with his name on dial as maker, presumably
WINSLOW, EZRA: Westborough, Mass., 1850s–1860s
WINSLOW, JONATHAN: Springfield, Mass., *c.* 1820s–1840. Name appears on short tall-case clocks in painted pine cases

WINSTANLEY, HENRY: Brooklyn, N.Y., 1840s

WINSTON, A. L. & W.: Bristol, Conn., 1840s

WINTERBOTTOM, THOMAS: Philadelphia, 1750; mentioned as a runaway bound out to Joseph Wills. Probably a redemptioner, or one who sold himself into service for a number of years in order to have passage to America paid

WINTERHALDER, CHARLES: Santa Cruz, Cal., 1855–1865

WINTERODE, JACOB: Dauphin County, Pa., tall clocks, n.d.

WISE, WILLIAM: Brooklyn, N.Y., from *c.* 1834. Later William Wise & Sons, active to 1930s

WISMER, HENRY: Plumstead, Pa., late 1790s–1820s

WITHINGTON, PETER: Mifflinburg, Pa., 1810s–1840s

WHITMAN, BENJAMIN: Reading, Pa., 1790s–1820s

WITMER, ABEL: Ephrata, Lancaster County, Pa. Worked as clockmaker while an inmate of, or connected with, the Seventh Day Baptist monastery in its days of disintegration. Space for several workmen was provided at no charge. The body of lay members and inmates was dwindling, the premises were tax free, and the entire fabric was loosely held together. Research would seem to indicate that Abel Witmer simply had shop room and living quarters rent free at the Cloisters but made clocks for anyone who came to purchase them, 1790–1820

WITT, CHRISTOPHER: Germantown, Pa., 1703–1765. Physician, mystic, scientist, clockmaker. Made excellent tall-case clocks, tower clocks, and instruments. Taught Sower, who, as a clockmaker, spelled his name Sauer, and others. Witt was the son (or grandson) of a Dutch clockmaker who entered England *c.* 1660. Witt had great influence on all the so-called "mystical" sectarians in Pennsylvania. Many of these, reported to have had their inspiration from Germany, were actually inspired, energized, and encouraged by Witt. He may have financed certain of the activities and publishing ventures. Also taught medicine and liberal arts

WITWER, ISAAC: New Holland, Lancaster County, Pa., 1850s. Actually made good tall clocks, brass movement, eight-day type, between 1850 and 1855. It should be noted that many suburban and rural clockmakers of Chester, Lancaster, Berks, Dauphin, Lebanon, Delaware, York, Adams, Schuylkill and Bucks counties of Pennsylvania made tall clocks to order for rural custom much later than has been imagined. This type of clock was often preferred to the cheap mantel clocks of Connecticut, and the custom of the clockmakers here considered was not primarily concerned with the price of the clock. They wanted good, big clocks

WOLF, HENRY: Marietta, Lancaster County, Pa., 1850s. Another maker of tall clocks working several decades after tall-clock production is supposed to have stopped

WOLF, THOMAS D.: Westtown, Chester County, Pa., 1810s

WOLTZ, GEORGE: Hagerstown, Md., 1770s–1812. At the present time, L. S. Spangler, Esq., of Hagerstown, Md., is writing a series of monographs on the clockmakers of Hagerstown including Woltz, which are appearing in a local newspaper. It is to be hoped that Mr. Spangler's valuable contribution will be printed in booklet form for the use of clock collectors

WOLTZ, SAMUEL: Hagerstown, Md., 1800–1805

WOOD, DAVID: Newburyport, Mass., 1790s–1820s

WOOD & HUDSON: Philadelphia, and Mt. Holly, N.J., 1780s–1820s

WOOD & HUDSON: Mt. Holly, N.J., 1790s–1810s

WOOD, JOHN: Philadelphia, advertising in 1755 to 1790. Made clocks and imported dial plates, blanks, hands, and other parts which he sold to other clockmakers. John Wood led the Clockmakers Company in the victory celebration procession, July 4, 1786, at Philadelphia; he was a master clockmaker, closely associated at one time with Rittenhouse, and may have imported much material for the use of Rittenhouse. There are records of Rittenhouse dealing direct with English export houses. This is further covered in the note under David Rittenhouse in this list

WOOD, JOHN, JR.: Philadelphia, 1780s–1810s

WOOD, JOSIAH: New Bedford, Mass., from 1800s

WOOD, M.: Rockport, Ind., 1840s

WOODFORD, ISAAC: New Haven, Conn., 1840s–1850s

WOODING, E.: Torrington, Conn., 1820s–1830s

WOODRUFF & WHITE: Cincinnati, Ohio, 1820s–1830s

WOODRUFF, JOHN, II: New Haven, Conn., 1840s–1850s

WOODWARD, A.: Middletown, Conn., 1780s–1790s

WOODWARD, ——: Amherst, N.H., *c.* 1840s

WOOLF, B.: Charleston, S.C., late eighteenth and early nineteenth century

WOOLSON, THOMAS, JR.: Amherst, N.H., 1800s–1840s

WOOLSTON, R.: "Glastonburg, Montgomery County, Pa., n.d." is the somewhat vague reference reported by a researcher, 1945

WOOLWORTH, CHESTER: New Haven, Conn., 1840s–1850s

WORDEN, C. M.: Bridgeport, Conn., 1850s–1860s

WORTON, ROBERT: Philadelphia, 1840s

WRIGHT, CHARLES: New York City, 1800s–1812; Utica, N.Y., 1812–1820s

WRIGHT, HARVEY: Bristol, Conn., 1831

WRIGHT, JOHN: New York City, 1710s–1730s

WRIGHT, SAMUEL: Lancaster, N.H., 1800s–1820s

WYMAN, ROGERS & COX: Nashua, N.H., 1832–1838. Factory operating under proprietorship of L. W. Noyes

YALE CLOCK CO.: New Haven, Conn., 1880s

YARNALL, ALLAN: Willistown and West Chester, Pa., 1825–1832

YATES & KENT: Trenton, N.J., 1780s–1790s

YATES, JOSEPH: Trenton, N.J., late 1780s–1800s; Freehold, N.J., after *c.* 1805

YEADEN, RICHARD: Charleston, S.C., advertised in 1771

YEAKEL, SOLOMON: Northampton, Pa. (now Allentown), *c.* 1790s–1830s

YEOMANS & COLLINS: New York City; James Yeomans advertised alone, 1771–2–3; advertised as this firm, 1769

YEOMANS, ELIJAH: Hadley, Mass., 1760s–1770s; Middletown, Conn., 1780s–1790

YORKEE, JACOB: Manheim, Lancaster County, Pa., 1790s–1810s

YOU, THOMAS: Charleston, S.C., 1750s–1780s; probably also a dealer

YOUNG, B.: Watervliet, N.Y., *c.* 1800–1820

YOUNG, CHARLES: Chambersburg, Pa., *c.* 1750–1780. Clock by him pictured in Chapter X

YOUNG, DAVID: Hopkinton, N.H., n.d.

YOUNG, FRANCIS: Clockmaker of Philadelphia, advertising in 1777

YOUNG, JACOB: Northern Liberties, Philadelphia (Manheim Section), 1760s–1770s. Clocks signed "Jacob Y" Manheim, are by this man and not by Jacob Yorkee, Manheim, Lancaster County, Pa. This maker, Young, also spelled name Younge and Yonge

YOUNG, JACOB: Hagerstown, Md., 1775–1790. There is some data which indicate that Jacob Young of Hagerstown was the son of Jacob Young who was working at Philadelphia, and listed immediately above

YOUNG, SAMUEL: Charlestown, Virginia, 1790s–1820s

YOUNG, STEPHEN: New York City, 1800s–1810s

YOUNG, S. E.: Laconia, N.H., 1850s–1860s

YOUNG, STEPHEN: New York City, 1810s

YOUNGS, BENJAMIN: Windsor, Conn., 1757–66; Schenectady, N.Y., 1767–1780; Watervliet, N.Y., 1780–1815. Son, Benjamin, dropped the final *s* and spelled his name Young

YOUNGS, EBENEZER: Hebron, Conn., 1778–1780s

YOUNGS, SETH: Hartford, Conn., 1730s–1742; Windsor, Conn., 1742–1760

ZAHM AND JACKSON: Lancaster, Pa., 1850s
ZAHM, G. M. & Co.: Lancaster, Pa., 1850s
ZAHM, H. L. & E. J.: Lancaster, Pa., 1850s
ZELLAKS, DROSSON: St. Augustine, or St. Johns River, Fla.; Minorcan or Greek clockmaker
ZIMMERMAN, ANTHONY: Reading, Pa., *c.* 1770–1790
ZUBER, JOHN J.: Upper Hanover, Pa. n.d. Tall clocks

Co-operating in the compilation of this list, the research, and the checking of previously noted clockmakers and manufacturers, are the Historical Societies of:

Nashua, N.H.
Washington County, Ind.
State of Missouri, St. Louis
Berks County, Pa.
Western Reserve, Cleveland, O.
York County, Pa.
Albemarle County, Va.
Santa Cruz County, Calif.
Nantucket, Mass.
Washington County, Md.
Jefferson County, W.Va.
Burlington County, N.J.
State of Virginia, Richmond, Va.
Charleston, South Carolina
Warren County, Ohio
Peacham, Vermont
L'Anguille Valley, Logansport, Ind.
Dutchess County, N.Y.
Chester County, Pa.
Bangor, Maine
Plymouth County, Ind.
Old Colony, Taunton, Mass.
Hart County, Ky.
Lexington, Mass.
Waseca, Minn.
Old Dartmouth, New Bedford, Mass.
Dayton, Ohio
Delaware County, Pa.
Bucks County, Pa.
Lancaster County, Pa.
Bristol, R.I.
McLean County, Ill.
Fitchburg, Mass.
Haverhill, Mass.
Philadelphia Athenaeum, Philadelphia, Pa.
Broome County, N.Y.
State of Maine, Portland, Me.
City of Rochester, N.Y.
City of Lancaster, Pa.
City of Newport, R.I.
Museum of City of New York, N.Y.
Clay County, Ind.
Brattleboro, Vermont
State of Vermont, Montpelier, Vt.
Dedham, Mass.
Lebanon County, Pa.
Montgomery County, Pa.
St. Petersburg, Fla.
Upshur County, West Va.
Snyder County, Pa.
Cape Girardeau County, Mo.

Bradford County, Pa.
Crawford County, Pa.
New Bern, N.C.
Adams County, Pa.
State of New Hampshire, Concord
Potter County, Pa.
Lee, Maine
Pottstown, Pa.
Passaic County, N.J.
Tioga County, Pa.
Spencer County, Ind.
LeRoy, N.Y.
Tippecanoe County, Ind.
San Mateo County, Calif.
Herkimer County, N.Y.
Ottawa County, Ohio
Vineland, N.J.
Cameron County, Pa.
Little Compton, R.I.
Schuyler County, Ill.
Olmsted County, Minn.
Westchester County, N.Y.
New Gloucester, Maine
Manchester, Vermont
Morgan County, Ill.
Marblehead, Mass.
Hartford County, Md.
Wayne County, Ind.
Chicago, Illinois
Dauphin County, Pa.
Windham County, Vermont
Onondaga, Syracuse, N.Y.
Reading, Mass.
Milton, Mass.
Medway, Mass.
Jackson County, Ind.
Northampton, Mass.
Clark County, Va.
Evanston, Ill.
Cortland County, N.Y.
Oneida, Utica, N.Y.
Switzerland County, Ind.
Guernsey County, Ohio
Beloit, Wis.
Ripley County, Ind.
Knox County, Ohio
Fayette County, Ind.
Dearborn, Mich.
Crawford County, Ohio
Moultrie County, Ill.
Allen County, Ind.
Chenango County, N.Y.
Kenosha County, Wis.
Boone County, Ill.
Chatham, Mass.
Aurora, Ill.
Erie County, Pa.
Wilmington, N.C.
Columbia County, Pa.
Oswego, N.Y.
Philadelphia Museum of Art, Philadelphia, Pa.
Suffolk County, L.I., N.Y.
Sandwich, Mass.
Historical Soc. of Frederick County, Frederick, Md.
North Attleboro, Mass.

# CHAPTER XII

"Sir," said Dr. Johnson, "a dictionary is like a watch; the worst is better than none and the best cannot be expected to go quite true"

Acorn Clocks: *See* pictures in Chapter X

Angelus: The evening bell to prayer

Anniversary Clock: Presumed by many to be a twentieth-century innovation; a clock that runs an entire year. Daniel Quare of London made them in 1690

Annular Ringed Clock: A ring or band on which the hours appear, moving to bring the proper hour over a pointer and thus indicate time. Usually the movement is in a globular housing and the ring of numerals is a band around the globe

Arbor: The axle of a clock wheel

Arched Time Track: A series of two line arches, or waves, arranged between the numerals, carrying the minute divisions. Used in this fanciful, decorative form on but few clocks; most clocks have time tracks in the form of simple circles

Astrolabe: Instrument to measure altitudes; to shoot the stars. An ancient measuring instrument; not a clock

Astronomical Clocks: Moon phase, sunrise, heavenly aspects, orrery, and other featured clocks are so called

Atkinson Panels or Tablets: Decalcomania transfers made by W. Atkinson of New York City, *c.* 1865–1875. Many used to decorate Connecticut clock tablets

Back Pendulum: Pendulum mounted at the back of a movement

Balance Alarum: A balanced beam, one arm of which was a funnel of sand and the other of which contained a ringing bell. When the sand ran out the bell tilted and rang

Ball Feet (Brass): On many old tall-case clocks of dates prior to 1750 the bottoms, or chests, of the cases were finished with a molding but not with feet. The "feet" used on such cases were brass balls affixed to long screws which were run into the bottoms of the cases. Leveling off the clock was quite easy: one simply screwed the ball feet in or out. Certain old cases have survived without any footing and, unfortunately, without the brass ball feet. The immediate cry when such a case is discovered is "restore the feet." However, wise would-be restorers who have examined the bottoms of the cases for indications of what kind of feet were on the case originally have found nothing but four screw holes. The proper restoration is to apply four brass balls—a diameter of about 1½ inches will suffice for most clocks—and nothing else

Balloon Clock: Any clock in the general shape of a balloon

Banjo Clocks: *See* Chapters V and X

Barrel Clock: A drum clock; the casing being drum-shaped

Baseball Clock: *See* page 141

Basket Top: Term is used in reference to clocks with basket-shaped tops of pierced metal, with handles. The "basket" shape is of course in reverse of normal position and the handle is affixed to what would be the bottom, not the top of the basket

Belfry (of a clock): The hood in which the movement of a tall clock is cased

Bell Sundial: An invention of the Abbe Galais of Paris, *c.* 1780. He poised a burning glass over a dial to concentrate the rays of the sun at noon on a tow linen thread which, burned through, released a hammer which hit a gong bell. Similar in idea to the sundial gun

Belsire: Grandfather

Bedpost Clock: Seventeenth-century clock of brass, standing on posts or pillars somewhat resembling bedposts. Not a clock to affix to bedposts as has been imagined by some

Bell Marine Clock: Maritime-type clock mounted on a pedestal in the form of a binnacle; entire assembly covered by a glass bell. Date is *c.* 1870

Bell Top: Casket or coffer tops of pleasing design on early type clocks, from 1690–1700

Bench Key: Ring to which four to six clock-winding keys shafts are attached

Bird-Cage Clock: Several definitions are to be considered: (1) A clock movement in the bottom of a bird cage. (2) Name for clock with specially made lantern pinions. (3) Spring-driven brass clocks of early to mid-seventeenth century, often miscalled "bracket clocks"

Blacksmith's Clocks: Iron clocks, supposedly earlier than brass. Dates range from sixteenth to seventeenth century. Warning: Question the authenticity of every one you find, unless backed by unconditional warranty over sufficient period for expert opinion

Blinking-Eye Clocks: Cast-iron clocks such as Topsy, Sambo, and the Continental, made by Bradley & Hubbard, The Waterbury Clock Co., and other Connecticut makers, from *c.* 1867. Painted in colors and having eyes that "blink" as the seconds are ticked off. Also tall-case clocks having a tympanum feature of a head with cut-out eyes which blink, or roll

Bristol Men: Reference is to Welsh, Irish, Scots, and Englishmen who, between 1654 and 1679, sold themselves by deed, in exchange for passage to the colonies. There were clockmakers and cabinetmakers in this company

Bull's-Eye Door: Circular orifice in tall-case clock doors, glazed, to permit view of pendulum swing

Caboose Clock: Brass-cased chronometer mounted on a panel from which extends an arm supporting an oil lamp. Used in cabins of locomotives, steamboats, et cetera. May date from 1850 but more likely *c.* 1865–70

Calendar Systems: Timekeeping by the year. The Julian system assumed the year to be 365¼ days and hence allocated a leap year every four years. This system is now thirteen days later than our present calendar system. Our system is the Gregorian. France had a "Republican" calendar system during the revolution. Jewish and Mahommedan calendars are based on lunar months of from twenty-nine to thirty days

Candle Clock: Made by W. H. & S. Jackson of Clarkenwell, England, *c.* 1825–1850. This "clock" had a glass dial and hands, mounted upon a burning Palmer patented candle. There is no movement. A flywheel turned by the heat of the candle was the only motive power and regulating feature. The clock face, of course, was illuminated when candle burned

Candle Dial: Candlestick of brass, with a horizontal gnomon and a dial. A candle placed in the socket and burned cast a shadow on the dial. An 18th century conceit or novelty

Canadian Trade Clocks: *See* Chapter X for example. A Connecticut pillar-and-scroll variant with magnificently carved crest of the arms of Great Britain

Canonical Hours: The seven hours of prayer, originally belled for the people. Names of the hours: matins, prime, tierce, sext, nones, vespers, campline

Sixteen of the many variants of the William and Mary, Queen Anne, Georgian, Adam, Chippendale, Hepplewhite, and Sheraton styles as reflected in tall-clock case tops or hoods. The scarcest type is the broken pediment. We cannot always assign the date of the style to clock cases made in any of these styles. There is a hollowed pediment case pictured in this volume made *c.* 1810. Yet the style was used as early as 1760–70.

CARPENTER CLOCKMAKER: Casemaker who purchased or traded movements, casing them in his cases and designating the finished clocks as of his production. Not always are such clocks marked with the name of the casemaker

CARRIAGE CLOCKS: Small portable clocks of brass with handle at top, originally in an extra leather case

CARTEL CLOCK: Elaborately carved casings for wall clock movements, sometimes gilded or parcel gilt. Only one American-made example was reported in the research project for this book; made by Daniel Forrer, Lampeter Square, Lancaster, Pa., *c.* 1756

CAST-IRON CLOCKS: *See* Chapter IX. Some cast-iron clocks are only cast-iron fronts, backed with a wooden boxlike section

CATHEDRAL CLOCKS: Gothic clocks, steeple clocks, and variants, including some unholy horrors in the form of jigsaw work. Most date from *c.* mid nineteenth century

CENTER WHEEL: The minute wheel of a clock; the arbor is connected to second hands when these are on clocks

CENTURY CLOCK: Exhibited at the Centennial Exposition, designed to run one hundred years by virtue of a prodigious weight which fell less than an inch a year. Designed and built by J. W. Hill of Kansas, 1873. Very few made

CHOPS: Small brass blocks between which a pendulum swings; used to avoid torque

CHRONOS: Father Time

CLEPSAMMIA: Thief of sand; hourglass; sand glass of any duration

CLEPSYDRA: Water thief; water clock. *See* Chapter IIII

CLOCHE: Glass bell or dome; also a bell, or to strike a bell. *See* Chapter I

CLOCK CUPBOARD: The original name for the casing of a tall clock; a most logical name. The case is, actually a cupboard in which to put a clock movement and lines with weights

CLOCK FLOWER: Both the sunflower and the heliotrope were once called clock flowers. The rays of the sun affect the bloom and cause the flower to follow the sun in its seeming path across the sky. A glance at the heliotrope or sunflower would give the observer the approximate time. The "four-o'clock" was called the tea flower because it popped open at teatime, around four o'clock in the afternoon

CLOCK HANDS: Many varieties used; reader desirous of further study should first consult *American Antique Furniture* Volume II, by Edgar Miller Jr., in which many varieties are pictured

CLOCK LAMP: Pewter or Britannia base upon which is poised a glass fluid reservoir. The ensemble is a lamp which, consuming the fluid, reduces the level in the reservoir. This serves as an indicator of time. Dutch, not German in origin. Sold in the colonies and the States from *c.* 1770 down to 1850s. Not scarce or rare

CLOCK LEAD: The weights of a clock

CLOCK LINE: Cord of the weights

CLOCK PITCHER: Copper and silver luster pitchers from six to ten inches high, bearing a clock face on the side

CLOCK SETTER: Caretaker or overseer of a town clock or any public clocks. Also a man who would, for a fee, attend to clocks in homes or offices

CLOCK SPURS: Pointed spikes affixed to bottoms of back posts of early clocks to provide anchorage and at the same time holding the case of the clock far enough from wall to permit pendulum to swing. Used on some seventeenth-century clocks

CLOCK WINDER: (1) key or crank to aid in winding a clock; (2) man winding and setting clocks for a fee

COLUMBUS CLOCK: *See* Chapters I and IX

CONTINENTAL CLOCK: A blinking-eye clock, pictured in Chapter IX

CUPID ALARM CLOCK: A more or less standard, round, metal-cased alarm clock surmounted by a figure of Cupid almost the size of the clock itself. Cupid holds a mallet. The mechanism moves the arm of the figure and the mallet strikes the gong. Made from 1882 by the Ansonia Clock Company

DECIMAL TIME: A proposed "reform" in time-unit measurement that would break up a day into twenty hours of one hundred minutes each, one hundred seconds to the minute. Probably as much chance of this as that of passage of a bill once introduced in a Southern state, to establish "pi" as 3, rather than 3.1416, in order to make figuring easy!

DIAL: From the Latin, dies: day. The face of a clock

DIAMOND-HEAD BANJO: Pictured in Chapter X

DIORAMA CLOCKS: Clock movements operating a three-dimensional show of automatons

DOLMEN: A hedge of stones set at points n.e., s.w., with a gnomon stone, tilted, to cast a shadow

DORIC CLOCK: Importation by Kramer of Boston, 1825. Greek revival casing with very small dial

DRIVING WHEEL: Main wheel of a clock—the wheel to which the driving power of the weight or spring is applied

DRUM CLOCK: (1) Table clock in the general shape of a drum. (2) Wall or mantel clock in which the main casing is of drum shape

DUTCH WAG: Tall-case movement without casing, hung on the wall and used as a wall clock. American term is hang-up clock; also known as wag-on-the-wall

DWARF CLOCK: What is now called a grandmother clock, a small tall-case clock, was once called a dwarf clock

EAGLE HAND: Clock hand pointers in the form of eagles. Simeon Crittenden and other clockmakers used hands of this type

EGG DIAL: Oval-shaped dial

EGLOMISE PANEL: Fashionable name for painted clock tablet; named for one Glomi, French or Swiss decorator, who painted in gold leaf on glass. An Eglomise panel should be of gilt on glass panel; as the term is used now it refers to any painted panel

ELECTRIC CLOCKS: *See* Chapter IX

EMPIRE BANJO: Later version of the early nineteenth-century banjo; it is coarser in cabinetwork, has carved wood rather than brass side brackets, sometimes fret-sawed; beveled frames; glass panels with plain gilt borders. These are easier to fake than the finer banjo clocks

EPACT: Excess of solar over lunar time calculation

ESCAPEMENT: The heart of every timepiece of mechanical nature; the device by which the escape of power is regulated. Three major types of escapement are now in use: the dead beat, the detached, and the recoil

EXHIBITION CLOCK: A display clock of any kind was so called in nineteenth century

EXTENSION CLOCK KEY: A clock-winding key with universal joint on a long shank; used in winding tall clocks, wall banjo clocks, et cetera. Better adapted to winding spring-driven clocks as a weight clock would require more purchase than that permitted by the thumbpiece of this device

FISHERMAN CLOCK: Fisherman, or fishing lady, in cut out, arranged in the tympanum of a clock dial, and continually casting a rod when the clock is running

FRANKLIN CLOCK: (1) Clock invented by B. Franklin. *See* Chapter IX. (2) Clock by Hoadley and other Connecticut makers, using the slogan "Time is Money" and other mottoes by Franklin, on pendulums, tablets, and dials

FRIESLAND CLOCK: Ornate Dutch clocks of seventeenth century and later

FUSEE: *See* page 7

GABLED HOOD: Hood over a tall clock, cased, or wag, resembling the gable end of a house; also called a portico

GNOMON: The pointer piece of a sundial which casts the shadow

GOTHIC CLOCK: Variant of the steeple clock. Made up to 1880s and even later

GRECIAN CLOCK: Clock case in the Greek-revival style

GRIDIRON PENDULUM: Alternating rods of steel and brass, set in a frame and used as a bob. This type pendulum bob is supposed, by virtue of the fact that the two metals contract and expand respectively at same rate at any given temperature, to compensate for temperature changes and thus keep more correct time. Some gridiron pendulums were "faked" and used on cheap clocks to make them look good

HALF CLOCK: Tall-clock type case made without a base or chest, with a tapering bracket at bottom, used as wall clock. *See* picture in Chapter III. Seth Thomas made a variant of this type clock, in smaller size, *c.* 1825–1830. This is not pictured. "Half clock" is also the term of record for the mantel clocks by Simon and Aaron Willard which are also designated as two-story and as case-on-case clocks

HALF KIDNEY: Door orifice and dial shapes used by Willards and others on mantel clocks pictured on page 183

HAND-HAND: TRUE HAND: The term "hand" for the pointer of a clock is said to derive from use of a cutout hand on a rod on early clocks. The fleur-de-lys seems to have been used as a pointer in preference to an imitation of the human hand, but the term "hand" remained in use. When the hand of a clock is actually in imitation of a human hand the somewhat awkward term hand-hand is sometimes used to designate this feature. A turning hand is found used as a second hand on some Connecticut clocks of the nineteenth century; also the hand-hands are found on some American tall clocks of the eighteenth century

HELIOTROPE: The name of this flower derives from *helios* (sun) and *tropos* (to turn). It turns with the sun and hence was once called a clock flower. The sundial at one time was called a "heliotropion"

HORLOGE: Any mechanism for telling time

HOURGLASS: Globes of glass, in pairs, one filled with sand, which pours into the empty globe through a fine orifice. Many sizes and shapes. Early globes are fastened together at the orifices or necks, and protected by a wood or metal cage or case. Batteries of three to six sand glasses were once made for timekeeping purposes

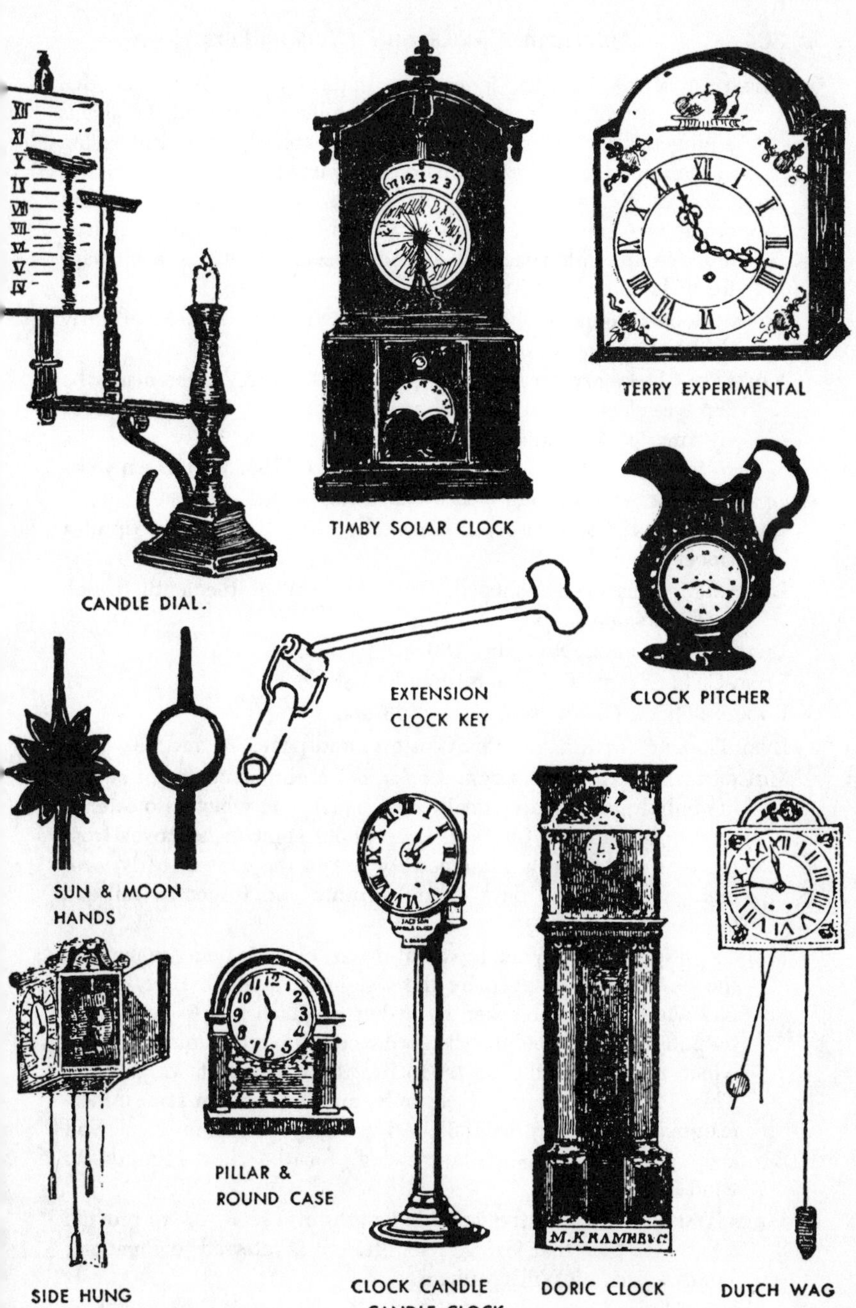
TERRY EXPERIMENTAL
TIMBY SOLAR CLOCK
CANDLE DIAL.
CLOCK PITCHER
EXTENSION
CLOCK KEY
SUN & MOON
HANDS
PILLAR &
ROUND CASE
SIDE HUNG
WALL CLOCK
CLOCK CANDLE
—CANDLE CLOCK
DORIC CLOCK
DUTCH WAG

INVERTED MOON PHASE: Moon phase indicator placed on the dial proper, sometimes under the center. When so placed the slot is arranged fanwise, from center. Some moon-phase indicators are in the upper section of the main dial, immediately over the center

IRON CLOCKS: Reference is to the cast-iron clocks made by Jerome and others in Connecticut and not to the blacksmiths' clocks of iron made in fifteenth, sixteenth, and seventeenth centuries. *See* Chapter IX for pictures of cast-iron clocks

JACKS: Robots actuated by heavy weights striking the bells of early clocks. Chapter I tells more about them

KINABLE: Clockmaker of France in period of Louis XVI who made the first lyre clocks, some of which were imported to the United States of America immediately after the Revolution. They were the *crème de la crème* of clockmaking in 1784–1785. Within ten years or so we were making clocks like them

LANCET CLOCK: Clock case with a round pointed top, like the tip of a lancet

LENTICLE: Lens or lens-shaped, from the seed of the lentil, which is of the same shape

LIGHTHOUSE CLOCK: *See* page 186

LONG-CASE CLOCK: Tall case or grandfather clock

LOOKING-GLASS CLOCK: *See* pages 106 and 111

LYRE CLOCK: *See* Kinable, this Glossary, and pages 74 and 182

MCGRANE LOCOMOTIVE CLOCK: Looks like a chronometer not swung in gimbals, mounted vertically on a panel from which also extends an arm terminating in an oil lamp about eight inches away from the dial of the clock. Designed for use in the cabs of early locomotives before the days of an accurate and inspected railroad timekeeper

MAINTAINING POWER: When a weight-driven clock is being wound up the power usually given by the weight is nullified. Early clocks had winding holes blocked by a shutter which had to be opened by pulling a cord; pulling the cord wound up a one-minute spring which maintained the power to run the clock as it was wound. This is a feature of fine clocks only, and is found on some American-made clocks up to 1835. An ordinary pendulum clock will keep going, from pendulum swing, for the time required to wind it

MEAN TIME: Average of the variable lengths of a solar day to provide a basis for time that just isn't so. Student is referred to *Time and Timekeepers,* by Willis Milham

MIRROR-DOOR CLOCK: Tall-case clock in which the panel of the pendulum door is made of a piece of mirror glass. A vogue of the first half of the eighteenth century

MOON PHASE: Age of the moon told pictorially by a disk carrying the waxing moon as a moving display, from behind a hemisphere across the sky, to wane under another hemisphere. Since a lunar month is 29½ days, this feature must be corrected at least once a month on most clocks having it

MOZART CLOCK: One-year clock made at Bristol, Conn., 1859–60; named for Don. Mozart, the inventor

MURAL CLOCK: Wall clock. Term is now reserved, by some editors and writers, for application only to important wall clocks

MUSICAL CLOCKS: Many varieties. Any clock playing a tune on bells or chimes is considered musical. Benjamin Willard in 1770s advertised musical clocks playing a different tune every day and a psalm tune on Sundays. See page 43 for picture of musical-clock mechanism

NAVY CLOCK: Papier-maché clock of Connecticut make, by Chauncey Jerome, displaying many navy emblems. *C.* 1848. *See* page 107

NEWPORT BANJO: Looking like a Willard or other fine banjo, the difference is in the movement which is characterized by triangular open plates rather than rectangular solid plates. A specialist's interest. Made at Newport, R.I., contemporaneously with Willard banjos

NIGHT CLOCKS: Many varieties. *See* candle clock, candle dial. Also a clock with numerals cut out in open-silhouette, dial revolving to bring the numerals within a slot illuminated by a candle or lamp within the clock. Also the luminous dial introduced by Seth Thomas Company in 1880s

NOON MARK: Cut or painted mark on window sill, or door stile, on which a shadow, cast by the structure, fell at noon or when the sun was at its highest point. Used to check clocks before the days of radio and telephone and when the question, "What time is it?" was one you had to answer yourself

O.O.G: Clock manufacturer's designation for double O-G molding

PAPER DIALS: *See* Chapter IX for pictures of two

PARIAN CLOCK CASE: A clock case made by C. W. Fenton of Bennington, Vt., 1852, and exhibited at the Crystal Palace, New York City, 1853. Parian is an imitation marble made of pottery, hard-fired and unglazed. Some Connecticut clockmakers (Jerome, Ingraham, Seth Thomas, Welch, Spring & Co., and J. C. Brown) are believed to have cased movements in Fenton's Parian cases. A very few, apparently, were so cased, for the item is excessively rare. Two classes of collectors, clock enthusiasts and pottery enthusiasts, seek examples of this clock case

PARLIAMENT CLOCK: Imagine the head of a tall-case clock with scroll or bell top and epis, but no neck or throat and no base; just a bracketlike tail supporting the head to make it a wall clock. This and several other "mural" type clocks were called "Parliament." Dates range from *c.* 1720–1850. See Chapter V and picture of Amana clock on page 116 which is a form of Parliament clock

PECKING BIRD CLOCK: Term used to designate a tall clock with a telltale or motion indicator in the form of a constantly pecking bird perched in the tympanum

PENDULUM OVER DIAL: Precisely what the name implies; the pendulum and escapement are above the main time train mechanism and dial. Many forms. One is pictured on page 175

PERAMBULATOR: Same as "way wiser"; a device that counted the mileage of a carriage. Made by clockmakers generally. Advertised by Simon Willard

PICTURE CLOCK: A picture or scene including some sort of clock tower made realistic by cutting a hole in the canvas and putting a real dial in the tower with a real clock behind it to serve as a timepiece. Also any clockwork, whether plane, with cutouts or three-dimensional figures, which have motion imparted when the clock is running. Some curious examples are known. Mostly Italian, Swiss, Dutch, and French. A sort of peasant art extended to clockmaking

PILLAR CLOCK: French-style clock characterized by four upstanding pillars between which the movement and dial are set at top and in which the pendulum swings. Thousands imported in nineteenth century, some very fine, of marble and ormolu. L. Watson of Cincinnati made clocks of this type in 1820s. *See* picture, page 49

PILLAR-AND-CREST: Variant of the pillar-and-scroll in which the scroll is replaced by a carved, cutout, or stenciled cresting. *See* page 178 for Canadian clock owned by Mr. & Mrs. Frank Beavens, made in Connecticut for the Canadian market. It is a pillar-and-crest clock

PILLAR-AND-ROUND: Hardly a variant of the pillar-and-scroll; two pillars surmounted by a half-round arch. Thousands made in sizes six to sixteen inch by Connecticut makers, 1850 to 1900

PILLAR-AND-SCROLL: *See* Chapter VI

PINEAPPLE CLOCK: Heavy side pillars surmounted by carved or stenciled pineapple forms, between which is a scroll of carved or stenciled fruits in colored bronzes. Connecticut, 1830s–1840s. *See* page 100

POINTED GOTHIC: Same as Lancet top

PORTICO CLOCK: Any clock movement supported within a portico or porch of colonettes or small columns

PORTICO TOP: Same as gabled hood

PREVEAR TRANSIT: Sun transit. *See* page 151

PULL-UP CLOCK: Clocks wound by pulling on the weight cords

PULL REPEATER: Cord attached to the "repeat" mechanism of a fine clock; pulling on cord repeats the last strike of the clock; a nighttime convenience

REMONTOIR: Clock that rewinds itself every minute or so from a primary weight, to a secondary weight or other power source; very accurate clocks. A specialist's type of clock. Usually have dead-beat escapement and several dials. Nineteenth century

REVERSED O-G: The standard O-G molding in reverse; it curves forward somewhat like a bolection molding; giving the effect of a swell front. Made by Jerome and others *c.* 1845–1850; not a popular model

ROCKING SHIP: Another type of telltale. *See* Chapter IIII

ROLLING CLOCK: A clock movement that rolls down an incline, thus forming its own weight. Invented about 1660 by the Marquis of Worcester, who was quite an engineer. This novelty clock of the seventeenth century was revived as an idea in the nineteenth century

ROLLING EYE: A telltale on tall clocks. *See* Chapter IIII

ROUGH-AND-READY CLOCK: Narrow molding case, five-inch dial, painted tablet Connecticut clock of the 1840s

SAMBO: *See* blinking-eye clock

SAND CLOCK: A novelty clock, the "movement" of which is a spindle, a length of cord wound around it, and a heavy ball resting in a large box of sand. Sand, permitted to escape, lowered the heavy ball, unwound the cord, and turned the spindle; hence the hands turned and told a sort of "time." This was advocated as a cheap clock for the people *c.* 1815 but it was not made. Connecticut clockmakers developed a real clock to sell for little money. These sand clocks were actually made 1750 to 1850. Any found today, however, must be scanned with skeptical eye; they are easily faked

SEESAW CLOCK: Another form of telltale, the seesaw or teeter, gives this clock its colloquial name. Found on tall clocks

SHAKER CLOCKS: Tall clocks in severaly plain cases, unornamented dials, and time only. Probably made only for their own use by Shakers

SHARP GOTHIC: The steeple clock designed by Elias Ingraham, 1840s

SHEEP'S-HEAD CLOCK: Name given lantern or bird-cage clocks of seventeenth century

SHELF CLOCKS: Eli Terry did not conceive of the idea of a shelf clock, but of the idea of a very cheap shelf clock, mass produced; fine shelf clocks were made in Connecticut by Jocelin. Heman Clark's shelf clocks were finer by far than Terry's

SHIELD CORNERS: Spandrels on dials in the form of shields; some painted on. These are often the shield of the United States. Sometimes inlaid on cases

SIDE-HUNG WALL CLOCK: Ancient form of hang-up clock; one of the "sides" was hung against the wall. The face of the clock was to the left and the normal "back" of the clock to the right. The other "side" faced out; this was fitted with a door to provide easy access to the movement. Bob pendulum-type clocks, weight-driven, seventeenth century

SIDEREAL TIME: Star time; astronomical time. Sidereal time shows an advance on mean solar time (averaged solar time) of three minutes fifty-six and one half seconds per day. Thus a clock showing sidereal time is simply a clock running faster per day by the amount mentioned than a regular clock. It would gain a day a year. Why? Read Willis Milham's *Time and Timekeepers* if you must know

SILVER GRANDMOTHER: Miniature tall-case clock in pure silver case; timepiece is usually a watch movement. Made in France and Netherlands, also in England. Mostly nineteenth century. All-silver cases of larger size are of course known

SKELETON CLOCK: Clocks exposing the movement in a framework of straps rather than solid plates

SOLAR TIME: The duration of a solar day divided by 24×60×60! Since the solar day varies in length, solar time has been discarded for mean solar time. Confusion begins with what we call solar or sun time; the correct phrase is true, or apparent solar time . . or what it seems to be but isn't. Read the books recommended in the Bibliography for further confusion if you are easily confused, and complete enlightenment if you have a mathematical sense

SPOOL BANJO: Spool turnings used as rests for the brass side brackets on a banjo clock

STARRED MIRROR CLOCK: One of Chauncey Jerome's novelties; the ordinary O-G-type case with a mirror panel showing stars over the surface. Date is *c.* 1845–1850

STRAP FRONT: Term designating the framing of a movement within straps of wood or brass rather than within solid plates

SUNFLOWER: This flower often appears as an item of decoration on clock papers, watch papers, et cetera. This is not by accident. The sunflower was once known as the clock flower because this bloom follows the sun in its path across the sky and always, more or less, presents its full face to the sun, twisting on its thick stem from morning until evening

SUNFLOWER CLOCK: *See* page 134

SUN-AND-MOON HANDS: Clock hands of Masonic significance obscure to anyone not a Mason. The sun, or major light, is on the hour hand and the moon, or lesser light, on the minute hand. Representations of the sun and moon are known (1) engraved on solid metal, (2) cut out of the solid metal, (3) painted on bosses that are a part of the hands. There may be others. Type two is pictured

SWAYING BIRD: Same as pecking bird. Isaac Chandlee made at least one swaying, or pecking, bird clock

SWORD CLOCK: Cased clock movement which acts as its own weight as it travels downward over the blade of sword, toothed to engage gears within the clock. Eighteenth and early nineteenth century. Warning! Faked ones are in circulation

TAILORS, NINE TO MAKE A MAN: This famed old phrase, "It takes nine tailors to make a man" is often thought to refer to clothiers. It doesn't. The term is "tollers," and it means that it took nine tollings of the bell to designate the burial of a man

TERRY EXPERIMENTALS: Any Terry-type thirty-hour, wooden-movement mantel clock in any casing, before the final pillar-and-scroll, with clear dial, hidden escapement and pendulum, and painted tablet. Various types are pictured in Chapter VI but not all. Pictured is Terry's first experimental, now owned but not for sale, by one of the antiques shops of New York City. The date is *c.* 1812

TICK-TACK-TOE CLOCK: Reference is to the case, the front of which is like the tick-tack-toe frames of *c.* 1875

TIDE CLOCK: Any fine clock with tide indicator; a variable depending upon the phases of the moon

TIMBY SOLAR CLOCK: Made by S. Whiting, of Saratoga Springs, N.Y., under patents granted Timby for a clock showing solar time all over the earth

TIME STEPS: Stair of four steps on which stand tubs or cans with drip spouts to act as a clepsydra. Chinese in origin; known as Hon Woo et Low

TIME, KINDS: Solar, sidereal, and mean time, are the "times" generally referred to in reference books. There are at least six other designations all of which deal with the fact that time, as a measurement, using the earth's rotation on its axis as a standard, is a variable, from the rotation of the earth itself and from every other viewpoint, whether the sun, the stars, or what. A study of the higher sciences dealing with time is not light reading. Perhaps that is why most experts in clock collecting prefer to study the more exact science of movement construction

TIN-PLATE CLOCKS: Clocks having movements of tin plate; that is, tin-plated sheet iron. Patented and made by Joseph Ives of Bristol, late 1850s or early 1860s

"THOMAS-TERRY": Designating the pillar-and-scroll cased thirty-hour wooden movement made by Seth Thomas under the Terry patents. It is not clear that Thomas's license from Terry was for anything but the making of the movement patented by Terry. Also it is not yet clear, in spite of decades of pillar-and-scroll tradition, that Terry was the first maker, after Heman Clark, to use the pillar-and-scroll case. There is good cause to suspect that Seth Thomas used the Heman Clark pillar-and-scroll-type case *before* Terry, to case the movements he, Thomas, was making under licensed agreement with Terry

THREE-TIER PILLAR: Novel variant of the pillar-and-scroll, made by Chauncey Jerome. The case is made in three tiers, or levels, and each tier is fitted with separate columns. The top tier is surmounted by a carved eagle cresting rather than a scroll. Jerome cased only eight-day brass movements in this case: the movement having the Ives roller pinion and hour strike. *See* page 105 for picture

TIN-CAN WEIGHTS: Actually sheet-iron cans filled with stones to serve as weights. Shipping Connecticut clocks any great distance, as for example to the Ohio country, added considerable weight to a load if there were weights in the clocks; hence tin cans, shipped in the clocks empty, were used instead of solid weights; the buyer filled the cans with stones

TOLLER: A single strike of a bell. A bellman once told us (he was a gentleman from Scotland) that a ring, or peal of a bell, was two bangs of the clapper against the bell while a toller was one. You cannot toll a bell by "ringin' it," he said; "it takes a separate pull to do your tolling unless you be a very smart bellman." This is reporting; we do not know and cannot vouch for its truth

TOPSY CLOCK: *See* blinking eye clocks

TORY CLOCK: TORY'S CLOCK: During the Revolution there were committees who collected all lead clock weights and substituted iron weights for them. The lead was needed for bullets. Hence any eighteenth-century clock, made before 1776, with lead weights, is called a Tory's clock. It is largely a pleasantry now; chances are many of the iron-weighted clocks were reweighted with lead after the Revolution

TYMPANUM: The arched section over the dial of a clock

UERWERKPLAET: Paper clock dials for pasting on wood or iron panels. Made in book form in the Netherlands, *c.* 1785–1825 and sold in considerable quantities for making cheap clocks. *See* page 148

WALLPAPERED DIALS: Misnomer. What is meant is a clock dial of paper, cut round and mounted on wallpaper, which provides the decorative part

WARNING CLOCK: Seventeenth- and eighteenth-century term for alarum clock

WATCH CLOCK: Also a term for an alarum clock

WASHINGTON CLOCK: Ormolu, marble, and brass clocks made as memorials to Washington. Made in France. One is pictured on page 144

WINGS: Appendages on the sides of early clocks to mask the wide swing of a bob pendulum

WOODEN CLOCKS: This term always applies to the movement. Not all wooden-movement clocks are cheaply made; some are known with black walnut wheels and ivory bushings. Some clocks are known with boxwood and even lignum-vitae parts and pinions. The all-wooden clock movement seems to have originated in the French Jura, spread to the Swiss Jura, and from there to the Black Forest of Germany and to the Netherlands. Wooden-movement clocks appear to have been made in the French Jura *c.* 1550. They were made all over Europe, apparently, by the seventeenth century, but not in mass-production quantities

YEAR: The measure of a circuit of the earth on its orbit around the sun. Most people, thinking of this orbit and the fact that we do not make the circuit in precisely three hundred and sixty-five days, wonder how in all creation we make it in a fraction of a day more without our being aware of it. We are apt to forget that our earth is spinning on its own axis at the same time and that the sun doesn't ring a bell to tell us when a year is up. If we didn't compensate for the extra time beyond three hundred and sixty-five days taken to make the circuit, the only thing we'd notice, over a period of years, is that the accumulation of extra days would be pushing our seasons around. If we never fixed the calendar we'd have roses at Christmas, in Boston, and snow on the Fourth of July. And then, after centuries, we'd be back to roses in June and snow at Christmas. *See* calendar systems in any good encyclopedia and in any of the scientific journals on file in libraries

## BIBLIOGRAPHY

ATKINS & OVERALL: Some Account of the Worshipful Company of Clockmakers of London, 1881.

BAILEY, ROY R.: Through the Ages with Father Time.

BAILLIE: Watchmakers and Clockmakers of the World, 1929.

BENSON, JAMES W.: Time and Time Tellers, 1902.

BOOTH, MARY: New and Complete Clock and Watchmakers' Manual, 1860.

BREARLY, H. C.: Time-Telling Through the Ages, 1919.

BRITTEN, FREDERICK J.: Old Clocks and Watches and Their Makers, 1922.

CESCINSKY & WEBSTER: English Domestic Clocks, 1913.

CHANDLEE, EDWARD E.: Six Quaker Clockmakers, 1943.

CYNYNGHAME, H. H.: Time and Clocks, 1906.

DENT, F.: Treatise on Clocks and Watch Work, 1855.

DERHAM, WILLIAM: The Artificial Clockmaker, 1696 (Many subsequent editions)

HAYDEN, ARTHUR: Chats on Old Clocks, 1917.

HOOPES, PENROSE: Connecticut Clockmakers of the 18th Century.

——: Early Clockmaking in Connecticut.

JAMES, ARTHUR: Time and Its Measurement, 1909.

JEROME, CHAUNCEY: History of the American Clock Business, 1860.

MILHAM, WILLIS: Time and Timekeepers, 1941.

MILLER, EDGAR: American Antique Furniture.

MOORE, HUDSON: The Old Clock Book, 1911.

NUTTING, WALLACE: The Clock Book, 1924.

——: Furniture Treasury, Volume III, 1933.

SAUNIER, CLAUDIUS: Modern Horology, A Treatise on, 1887.

THOMSON, ADAM: Time and Timekeepers, 1842.

WILLARD, JOHN WARE: A History of Simon Willard, Clockmaker and Inventor, 1911.

# *SUPPLEMENT*

THIS supplement represents the work of the late Carl W. Drepperd and his associates in a concerted effort to augment the previous compilation of clockmakers listed in the first edition of *American Clocks and Clockmakers,* first published in 1947. Until his death in 1956, Mr. Drepperd was engaged in energetic research in order to compile the names of bona fide clockmakers who had been overlooked in the first edition of this book.

Aided by a very large number of volunteer research workers, Mr. Drepperd assembled these (previously unlisted) names of clockmakers in each issue of a short-lived journal during 1949-1950, *Time Pieces Quarterly,* published by the American Clock and Watch Foundation. In his capacity as a member of the editorial staff, Mr. Drepperd inserted regular installments of "additional clockmakers." The purpose of these listings, as announced in *Time Pieces Quarterly,* was to pave the way for an enlarged section or supplement of clockmakers in a forthcoming edition of *American Clocks and Clockmakers.* New names began to roll in, unearthed by diligent investigators who found them in old advertisements, on old clocks, and other places.

The publishers of this new edition of *American Clocks and Clockmakers* take pleasure in presenting this fresh material, which includes the names of clockmakers discovered by Mr. Drepperd's independent investigation, as well as those names contributed by associates, friends, readers and the many individuals who admired the author as a ranking authority in the world of American antiques.

This carefully compiled supplement does not pretend to be all-inclusive. The names of *Clockmakers* only were collected and not those of clock merchants or piece-workers in clock factories. The reader will note that the first edition in its entirety has been reproduced in facsimile. This new material is simply inserted as a supplement in order to enlarge and bring up-to-date a valuable reference on the history of clockmakers in America. The following list is in its own alphabetical order and on occasion a name already noted in the "first edition" may reappear with new or corrected details.

## ADDITIONAL NAMES OF CLOCKMAKERS

ACKER, JOSEPH D.: West Chester, Pa., 1850s. This man is listed in the supplement to the first directory of West Chester

ADAMS, E. W.: Seneca Falls, N. Y., 1820s–1850s. A brass movement, 8-day mantel clock by him bears this inscription: "E. W. Adams, Horologist, Manufacturer of Town Clocks, Time Clocks and Regulators"

ADAMS, THOMAS F.: Baltimore, Md., to 1807. Thence to Petersburg, Va., to 1809, then to Edenton, N. C.

ADKINS (ATKINS), ELBRIDGE (ELDRIDGE): Bristol, Conn. Made pillar & scroll cased wooden 30 hour movements and other shelf clocks. Both names are known to have been used. "Elbridge Adkins" is the spelling on a clock paper in one clock reported; Eldridge Atkins on another

ALLEBACH, HENRY: Reading, Pa., 1820s. Advertised in 1829

ALLEN, A. & SON: Rochester, N. Y., 1850s–1870s

ALLEN, ISAAC A.: Enfield, Connecticut, 1860s

ALLENSPACHERN, JOSEPH: Philadelphia, 1780s. A Hessian deserter from the British army

ALMY, JAMES T.: New Bedford, Mass., 1840s–1850s. Probably dealer only

ALSOP, THOMAS: Philadelphia, 1830s–1850s

AMERICAN CLOCK CO.: New York City, 1850s

ANDREWS, D. B.: Cincinnati, Ohio, 1850s

ANDREWS, JAMES: New York City, 1810s

ANGELUS CLOCK CO.: Philadelphia, incorporated 1874; Thomas E. Cahill, President, John Rogers, Secretary and Treasurer. Made 8-day striking clocks which sounded the Angelus bell at 6 A.M., noon and 6 P.M. Clock cases in form of cathedral door with 4 inch spire finial

ANSONIA CLOCK CO.: Branch of Ansonia Brass Co. (Est. 1844) began making clocks 1849. Incorporated as separate company, 1877, with factory at Brooklyn, N.Y. Fire destroyed factory 1880. Rebuilt 1881

ANSPETH (ANSTETH) J. ROLLIN: Buffalo, N.Y., 1880s–1890s. Made clocks with triangular dials of copper with stamped-in numerals

ARDERY, R.: Zanesville, Ohio, 1850s–1870s

AUSTIN, SEYMOUR: Hartford, Conn., 1800s; Western Reserve, Ohio, 1810s

AVISE, M.: Reading, Pa., 1820s. Advertised in newspapers 1827

AYERS, T.R.J.: Keokuk, Iowa, 1860s–1870s

BACHMAN, JOSEPH: New York City, 1850s

BAERR, WILLIAM: Weaverville, California, late 1850s–1860s. Watch and clockmaker

BAILEY, GAMALIEL: Mount Holly, N.J. from 1807 to 1821. See also pp 200, American Clocks & Clockmakers. Bailey removed to Philadelphia, 1827 where he remained to 1832 or 1833 and then moved to Cincinnati, Ohio

BAILEY, JOHN: Hanover, Mass., b. 1751; d. 1823. Son of Colonel John Bailey and known properly as John Bailey, Jr. Made clocks from 1760s; said to have constructed a clock when only 11 years of age. Had two sons, both clockmakers, John Bailey III and Joseph Bailey

BAILEY, JOHN, III: New Bedford, Mass., 1790s. Then at Lynn, Mass., to c. 1850

BAILEY, JOSEPH: New Bedford, and Lynn, Mass., 1790s to 1840s

BAILEY & KITCHEN: Philadelphia, Penna., 1840s. Probably dealers only but clocks with the name on dial are reported

BAILEY, PUTNAM: Goshen, Conn., 1830s

BAKER, DAVID: New Bedford, Mass., 1840s–1850s

BAKER, SAMUEL: New Brunswick, N.J., from c.1810s to 1850. A watch paper, engraved by Simmons, and used by Baker, was issued c. 1820s. On this paper he calls himself a clock and watchmaker

BALL, B.: New Haven, Connecticut, 1860s

BANDELL & CO.: St. Albans, Vt. n.d. A beautiful banjo clock with this name was examined in 1948; the name was almost obliterated from dial

BANFIELD, FORRISTALL & CO.: Boston, Massachusetts, 1860s

BANNAKER, BENJAMIN: Ellicott's Mills and Baltimore, Md., from c. 1781. Pupil of Andrew and perhaps also of Joseph Ellicott, the latter founding the village, Ellicott's Mills in 1770, migrating from Bucks County, Pa., Bannaker was partly Negro. He became a very good mathematician and published an almanac from 1791. Made clocks

BARRETT & SHERWOOD: San Francisco, Cal., 1850s–1860s; made clocks and chronometers

BARRINGTON, JOSEPH: Dumfries, Va., 1790s to 1820. Then at Salisbury, N.C. Made self-winding clocks and other rarities and advertised them

BARTELS, FRANZ: Jersey City, N.J., 1860s–1870s

BARTHOLOMEW, W. J.: Brooklyn, N.Y., 1850s–1860s

BATES, AMOS: New Bedford, Mass., 1830s–1850s. Chronometer maker

BAUMANN, G.: Columbus, Ohio, 1840s. "*Clockmaker* and watch repairer" in 1845 directory of city

BAYLEY, LEBBENS: This maker, listed on page 203 of first Edition of American Clocks & Clockmakers, is not authenticated. This entry establishes full authentication. In a clock by Lebbens Bayley, owned by J. L. Berkely, Esq., of Freeport, Me., is this inscription: ". . . .Made by Mr. Lebbens Bayley of North Yarmouth, Maine, in the year 1800 and set up in my house in June 17th of that same year" (signed) Thomas Bicknell. This clock is an 8 day brass movement, time & strike, in tall case of pine

BEALS, J. J. & Co.: 1867, Boston

BEALS, WILLIAM: Boston, Mass., 1853

BEASLEY, JOHN M.: Fayetteville, N.C., from 1830s

BEATTY, GEORGE: Harrisburg, Pa., 1808–1848. Born 1781 at Ballykeel, Ireland, apprenticed to brother-in-law, Samuel Hill. Made watches, tall clocks and mantel clocks with time, strike and moon phase. Used Osborn dials. Some of his movement plates have mark "GA" in a rectangle

BECHTLER, CHRISTOPHER: Philadelphia, Pa., 1830s. Moved to Rutherfordton, N.C. He produced the famous Bechtler gold coinage

BELL BROTHERS: San Antonio, Texas from 1850s. Claimed to have been "manufacturers" but probably only dealers and distributors.

BELL, WILLIAM: Boston, 1820s–1840s. Maker of clock and watch glasses, not clocks and watches

BENEDICT, ALBERT: Lewisburg, Pa., 1860s

BENEDICT, ANDREW C.: New York, c. 1810s–1830. Clock and watchmaker, shop at 23, the Bowery

BENEDICT, MARTIN: New York City, 1830s

BENJAMIN, EVERARD: New Haven, Conn., 1840s–1860. In 1846-7 firm was E. Benjamin & Co. Later firm was Benjamin & Ford, the partner being George H. Ford

BENNETT, R. JONES: Easton, Maryland, 1820s. Advertised in Republican-Star, 1827 as clock & watchmaker

BENNY, JAMES: Easton, Maryland, 1820s. Advertised in Republican-Star, 1926 as clock & watchmaker

BENNY, JONATHAN (Not Jack Benny): Easton, Maryland, 1800s Later at Pittsburgh. Advertised in Republican-Star, 1802

BENTLEY, CALEB: Chester County (West Whiteland and other locales) Penna, and Taneytown, Maryland after 1787. Brother of Eli Bentley. Both men were also silversmiths and watchmakers

BENTLEY, ELI: Taneytown, Md., b. Doe Run, Chester Co., Pa., Feb. 16, 1752, d. Taneytown, Md., 1822

BENTLEY, GEORGE: Taneytown, Maryland, c. 1810 and later. Son of Eli Bentley. A clock with "G. Bentley, Taneytown" on dial is owned in this village

BERINGER, A. & J.: Albany, N.Y. 1830s

BERKE (OR BURKE) AUGUST: Louisville, Ky., 1860s

BERKLY, J.: Lewisburg, Pa., 1800s–1820s. Signed his clocks with title "clockmaker" in addition to name and place. Made hang-up type movements, many of which were fitted into cases by purchasers. Therefore, a variety of cabinetmaking, both as to quality and style, is noted in the cases of clocks by Berkly. It is believed this maker produced only uncased, hang-up type movements, as did Eli Terry in his early project

BIGELOW BROTHERS; BIGELOW & BROTHERS: Boston, Mass., 1840s. Extensive importers of French clocks

BIGELOW, JOHN B.: Boston, Mass., 1840s

BIRCE, J.: Brattleborough, Vermont, 1820s–1830s

BIRGE, J.: Brattleborough, Vt., n.d., but c. 1800s

BISHOP, JOSEPH: Wilmington, N.C., from 1810s

BISPHAM, SAMUEL: Philadelphia, from 1692 when, as a clockmaker, he purchased land upon which to erect a house and shop. Bispham is believed to have been working in South Jersey prior to 1692. Only one example, a tall case clock discovered by Mark Shanaberger and now owned by Harry Burke of Philadelphia, is known. This is an 8-day brass, time and strike movement clock

BLACKFORD, EDWARD: N.Y. City, 1830s

BLAKESLEE, E.: Cincinnati, Ohio, 1850s–1860s. This man was a representative of Seth Thomas. He sold clock parts, assembled clocks, and sold completely cased clocks

BLAKESLEE, EDWARD K.: Cincinnati, Ohio, 1840s–1850s. Made a "Patented marine timepiece or lever clock for steamboats, canal packets and railroad cars, for use like a watch, in any position, serving as admirable chronometers"

BLAKESLEY, HARPER: Cincinnati, 1820s–1830s

BLANCHARD, JOSHUA: Cincinnati, 1820s–1830s

BLISS, JOHN & Co.: N.Y. City, 1860s. Chronometers

BLISS, WILLIAM: Cleveland, Ohio, 1810s–1820s

BLOOMER, WILLIAM: Mt. Victory, Ohio, 1860s

BOIFEUILLET, JOHN P.: Savannah, Georgia, 1850s–1860s

BOOTH, HIRAM N.: N.Y. City, 1840s

BOTTSFORD, J. S.; Troy, N.Y., c. 1840s–1850s

BOTSFORD, S. N.: Norfolk, Va., c. 1850. Clock and watchmaker, Main Street, is designation on a watchpaper of record and in a Norfolk directory of the period

BOWER, HENRY: n.d.,n.p. A grandmother clock, once owned by Mrs. M. B. Cooke, now Pottstown, Pa. is pictured in Nutting's Clock Book (#108). Nutting's notes state "inscription on dial read Hy. Bower" but he fails to give the complete inscription on the dial which shows in the picture but not clearly enough to decipher. The name is in Latin characters, the balance of inscription is in Gothic characters. The clock dates 1810–1830

BOYD, H.: Blairsville, Pa., 1830s. Clock, watchmaker, and silversmith. Eight-day tall clocks with painted dials reported.

BRACKETT, JEFFREY: Boston, Mass., 1830s–1850s

BRACKETT, O.: Vassalboro (no State Designation) appears with this name on an unusual mantel clock in maple case. There is record of an Oliver Brackett in a card in our files without state or place designation and without date. The clock responsible for this entry is of first half of 19th century and is owned by Mrs. Teina Baumstone who reported it

BRADLEY, B. & Co.: 1867, Boston

BRADLEY, H.: Mantua, Ohio, 1810s

BRADYCAMP, LEWIS: Lancaster, Pa., 1836–1870. Apprentice of Martin Shreiner. Made tall case clocks to 1870

BRAINARD, O. T.: Tama City, Iowa, 1860s

BRANDT (or BRANT, or BRENT), ADAM: New Hanover, Montgomery County, Pa. Reported as working from middle of 18th century. Place is incorrectly attributed in first edition of American Clocks & Clockmakers as "now Hanover, Pa." Hanover is in York County, New Hanover was in Montgomery County. Tall case clocks by Adam Brent, Brant and Brandt are reported. The mid-18th century date of working is given from reports only

BRASIER, AMIABLE: Philadelphia, 1820s

BREESE, LAMAN: Wellsburg, Va., 1830s

BRENNEISEN, SAMUEL: Reading, Pa., 1790s. Removed to Adamstown, Lancaster County, Pa., between 1807 and 1810. Listed in American Clocks & Clockmakers, first edition, as working only at Adamstown and Reamstown. Data here is correct in respect of earlier activity

BRENEISER, WILLIAM: Reamstown, Lancaster County, Pa., 1780s to 1830s. Made tall clocks

BREWSTER, E. C. & Co.: Bristol, Conn., "manufacturers of patent spring 8-day repeating brass clocks" appearing on a clock paper signed by this variant of the Brewster-Ingraham interests in Bristol clockmaking. Date is in 1840s or 1850s

BREWSTER, N. L.: Bristol, Conn., made Ives patent roller pinion clocks c. 1846–1850

BRICKARD, H.: Bainbridge, Pa., 1860s

BRICKETT, WILLIAM: Boston, Mass., 1860s

BRIGHT, JACOB: Sunbury, Penna., c. 1790-1810. Tall case clocks reported. One in walnut case with broken arch top

BRINCKERHOOF, C.: New York, 1790s–1800s. Brass founders who produced blanks and bells for clockmakers

BROCK, FERDINAND: Carondelet, Mo., 1860s

BROCKETT, JESSE: New Haven, Conn., 1860s

BROKAW, JOHN: Woodbridge, N.J., 1770s–1780s. This, and several other names of New Jersey makers have been supplied by the late Phillipse R. Greene who checked the entire list of New Jersey Clockmakers in "American Clocks & Clockmakers" and verified dates

BROOK, JOHN: N.Y. City, 1830s

BROOKS, BARNARD: Salem Cross Roads, Westmoreland County, Pa., 1830s. This entry is based on hearsay evidence and legend

BROOKS, WILLIAM P.: Boston, Mass., 1860s

BROWN & BUCK: Columbus, Ohio, 1840s–1850s. Advertised 1850. Probably dealers and not makers or manufacturers

BROWN, F.: Savannah, Georgia, 1850s

BROWN, GEORGE: Bristol, Conn., (Forestville section) from

1856. Originally appraised, from his clocks, as working from 1840s, it is now definitely established he manufactured clocks from 1856 to 1862. George Brown had a factory at Bristol but it was chiefly a manufactory of toys and toy parts. Of course the toys were of the mechanical type. Very few clocks, apparently, were made and examples are now scarce. This man had no connection with J. C. Brown. George Brown's clocks do have papers and it is from one of these, found in a clock in 1949, that this maker can be here listed definitively as to name, date and place.

BROWN, JOHN: Lancaster, Penna., Revise data in 1st Edition of American Clocks and Clockmakers to read: working from 1820s to 1860s

BROWN, ROBERT: Baltimore, Maryland, from 1840s. Located at 206 Baltimore Street. These data in extension of information given in respect of this maker in American Clocks & Clockmakers

BROWNE, LIBERTY: Philadelphia, 1800s

BROWNOLD, D.: Louisville, Ky., 1860s

BRUGHNER, JACOB: Brooklyn, N.Y., 1840s–1850s

BUEL, DAVID: East Hampton, Conn., 1830s. Did not make clocks. He was a manufacturer of clock bells

BUERK, J. E.: Boston, Mass., 1860s. Inventor of Buerk watch-clock and of a watchman's time detector clock

BURDICT, S. P.: Philadelphia, c. 1870s–1880s. Inventor of patent lever, 8 day cathedral gong and musical clock using a music box. Examples are excessively rare

BURGI, FREDERICK: Swiss clockmaker of Trenton, N.J., from 1770s

BURKLE, JACOB: Pittsburgh, Pa., 1830s

BURNHAM, E. B.: Salisbury, N.C., from 1820s. Firm of Elliott & Burnham

BURRITT, JOSEPH: Ithaca, N.Y., 1830s. A newly found directory of 1831 states Burritt was "a *dealer* in clocks, andirons, brass castings, etc." He is not credited as a maker. Therefore this correction

BURROWES CLOCKS (THOMAS BURROWES): Strasburg, Lancaster County, Pa., 1787–1810

BYINGTON, LAWLER (also LAWYER, LOVING): Newark, Tioga

County, N.Y., a dealer in Chauncey Boardman clocks; doubtful as a maker in spite of fact that clocks do bear his name on dials and on clock papers

BYINGTON, LORING, (or LAUREN, or LAWYER): Bristol, Conn., clock peddler working for Eli and George Bartholomew, 1828–32. He sold the hollow column clock in the columns of which the weights of the clock were hidden. These were 30-hour wooden movement clocks. Byington was also in business for himself at Bristol as Byington & Co., 1843–49. The records of the town of Bristol report this firm as Loring Byington & Co. In 1852–53 he was in business again as Byington & Graham. In 1849–52 he seems to have had a distribution office and shop at Newark, Tioga County, N.Y., selling clocks by Chauncey Boardman of Bristol. Such clocks with the Byington label and the Newark place designation are of record

CALDERWOOD, A.: Philadelphia, 1800s

CAMPBELL, ______: Philadelphia, 1790s–1820s. Tall case, 8-day brass movement clocks with painted metal dials, generally time and strike, some with moon phase, seconds dial, and day of month slot. Sheraton style cases, some inlaid. No clocks known marked other than "Campbell, Philadelphia." Examples are scarce. Arthur Sussell reports finding only two in over 30 years of dealing in fine clocks

CAMPBELL, ALEXANDER: Brooklyn, N.Y., 1840s–1850s

CAMPBELL, JAMES: Union Town, N.J., c. 1790s–1800s. Tall case clocks reported without state designation. The New Jersey attribution here given is fairly certain

CAMPBELL, JOHN: N.Y. City and Brooklyn, 1840s

CARPENTER, JAMES: Harrison, (or Harrisontown) N.J. This state attribution is given as first choice; it may be N.Y. Working in early 19th century

CARRELL, J. & D.: Philadelphia, 1770s–1790s. Clocks, parts, and castings

CARRELL, JOHN: Philadelphia, from 1790s. Clocks, tools and parts

CARSON, THOMAS: Albany, N.Y., 1830s

CARTER & WELLER: Stockbridge, N.Y., 1930s. Reported as assemblers and salesmen of Connecticut movements

CHAMPNEY & FELTON: Troy, N.Y., 1850s. Probably dealers

Chappel & Sartwell: (Revision of data on firm as listed in first edition of American Clocks & Clockmakers.) This firm operated in Chautauqua County, N.Y., from the town of Busti, immediately south of Jamestown. Made hang-up and tall case clocks. Designation of place on their clocks "Chautauqua Co." refers to the county and not the place so named. Complete tall case clocks by this firm reported by Erik Erikson of Jamestown, N.Y., and C. B. Sampson of the same city, who supplied this important correction. The dates of operation fall within the decades 1830s–1840s

Chase, William H.: Salem, Mass., 1840s

Cheeseman, James L.: N.Y. City, 1830s

Child, S. & T.: Philadelphia, 1850s

Claymore, Robert: Germantown, Pa., 1765–1780s. Mulatto slave of Dr. Christopher Witt given freedom under will of the master clockmaker who taught Claymore and willed him his clockmaking tools and equipment

Choate, George W.: New Bedford, Mass., 1840s–1850s

Clarke, A.: Philadelphia, from 1787

Clark, Benjamin & Ellis: Philadelphia, 1820s. Also clockmakers tools

Clark, Charles: Fayetteville, N.C., 1820s

Clayton, Samuel: Brooklyn, N.Y., 1840s–1850s

Cochran, L.: Northfield Centre, Vt., c. 1850s

Coffin, Simeon: Yarmouth, Maine, 1820s–1840. Not a clockmaker. Coffin was a cabinetmaker. He seems to have made cases for imported English brass movements

Cogswell, Joseph: Norwich, Conn., 1780s–1800s

Collins & Co.: Cranston, R.I. from 1830s to 1850s. Brass movement mantel clocks are known

Conant, W. S.: New York City. Manufacturer of brass and wood clocks at 177 Pearl Street, in 1845. These data extend that already given in American Clocks & Clockmakers

Conklin & Ritchey: Clinton, Illinois, 1850s, 1860s. Clocks with papers of this firm are Connecticut made. They were clock peddlers with extensive routes in rural Illinois

Connecticut Clock Co.: New York City, 1850s

Constant, Francis: Kingston, N.Y., 1850s

Converse & Crane: 1867, Boston

Cook, Benjamin E.: Northampton, Mass., 1840s–1850s

COOK, SAMUEL: Waterbury, Conn., 1820s–1830s. This maker born 1794, died 1835. Sheldon Museum, Middlebury, Vermont, owns a shelf clock made by this man

COOKE, BENJAMIN: Philadelphia, 1860s

COOKE, F. B.: (Additional data to be added to entry of Frederick B. Cooke, in first edition of American Clocks & Clockmakers.) This maker in Columbia, Lancaster County, and at York, Pa., within the date limits established by Drepperd, appears while at York to have marketed wood and brass movement one-day shelf clocks of Connecticut type, with papers or labels attributing manufacture to this maker at York. Further research is indicated in respect of this clockmaker who, at York, may have been acting as an agent for various Connecticut firms. Obviously the research would be a matter of movement identification

COOKE'S SONS, B.G.: Philadelphia, from 1853. From 1870 they were extensive wholesale dealers in Connecticut and other clocks

COOPER, JOHN: N.Y. City, 1840s

COPE, JOHN: Lancaster, Pa., 1790s–1800s

COPPUCK, GEORGE: Mount Holly, N.J., from c. 1824 to 1860s

CORBETT, THOMAS: Canterbury, N.H. Shaker clockmaker, 1810s

CORL, WILLIAM: This name, William Corl, is an error in any list of makers. It has appeared due to misreading the signature of Abraham Corl when signed Abm. Corl on clock dials. The "Ab" in script is mistaken for a "W" and, combined with the "m" is thus mistaken as an abbreviation for William, which it is not

CORLISS, A. G.: Portland, Maine, 1860s

CORY, LEWIS: Rahway, N.J., c. 1820s–1840s

CORYTON, JOSIAH: Alexandria, Virginia, from c. 1780s to 1799 or 1800. Tall case and mantel clocks, brass movements, imported in parts from London

COWPER, JOHN: Philadelphia, from 1710s to 1720s. Name also spelled COWPUR and COOPER. One of our really early clockmakers. Owner of tall case, brass dial clock, giving information has requested anonymity

CRAFTE (KRAFT), JACOB: Sheperdstown, Va., 1790s–1820s. This man is the same as the Jacob Kraft listed in first edition of American Clocks & Clockmakers. "Crafte" is the correct spelling and Virginia is the correct state designation, as

West Virginia was not a state during the period of this man's activity

CRAIG, JOHN B.: Pittsburgh, Pa., 1840s–1850s

CRITTENDEN, CHARLES: Tallmaga, Ohio, 1830s

CROCKER, J. R.: Valley Falls, R.I. Maker of clocks for toy banks, and so advertised in 1860s

CROCKER, WILLIAM: N.Y. City, 1840s

CROSBY, D. S.: New York City, 1850s

CURTIS & DUNNING: Burlington, Vt., 1820s–1840s. A fine Banjo clock with Masonic emblems, by this firm, and signed, is reported by Caleb R. Nash, Esq.

CURTIS, THOMAS: Lowell, Mass., 1860s

CURTISS, H. & Co.: Meriden, Conn., 1820s–1830s. Made modified pillar and scroll cased mantel clocks with 30 hour wooden movements of the "groaner" type. Data from Ira C. Baldwin, Esq., of New Britain

CUTLER, J. N.: Albany, N.Y., 1840s–1850s. Advertised in 1840s

DANIEL, GEORGE C.: Elizabeth City, N.C., from 1830

DANIELS, G.: Cincinnati, 1820s. Clockmaker and maker of clock models. No clock signed by him located. Did work for Luman Watson

DAUMONT, PETER (ALSO DAUMONT, H. & Co.): Indianapolis, Ind., 1860s

DAVENPORT, WILLIAM: Philadelphia, 1800s

DAVENPORT, WILLIAM: N.Y. City, 1810s–1820s. Chronometers reported

DAVIES, D.: Wellsburg, Virginia, 1830s–1840s

DAVIS, D. P.: 1867, Boston

DAVIS, PHINEA: York, Pa., from early 1800s. Lewis Miller's Sketch Books, owned by York County Historical Society, contain a picture of Davis at work with this data: "In 1806 made a watch pocket clock which he sent to London." Davis was a watch and clockmaker, silversmith, steamboat builder and locomotive builder for the B.&O. He was also a bellfounder. His iron steamboat "Codorus," navigated on the Susquehanna River

DAVIS, RILEY: New Bern, N.C., from 1850s

DAVIS, SAMUEL: (Additional data concerning this maker, listed in first edition of American Clocks & Clockmakers as working 1810-1820.) Samuel Davis is listed in the Pittsburgh

Directory of 1815 and in the 1850 directory. While we can assume it is the same man listed in both directories, we should not overlook the possibility of a father and son of the same name

DAWREY, CHARLES D.: Brooklyn, N.Y., 1840s–1850s. In 1850 Directory he is listed as a clock and dial *painter*. In others as a "maker"

DAYTON, JOHN D.: Brooklyn, N.Y., 1840s–1850s

DERAISMES & BOIZARD: N.Y. City, 1840s. Assemblers of French movements in fancy cases. Shop at 88 William Street

DE VACHT, FRANCOIS: Gallipolis (City of the French), Ohio, c. 1790s–1810s. The authority for this and other DeVacht (De Vacz) entries is John Heckewelder's narrative. Heckewelder was an on-the-spot commentator in respect of Gallipolis in 1792. He said, "The most interesting shops were those of the goldsmiths and watchmakers, who showed us watches, compasses and sun dials finer than I have ever (before) beheld." In a footnote, this same author gives the names of De Vacht, J. G., and De Vacht, Francois, and Didier, Pierre, who moved westward and finally became treasurer of the State of Missouri

DE VACHT, J. G.: Gallipolis, Ohio, 1790s–1810s

DE VACZ (See De Vacht)

DEXTER, WILLIAM: Stockbridge, N.Y., 1830s. Probably assembled and cased Connecticut movements

DICKENSON, ______: Boston, Mass., c. 1800s. A tall case clock in oak case with brass movement, 8-day, enameled dial, time and strike, with day of month slot, inscribed "Dickenson, Boston" was in the Martin E. Albert Collection in 1948. Both case and movement, or case only, may be English importations. The date is c. 1800s. No further information available

DICKERSON, JOHN: Morristown, N.J., from late 1770s to late 1790s. Said to have worked at spot near New Harmony, Indiana, from c. 1799 or 1800 to as late as 1825. Latter data not yet verified

DIDIER, PIERRE: Gallipolis, Ohio, 1790s–1800s. (See also DE VACHT)

DIEHL, JACOB: Reading, Pa., 1790s–1820s. Properly listed in first edition of American Clocks and Clockmakers, but these new data can be added, supplied by Earl T. Strickler of Columbia, Pa.: Jacob Diehl operated the shop of Daniel Rose to 1804 during the absence of proprietor, and thereafter conducted his own clockmaking establishment as Jacob Diehl

DIKEMAN, A.: New York City, 1780s to 1800s

DILLON, J. F. M.: Adell, Iowa, 1860s

DILLON, T. E.: N.Y. City, 1860s. Chronometers

DOBSON, JOHN A.: Baltimore, Md., 1860s–1870s

DOMINICK, FREDERICK: Philadelphia, early 19th century. Numbered his clocks, Number 9 reported by Gregory Slatoff, of Bristol, Pa.

DON, ALEXANDER (AND WILLIAM): Albany, N.Y. from 1810s. William Don came from Turniff, Aberdeenshire, Scotland. He is believed to have settled near Albany, 1810s. General William A. McCulloch, of Swarthmore, Penna., owns a William Don watch, purchased by his great grandfather, at Albany, but marked William Don, Turniff and numbered 84

DONALDSON, GEORGE E.: Doylestown, Pa., 1850s–1860s

DORCHESTER CLOCK & BELL FOUNDRY: Dorchester, Mass., operating in 1830s when statistical table reporter designated the factory as a clock and organ manufactory, combined with a bell foundry, employing 10 hands

DROZ, HANNAH: Philadelphia, Pa., 1840s

DROZ, JOHN: Cincinnati, Ohio, 1820s

DRYER, C.: Louisville, Ky., 1840s. Reported as a clock, instrument, and thermometer maker

DUCOMMUN, HENRY: Philadelphia, Pa., 1830s. He dealt principally in clock & watchmakers tools

DUFF, GEORGE C.: New Bern, N.C., from 1845

DUHME & CO.: Cincinnati, Ohio, 1850s–1860s. Reported as dealers and makers

DULTY, JOHN: Zanesville, Ohio, 1800–1810s

DUMOTETTE, J. B.: Philadelphia, 1800s

DUREN, H.: N.Y. City, 1820s to 1840s

DURFEE, WALTER H.: Providence, R.I., from 1870s. Had factory at rear 283 High St., where he produced oak cased tall clocks, time, strike, chime and moon phase, many of which are mistaken for much older workmanship

DYAR, A.: Lowell Mass., 1830s

DYER, WADSWORTH & CO.: Augusta, Georgia, 1830s–1840s. Connecticut clock manufacturers "front" firm for Southern states distribution

EALER, JOHN: Northampton (now Allentown) Penna. c. 1800s

EBERMAN, JOSEPH: Lancaster, Pa., to c. 1860. He is listed in Directory of 1857, in 1859 and in 1860. May be son of man of same name listed in Drepperd, as at Lancaster, 1800–1844

EBY, JACOB: Lancaster County, Pa., from 1830s to 1860s. May have been son of Jacob Eby of Sporting Hill, same County. Name sometimes in error appears as ELY

ECKEL, ALEXANDER P.: Greensboro, N.C., from 1845. Worked to 1890s

EDGERLY, S.: Roxbury, Mass., 1840s

EDGERTON, MATTHEW, SR.: New Brunswick, N.J., 1760s–1780s

EDMANDS & HAMBLETT: 1867, Boston

EDMUNDS, WILLIAM: Roxbury, Mass. 1820s–1840s. Banjo clocks reported

EELLS, EDWARD: Middlebury, Vt., from c. 1814 to 1830s or later. A monograph on this maker appeared in the second number of the magazine "Timepieces," 1949

EGGERT, D. SONS: N.Y. City 1860s. Chronometers

ELLERY, E.: Clockmaker reported as working at Newburyport, Mass., n.d.

ELLIOTT & BURNHAM: Salisbury, N.C., from 1821. Zebulon Elliott and E. B. Burnham "from New York" clock and watch makers

ELLIOTT, GEORGE: Wilmington, Del., Successor of Charles Canby. Probably only dealer and repairman, from 1852

ENGLE, JACOB: Carlisle, Pa., c. 1780s–1800s. Tall case clocks

ENGLE, STEPHEN D.: Hazleton, Pa., 1850s–1870s. Made an apostolic clock with astronomical attachment. Pictured in Leslie's Illustrated, Apr. 13, 1878. Clock was displayed throughout the country and publicized by the Engle Clock Times, published N.Y. Jan. 1884. "Hourly News and Minutes of the Day Run Solely on Tick." Issue is marked Vol. I, #1. Others may have been published

EPPS, W.: New Orleans, La., 1860s

EUREKA MANUFACTURING CO.: Boston, 1850s–1860s. They advertised regulators, astronomical, marine, school, hotel, office, calendar and house clocks and clockwork driven self-stirring coffee roasters in 1860s

ERNST, ______: Cooperstown, N.Y., c. 1810s–1840

EVANS, ELIJAH: Frederick, Md., from 1782; Baltimore, Md. from c. 1779 to 1780. A partnership at Baltimore was David & Elijah Evans as clocks bearing both names are reported. Clocks by Elijah, marked Frederick, Maryland, are scarce, but of record. All reported clocks are tall case

EVANS, GEORGE: Philadelphia, 1790s

EVANS, HENRY: Newark, N.J., 1850s

EVANS, WILLIAM M.: Cincinnati, 1850s

FABER, GEORGE: Sumneytown, Pa., 1770s; Reading, Pa., around 1772–1780

FALES, G. S., J. & J.: New Bedford, Mass., 1840s–1850s

FALES, JAMES & GILES: New Bedford, Mass., 1840s

FALLER, ADAM: Philadelphia, Pa., 1860s

FARMER, JOHN: Philadelphia, from 1693. Documentary reference designates this clockmaker as establishing himself the 24th day, 8th month, 1693

FARR & THOMPSON: Philadelphia, Pa. John C. Farr founded business in 1822; in 1849 a son of John C. and C. E. Thompson formed a partnership. It is not established this succession ever made clocks but from 1822 they were extensive importers

FAY, HENRY C.: Troy, N.Y., 1850s

FEHRENBACH, P.: Boston, 1860s

FEHRER, GEORGE J.: Shawneetown, Illinois, 1860s

FELLOWS, WADSWORTH & CO.: New York City, 1840s. Probably dealers only. But were American agents for Chronometers of Litherland, Davies & Co., London

FELTON, A. C.: Boston, 1860s

FENNO, JAMES: Lowell, Mass., 1830s–1840s

FISHER, CHARLES F.: San Antonio, Texas. Really a watchmaker and probably also a clockmaker. Worked in 1850s and 1860s

FISHER, LOUIS: N.Y. City, last half of 18th century

FOLLETT, M. M.: Madrid, N.Y., n.c., but first half of 19th century

FORBES, WELLS: Bristol, N.H., 1840s. A clock signed by this

maker at the place noted, dated 1842, is reported in complete verification of the inclusion of this name in American Clocks & Clockmakers

FORD, GEORGE H.: New Haven, Conn. (See Benjamin, Everard)

FORESTVILLE CLOCK CO.: Forestville, Conn., 1830s. Clock bearing this variant from other Forestville Mfg. Companies, or clock manufactory names, on its paper is owned by H. A. Yungmann of Milwaukee, Wis., who contributes this information

FORSYTH, HENRY: Philadelphia, Pa., 1860s

FOURNIER, STANISLAUS: New Orleans, La., 1830s–1850s. Made the first public electric clock of record for the Bank of Louisiana, 1849

FOWLE, J. H.: Northampton, Mass., 1850s

FRENCH, CHARLES: Clockmaker residing in Deleware County, Ohio, 1825. Employed by Knowles Linnell of St. Albans, 1826, to work in the Linnell clock factory. Remained in charge of operation at the factory to 1828, when he removed to Granville, Ohio, to follow his trade

FRISBIE, L. & J. & Co.: Chittenango, N.Y., around 1830

FROST, DANIEL: Reading, Mass., 1760s or 1770s to c.1800. A typographical error in American Clocks & Clockmakers lists this maker as Front, Daniel, with the vague place attribution of Reading, Mass., or Reading, Pa. The correct name is Daniel Frost and the correct place is Reading, Mass. An Excessively rare type of pilaster and scroll top mantel clock by this maker, in a case with scrolled and shell-carved valance with claw and ball feet, was sold in 1929 at the Reifsnyder sale for $3600 to Henry Ford. Mr. Ford later presented this clock to Matthew Sloane, president of the Brooklyn Edison Company, New York City. This clock stands 42 inches high and 19½" wide. Brass movement, 8-day, time and strike, with moon phase and day of month slot. A somewhat similar clock without maker designation but in a case bearing evidence of making by Bachmann of Lampeter Square, is perhaps the reason for the belief that this maker worked in Pennsylvania. This second clock, the only other example known, may have been made by Christian and Daniel Forrer

FROST, JESSE: Lynn, Mass., 1840s–1850s

FROST, JONATHAN: Bradford, Mass. Clock by this maker with this place designation is reported by Mr. Charles Kellogg of Marblehead, Mass. Jonathan Frost, as a clockmaker, appears in most standard lists. But this locale is a new piece of information

FRY, JACOB: Woodstock (no state mentioned) (no date). Tall case clock in excellent scroll topped hood; time and strike, seconds dial, moon phase, and day of month slot; dial with sunburst spandrels. Date probably c.1800s

FRYE & SHAW: N.Y. City, 1830s

FULLER, ARTEMAS: Lowell, Mass., 1840s–1850s

FUNK, JACOB: Lebanon, Pa., 1850s

FYLER, ——————: Torrington (or Torringford) (Conn.?) c.1820s–1830s. Large size mantel clock with 8-day wooden movement reported, marked Fyler, Torring (obliterated in part) on dial

GAILLARD, PETER: French clockmaker of Reading, Pa., settling in this borough about 1790. In 1794 he advertised his services stating he had long practiced his trade in France

GARDNER, BARZILLAI: Charlotte, N.C., from 1807. It is believed he learned clockmaking at York, Pa.

GARLAND, JOHN R.: Greensboro, N.C., from 1840s

GARRETT, THOMAS C. & Co.: Philadelphia, Pa., from 1826. Prior to that date, GARRET, PHILIP, who started the business c.1800. Both establishments were probably as clock dealers and importers in spite of names on dials of surviving clocks

GEMMILL, JOHN: Carlisle, Pa., from 1760s. A bonafide clock maker, already listed as working at other points in Pennsylvania, now definitely established also as working at Carlisle during the frontier days when this town was an important military and trading post. An excellent tall cased example, 8-day, time and strike, brass movement, brass dial, is extant with name and Carlisle designated as place of making. This clock was once owned by the late Senator Martin

GEORGE, WILLIAM: Philadelphia, Pa., from 1720s. Apprenticed to John Cowper, 1716

GERE, ISSAC: Northampton, Mass. The Hampshire "Gazette" of Northampton, for August 25, 1863, contains notice of an old clock by Gere that was "seven feet tall, and played a special tune every fourth hour, including "On the road to Boston," "Paddy whack," and "Lady Coventry's Minuet." This clock was sold by Gere for $150. (in 1800s)

GIBBONS, WILLIAM: Philadelphia, n.d.

GIBBS, BENJAMIN: Newburyport, Mass., 1810s–1820s

GIFFT, PETER: Kutztown, Pa., c.1800s–1820s

GILLMAN, ——————: Hallowell (probably Maine) n.d.

GILMUR, GEORGE: Philadelphia, 1800s

GIRARD, A.: Mobile, Ala., 1840s–1850s. Invented a sun transit and altitude finder c.1849

GOEWEY, P. D. F.: Albany, N.Y., 1850–1880s

GLOBE CLOCK CO.: Milldale, Conn., 1880s. Makers of the globe clock patented 1883

GOODWIN, HORACE: Hartford, Conn., 1840s. Doubtful as maker, definite as assembler and casemaker. This man had a pianoforte factory, jewelry store and clock and watch establishment

GOLATIEL, S.: Lancaster, Pa., 1850s–1860s

GOLDSMITH & CO.: Salem, Mass., 1850–1860s. Firm composed of William H. Chase, Caleb Newcomb, Nathaniel Goldsmith and James Fairless

GORDON, GEORGE I.: New York City, 1850s

GORGAS, JACOB: Norriton, 1680s–1710s, and other points in Pennsylvania. He taught his son John Gorgas, who in turn taught his son Jacob, and David Rittenhouse the art of clockmaking

GORGAS, SOLOMON P.: Mechanicsburg, Cumberland County, Pa., 1830s–1840s. This descendant of Jacob Gorgas, in 1856, founded the Irving Female College at Mechanicsburg

GORGAS, WILLIAM: Greensburg, Pa., 1830s, a descendant of Jacob Gorgas of near Ephrata, Lancaster County, Pa. Tall case clocks and shelf clocks by William Gorgas are reported

GOTSHALK, HENRY: Newbritain (Pa.?) around 1750s–1760s. A walnut cased tall clock with brass dial having pewter spandrels, and seconds slot, is reported with this name and locale, without colony or state designation

GOTTIER, FRANCIS: Charleston, S. C., 1750s

GRAFF, JACOB: Northampton (?) Pa., c.1790s, or after 1811

GRAFFENBERG, THOMAS: n.d., n.p. Wooden movement tall case clock has this name inscribed on back, in black ink, together with "No. 6"

GRAY & BAIL: Boston, Mass., 1860s

GREENAWALT, WILLIAM: Halifax, N.C., from 1820s

GREISHABER, E.: Louisville, Ky., 1840s. Had a shop at the corner of 3rd and Market Streets

GRIFFEN, BRYEN: Philadelphia, 1800s. Clockmaking still in doubt but was active maker of fine instruments

GRISWOLD, A. B. & Co.: New Orleans, La., 1850s–1860

GROSCH, SAMUEL: Marietta, Lancaster County, Pa., around 1790s–1810s and perhaps later. This maker may prove to be the producer of some of the finest mantel clocks in the American scene

GROSCLAUDE, F.: Savannah, Georgia, 1850s

GROVE, CHRISTIAN: Hanover-Town, Pa., c.1800s. (Hanover-Town is now Hanover, York County, Pa.) Clocks signed by this maker with the place of marking at "Hanover-Town" are reported. He has been generally regarded as a clockmaker of Heidleberg Township, York County

GRUEBY, GEORGE A.: Boston, 1860s. Calendar clocks

HACKEAR, MICHAEL: New Germantown, Perry County, Pa., no date but between 1810 and 1840. The Hackear, Hocker, Hatcher and Hocher names appear to spring from the same source "HOCKER" who was an immigrant from Europe, to Pennsylvania, before 1750. A tall case clock signed Michael Hackear and with the place name of New Germantown is extant. Since it is a tall case clock the date is probably before 1830. New Germantown is approximately 40 miles west of Harrisburg, Pennsylvania.

HAGEY, JOHN: Germantown, Pa., (in addition to data in Drepperd) this man was working at Germantown, Pa., suburb of Philadelphia, in 1810s

HAGEY, M.: Germantown, Pa., c.1820s–1840s

HAKES, A. H.: Norwich, Conn., 1860s

HALE, WILLIAM C.: Salem, Mass., 1850s

HALL, JOHN: Geneva, N.Y., c.1800s–1810s. First clockmaker of record at this place. Tall case hollow pediment example known; brass 8-day movement time and strike

HALLE, A.: Louisville, Ky., 1840s

HALLER, JACOB: Aaronsburg, Pa., 1790s–1810s. Inlaid walnut case tall clock with broken arch top, painted dial, 8-day brass movement with moon phase and sweeps second hand reported

HAM, SUPPLY: Portsmouth, N.H., 1800s–1860. Originally listed as working 1790s to 1820s in first edition of American Clocks & Clockmakers. It has been discovered that Ham was born March 6, 1788 and died October, 1862. He was working as an apprentice at the turn of the century and had his own shop from the late 1800s. He is still listed as a watchmaker in a directory of 1860-61

HAMILTON, S. P.: Savannah, Georgia, 1850s

HAMLEN, NATHANIEL: Augusta, Me., 1790s–1820s

HANDEL, BERNARD: Carlisle, Pa., from c. 1800s

HANDEL, JACOB: Carlisle, Pa., 1760s–1790s

HARRIS & CO., A.: Philadelphia, c. 1820s–1840s. A wall clock with fusee movement in painted tin case with this maker's name reported but not examined. May be a French or Swiss importation with a dealer's name added

HARRISON, SUSANNAH: New York City, 1850s

HART, M.: Pittsburgh, Pa., 1810s–1820s. Member of firm of Morgan & Hart

HART & WILCOX: Listed in American Clocks & Clockmakers without date, this firm was in existence in the 1800s and advertised in the Norwich, Conn., "Courier" October 25, 1808. Firm dissolved c. 1812 as in 1813 Judah Hart advertised as an individual

HARWOOD, BROS.: 1867, Boston

HASIE, MARK: New York City, 1850s

HASS (OR HAAS) JAMES: Philadelphia, Pa., 1860s

HASSAM (HASHAM), STEPHEN: Charlestown, N.H., 1780s through first quarter of 19th century. Made case-on-case clocks, some with half-kidney doors

HASTINGS, DAVID B.: Boston, Mass., 1840s. Probably a dealer

HAUGHWOUT, E. V. & CO.: N.Y. City, 1850s. Advertised, claiming to be manufacturers of bronze clocks and other items. May have been importers only

HAWLEY, F.: Panora, Iowa, 1860s

HAYDEN, S.: Boston, Mass., 1790s–1800. Advertised as "watch, clockmaker and gilder from London." May have worked as early as 1786

HAYES & THOMAS: Philadelphia, Pa., 1860s

HEADMAN, WILLIAM: Philadelphia, 1830s–1840s. Shop at 44th & 7th. Clockmaker and agent for Tobias & Co. Watches

HEDDERLEY, CHARLES: Philadelphia, 1790s. Reported as a maker of clock parts, a brass founder, clocksmith, and machinist

HEINITSCH, CHARLES: Lancaster, Pa., from 1780s. Recent study of account books of this man reveals he sold parts and tools as well as complete clocks. He was considered a merchant and apothecary. Some of his sales of parts were to John Eberman, clockmaker

HELM, CHRISTIAN: Philadelphia, 1800s. Reported as a watch and clockmaker

HENDEL, BERNARD: Carlisle, Pa., probably 1780s to 1810s. Broken arch cased tall clock, brass 8-day movement, time and strike, with moon phase, case banded with birdseye maple is known

HENDEL, JACOB: Carlisle, Pa., around 1800s

HENDERSON & LOSSING: Poughkeepsie, N.Y., 1830s–1840s

HERON, ISAAC: Philadelphia, prior to 1764. See pp 235 American Clocks & Clockmakers. After 1764 he worked at Bound Brook, N.J.

HERTZ, JACOB: Pennsylvania, n.d., n.p. Probably c. 1810s. 8-day, brass movement tall case clock with painted dial reported with this name

HETZEL, JOHN M.: New Town (Newton), N.J., from 1795. He advertised himself as a clockmaker

HILE, J. W.: Kansas City, Topeka and other points in Kansas, from 1860s; inventor and builder of the Century Clock mentioned on pp 299, American Clocks & Clockmakers. This clock was exhibited at the Centennial Exposition, Philadelphia, 1876. An enormous weight, said to be 200 pounds, falling less than three quarters of an inch a year, powered the clock movement, a 36 or 44 size watch–type movement. The weight had a 76 inch drop and therefore powered the clock for a century. These were offered at the Centennial at $1000 each. The case was reinforced with angle iron on the inside. The cords and pulleys within the case converted the annual three quarter inch fall of the weight into a constant source of power for the balance wheel of the movement

HILL, PETER: Mount Holly, N.J., from 1821 in which year he

took over the shop of Gamaliel Bailey. See also pp 235 American Clocks & Clockmakers

HILLIARD, GEORGE W.: Fayetteville, N.C., from 1820s

HILLIARD, WILLIAM: Columbia, S.C., 1810s–1820s. Also silversmith

HILLIER, THOMAS A.: Pittsburgh, Pa., 1840s–1850. Most likely a dealer

HILLS, GEORGE: Plainsville, Conn., 1850s. Probably George Hills of the firm of Hills, Goodrich & Co., working at same town in 1840s–1850s

HIRSH, A., H. & L.: Lancaster, Pa., from late 1850s. Clockmaking doubtful. Probably jewelers and watchmakers

HOBART, AARON: Boston, around 1770. Brassfounder making parts for clocks

HOCKLEY, THOMAS: Philadelphia, n.d., but probably 1790s–1800s

HOELSCHE, KILLIAN: Mount Joy, Lancaster County, Pa., 1850s

HOFF, GEORGE, JR.: Lancaster, Pa., working c. 1790 to 1830s or 1840s. Made tall case clocks. Son of George Hoff, Lancaster, working 1766–1816

HOFFARD, SAMUEL: Berlin, South Carolina. This entry corrects that of the same maker listed on pp 236 of American Clocks & Clockmakers, wherein the place is given as Berlin, Pa.

HOFFMAN, C. W.: Greensburgh, Pa., 1850s–1870s

HOLLENBACH, DAVID: Reading, Pa., 1826 to 1840s. Worked for Daniel Eyster or Oyster, 1822–1826. Advertised after 1826

HOLLINSHEAD, JOB: Haddonfield, N.J., c. 1800 to 1820s

HOLMAN, SALEM: Hartford, Conn., 1830s–1840s. Wood movement, one-day mantel clocks in decorated column cases

HOOPS, ADAM: Somerset, Pa., n.d., but probably 1790s–1810s

HOPPER, S.: Philadelphia, Pa., c. 1840s–1850s

HORAH, JAMES: Salisbury, N.C., from late 1840s

HORST, DAVID: Sporting Hill, Lancaster County, Pa., 1850s–1860s

HOSTETTER, S.: Hanover, Pa., c. 1820s. Watch papers bearing his name as clock and watch maker have survived

HOTCHKISS, ANDREW S.: N.Y. City 1860s. Listed as a manufacturer at 18 Cortland St

HOUGH (ALSO HUFF AND HOFF), JOHN: Newport, Indiana and nearby points, from 1820s. In civil records name may read Huff or Hoff and even Hopf, but Hough is correct and as name appears on clock dials by this maker. Said to have worked at New Liberty, Indiana

HOWARD WATCH & CLOCK CO.: 1867, Boston

HOWCOTT, NATHANIEL: Edenton, N.C., from 1830s

HOWELL, SILAS: New Brunswick, N.J., 1810s–1830s

HOSMER, M.: Hartford, Conn., 18th century. Lockwood pictures are outstanding example Vol. II pp 336, 3rd edition of "Colonial Furniture in America." This example was owned by CW. Lyon, Inc. in 1950. Curly maple case of superb cabinetwork, brass oval, moon phase, seconds dial, calendar slot, tune and strike, 8 day

HUBBELL & BOARDMAN: New Haven, Conn., 1860s. Advertised "clock calendars," by which they meant calendar clocks

HUDSON, JOSEPH: Albany, N.Y., 1850s. Probably a dealer

HUGHES, CHRISTOPHER: Baltimore, Md., 1859–1873

HUGHS, JOHN: Taneytown, Maryland, from 1810s. He made tower clocks, one of record for York (Penna.) County Court House and one for Lutheran church, Emmitsburg, Md. Said to have worked to 1840s

HUGUS, JACOB: Greensburg, Pa., 1800s–1820s

HUMPHREYS, DAVID: Lexington, Ky., 1780s–1790s. Advertised 1789 as a clock and watchmaker. Engraved first state seal of Kentucky

HUNT, JOHN: Farmington, Conn., 1830s–1840s. Listed in American Clocks & Clockmakers, first edition, as working at Plainville, Farmington, Conn. In 1949 report was received about an 8-day brass movement shelf clock with carved case and top, with a clock paper of John Hunt, Farmington, Conn.

HUNTINGTON, COLLIS P.: Clock peddlar for Conn. makers to 1841 when he set up a general store and added clocks at Oneonta, N.Y. In 1849 traveled to West and set up a store in Sacramento, Calif. Then became interested in Southern Pacific and other railroad building and amassed a colossal fortune and became one of America's greatest book and objets d'art collectors

HURDUS, ADAM: Cincinnati, Ohio, 1820s. Collaborator with Luman Watson in organ building. Was a clockmaker but no clock with his name, made in Cincinnati, has yet been located. A clock made by him in England (Lancashire) is in America and was exhibited at Chicago Art Institute from 1944

HUTCHINSON, SAMUEL: Philadelphia, Pa., from c. 1830s. Shop and store 231-½ Market Street

HUTCHSON, WILLIAM: Philadelphia, n.d., but probably first quarter of 19th century

HYVER, G. A.: New Orleans, La., 1850s to 1860

IMHAUSER TIME CLOCK CO.: New York, 1870s

IMHOFF, JACOB: N.Y. City, 1840s

INGRAHAM, ELIAS & CO.: Bristol, Conn., 1857–1861. This listing is at variance with certain information given under INGRAHAM, ELIAS, in the first edition of American Clocks & Clockmakers, where the Ingraham factory is listed as at Ansonia from 1856 to 1859. A clock by Elias Ingraham & Co., with paper bearing the Bristol, Conn., address is reported

INSKEEP, JOSEPH: Philadelphia, n.d., but c. 1790s–1800s. Tall clocks reported

IVES, BLAKESLEE & CO.: Bridgeport, Conn., 1870s–1880s. Made mechanical motion novelty clocks

JACKSON, RICHARD: East Springfield, Jefferson County, Ohio, (or Gillis Town) from c. 1803

JACKSON, THOMAS: Kittery, Maine, 1766. This additional information in respect of a maker already listed in American Clocks & Clockmakers comes from Vice-Admiral C. H. Cobb. The bill of sale for a clock by Jackson made at Kittery is preserved. It is dated 1766

JAMES (JOSHUA) & JOHNSON (ELI): Boston, 1818–1820s

JAMES (JOSHUA) & WILLIAMS (DEODAT): Boston, 1810s. From directories it appears James worked from 1810 to 1816 when this partnership began, lasting to 1818. After that Eli Johnson was his partner for a few years. See (James & Johnson)

JAMESON, JOHN: Springfield, Ohio, 1820s or earlier. Tall clock with 8-day brass movement, time and strike, moon phase and day of month indicator is owned by J. B. McGrew, a descendant of Colonel Werden, for whom the clock was made by John Jameson

JARRETT, SEBASTIAN: Germantown, Pa., c. 1760–1780s

JARVES, JOHN JACKSON: Boston, from 1787. "Cabinet, chair and clockmaker from London"

JENKINS, OSMORE: New Bedford, Mass., 1840s. Jenkins kept shop with William Pitman, jeweler

JEROME, CHAUNCEY: Austin, Ill., (clock with label of Jerome at this place, printed by Chicago Evening Journal printery, pasted in rosewood front case having decalcomania tablet. Movement in squat lyre shaped frame, springs at rear of arbor and slots cut in dial to provide space for expansion of spring)

JEROME & CO.: Label with this designation, printed by Renham & Co., New Haven, 1860s, is in a clock purchased in 1867

JEROME, S. B. & CO.: New Haven, Conn., from 1856. This firm advertised extensively as producers of extra quality clocks in tasteful styles, detached lever timepieces. They made traveling clocks and many small size clocks of 6 x 4½" front dimension or less. Firm was still advertising in 1877 and 1878

JEWETT, AMOS: Canaan, N.Y., 1790s and New Lebanon Community to 1830s. Made and numbered tall case clocks

JOHNSON, ANDREW: Boston, 1840s

JOHNSON, J. J.: New York City, 1850s

JOHNSON, WILLIAM S.: New York City. In 1845 advertised as manufacturer at 16 Courtland St. "engaged for years in the business" and now (1845) making 150 per day by steam power

JOHNSTON & PRICE: Hagerstown, Md., late 1790s. This firm was Arthur Johnston and Joseph Price of Baltimore

JOHNSTON, ROBERT: Cincinnati, Ohio; c. 1850s had a small factory at rear of 168 Vine Street in the Queen City of the West

JOHNSTON & SIMPSON: Hagerstown, Md., 1802–1804. Arthur Johnston and Alexander Simpson. Johnston was a keen man on "partnerships"

JOHNSTON, WILLIAM: Hagerstown, Md., 1820–1830s

JONAS, JOSEPH: Cincinnati, 1810s–1820s

JONES, HENRY B.: Easton, Maryland, 1820s. Advertised in Republican Star 1821 and 1822 clock and watchmaker

JONES, NOEL: Hudson, N.Y., or certainly in the vicinity of Troy, N.Y. Dr. Amos G. Avery reports an 8-day brass movement, tall case clock by this maker, indicating a date of making not earlier than 1790s and not later than 1830s

JONES & OLNEY: Newark, Tioga County, N.Y., around 1830s

JOSEPH, J. G.: Cincinnati, Ohio, 1820s–1840s

JUDD, HENRY G.: New York City, 1840s. Listed in directory of 1846–1847 as "clockmaker, 382 Greenwich Street"

JUSTICE, JOSEPH: Philadelphia, 1840s

JUVET, L. P.: Glenns Falls, N.Y., made Solar globe clocks

KABEL, JOSEPH: New York City, 1850s

KEIM, JOHN: Reading, Penna., from 1770s. Brass dialed tall clock of record with this name & place designation. Date is approximate; may be earlier or later

KELLEY, ALLEN: New Bedford, 1840s

KELLEY, EZRA AND SON: New Bedford, 1840s–1850s

KELLEY, ZENO: New Bedford, Mass., 1840s and 1850s. Advertised as clockmaker

KENT, LUKE: Cincinnati, 1810s–1840s

KENT, THOMAS: Cincinnati, 1820s–1840s

KERNER, LOUIS: Muskingum County, Ohio, c. 1850–1870. Made mirror clocks with mahogany cases and glass pendulum bobs

KILLAM, GEORGE: Pawtucket, R.I. Late maker, operating c. 1899 to 1910. Made banjo movements cased and sold by Tilden-Thurber of Providence, R.I.

KIMBALL, N.: Boston, c. 1810s–1820s. Reported as making banjo clocks

KIRKE & TODD: Wolcott, Conn., 1840s. Unique brass movement clocks with cast iron plates and musical attachments. A clock by this firm is in the Edward Ingraham Collection

KISSAMEE, EDUART: Entered USA through port of Saint Augustine, Florida, 1830s or early 1840s, from France. "Clock & Watchmaker." It is not known if place of same name, in Florida has any relation to this maker. Data from A. B. Controlle, Esq.

KISSAM & KEELER: New York City, 1840s. Claimed to manufacture clocks, furniture knobs and castors

KLINGMAN, JACOB: Reading, Pa., 1790 to late 1800s; York, Pa., 1810s–1820. This definitely answers query in first edition of American Clocks & Clockmakers as to whether name is "Kling" or "Klingman." It is Klingman

KLOCKENKEMPER & WINTHER: Clock & watch makers of San Antonio, Texas, from 1850s. Actual making by this firm is questionable

KNOWER, DANIEL: Roxbury, Mass., c. 1800s–1810s

KRAMER, M. & Co.: Boston, Massachusetts, from 1840s. This firm were NOT clockmakers. They were importers of French and German toys and clocks

KRAUSE (KROUSE), JOHN SAMUEL: Bethlehem, Pa., from 1780s. Died 1815. Business continued by former apprentice, Jedediah Weiss

KULP, JACOB: Franconia Square, Montgomery County, Pa., 1840s–1850s

KUNER, MAXIMILIAN: Vicksburg, Mississippi, 1850s–1860s

LACOUR, HENRI: Mobile, Ala., 1860s

LAMB, ANTHONY: New York City, c. 1740–1750s. Maker of clocks and mathematical instruments

LANE, AARON: Elizabeth, N.J. (as listed in American Clocks & Clockmakers, pp 248) also worked at Bound Brook, N. J., c. 1778–1780s

LANE, AARON, JR.: Elizabeth, N.J., late 1830s

LANE, H.: Bristol (no state designation) and no date. A tall case clock with painted dial is reported, by a volunteer who states "late type case"

LARGEN, ROBERT: Philadelphia, Pa., 1860s

LAWING, SAMUEL: Charlotte, N.C., from 1840s

LAWRENCE, WILLIAM: Sing-Sing landing, Mt. Pleasant, N.Y., mid-19th century. Data from a watchpaper that mentions man as a clockmaker

LEGOUX, A.: New York City, 1840s–1850s. Importer of French clocks of second baroque influence. Clocks with his name on dial reported

LEINBACH, ELIAS: Bowmansville, Lancaster County, Pa., from 1810s to 1850s. Listed as a clock and brushmaker. He was active in the anti-"free school" movement in 1850. A tall case clock reported

LESCHEY, THOMAS: Middletown, Pa., c. 1800s

LESLIE, ROBERT: Philadelphia, from 1745. Father of Major Leslie, Miss E. Leslie, an authoress, and C. R. Leslie, artist. Granted a patent in 1789 for an improvement in the mechanism of clocks and watches. Characterized as an ingenious workman. These data are in extension of the entry in Drepperd: "Leslie, Robert, (Sr.)" which is left as a query in his original entry

LESQUEREUX, L. & SON: Columbus, Ohio, 1840s–1850s

LEUPP, HARVEY (OR HERVEY): New Brunswick, N.J., 1800s–1810s

LEUPP (OR LOOP), PETER: New Brunswick, N.J., 1810s–1820s

LEWIS, GEORGE: Canonsburgh, Pa., 1830s. This man is known to local historians as a cabinetmaker, yet wood movement hang-up clocks in tall cherry cases with his name on dial are reported

LEWIS, ISAAC: Newark, N.J., from 1782

LEWIS, TUNIS: New York City, n.d., probably first half of 19th century

LILIENTHAL, EDWARD: New Orleans, La., 1860s

LILIENTHAL, J.: New Orleans, La., 1850s–1860. Shop at 28 Camp Street

LINDSAY, W. K. & CO.: Pittsburgh, Pa., 1830s. This is the same Lindsay listed as working as an individual, 1820s–1830s, in American Clocks & Clockmakers

LINDSLY, TIMOTHY: Reading, Pa., from 1815. Died 1825. Advertised in 1821

LINEBAUGH, H. W.: Keokuk, Iowa, 1860s–1870s

LITTLE, ARCHIBALD: Reading, Pa., 1810s–1820s

LOCKE, DR. JOHN: Cincinnati, Ohio, 1840s. Inventor of the magnetic registering clock, 1848. This clock had a make-and-break device which the Doctor called a rheoton. It was in the form of a glass tube with platinum contacts and mercury conductor. In 1849 the Congress appropriated $10,000 to be paid to Professor Locke for the erection of a magnetic clock in the National Observatory

LOCKWOOD, ALFRED (Later LOCKWOOD & SCRIBNER): New York City 1830s. Mantel or shelf clocks

LOOMIS, WILLIAM: Wethersfield, Conn., 1820s–1830s. Made Terry type wooden movements with short pendulum. His paper reads "Premium Clocks made by Wm. B. Loomis, Wethersfield, Connecticut"

LORING, JOSEPH: Sterling, Mass., from c. 1790. Account books are preserved. These reveal Loring made parts and units for Benjamin Willard. Loring is believed to have opened his shop at Sterling about 1789. Account books covering period 1791–1812 are owned by American Antiquarian Society, Worcester, Mass. Loring's production was chiefly tall case clocks. He died in 1846

LOVELL, GEORGE: Philadelphia, Pa., 1860s

LOVETT, JAMES: Mendon, Mass. b. 1728, d. 1814. Tall case clock by this maker with name and place on dial reported by owner, resident of Worcester, Mass., 1948

LUDEN, JACOB: Reading, Pa., 1850s–1860s

LUPP (OR LEUPP): John, at New Brunswick, N.J., 1777 to 1805 when his son, also named John, succeeded him; Lawrence, same town, working from 1806 to 1825; Peter, same town, also spelled name "LUPE" working from 1760s to c. 1800; Samuel V., same town, son of Henry, working from c. 1810 (not yet established that he made clocks); William, same town, working from c. 1790s to early 1840s, but no clocks made before 1805. Most likely a custom maker only as his trade was silversmithing. Similarly, Henry (see pp 249, American Clocks & Clockmakers) made only a few clocks as he was primarily a silversmith and hairworker. The Lupe, Leupp, Lupp family of New Brunswick were active enough to warrant a monograph on them

LUSK, WILLIAM: Columbus, Ohio, 1840s

LYON, GEORGE: Wilmington, N.C., from 1810s to 1840s

MCBRIDE & GARDNER: Charlotte, N.C., from 1807

MCCABE, WILLIAM: Richmond, Va., 1790s–1820s

MCCARTHY, THOMAS: Servant to David Rittenhouse who, after learning clockmaking from the master became a journeyman joiner and cabinet maker after 1806

MCDOWELL, F.: Philadelphia, c. 1790s–1800s. His shop was "two doors above the Draw Bridge"

M'FADDEN, JOHN B. & CO.: Pittsburgh, 1840s–1850s. J. B. McFadden, as an individual, is reported working 1830s and listed in directory of city

MCGREGOR, J.: San Francisco, Cal., 1850s–1860s. Also made chronometers

MCGREW, ALEXANDER: Cincinnati, 1810s

MCGREW, WILSON: Cincinnati, 1820s

MCKEE, JOHN: Chester, S.C., n.d., but probably last half 18th century. Sometimes listed or mentioned as John M. Kee.

Tall clock by this maker owned by Cecil Reid of Fredericksburg, Va.

McKINNEY, ROBERT: Wilmington, Del., advertised new and second hand clocks, 1845

MAGNIN, JOHN: New York, N.Y., 1840s. Imported and assembled clocks made by his own factory at Geneva, Switzerland. Clocks & Watches

MALLORY, GEORGE: New York City, 1840s. Shop at 333 Pearl Street. Probably a dealer

MALLS, PHILIP: Washington (no state or other designation; may be D. C.), working around 1800. Tall clock numbered 220 by this maker reported by the owner

MANN, WILLIAM: Baltimore, Md., 1860s

MARQUAND, ISAAC: Edenton, N.C., from 1790s. Removed to N.Y. City 1800s. Eventually became Marquand & Co., then Ball & Black, then Black-Starr & Frost, finally merged with Gorham Co. as Black, Starr, Frost & Gorham

MARTIN, JOHN: New York City, 1840s. Shop at 288 Spring Street

MARSH, GEORGE: Winchester, Conn., 1830s or 1840s. Mirror clock of tabernacle type lined with wall paper is known

MASON, H. G.: Boston, 1840s. This is a reversal of the initials of Mason, G. H. in Drepperd. H. G. is correct sequence

MASON, P.: Somerville, N.J., n.d., but probably first half of 19th century

MARTIN, ALBERT: Philadelphia, Pa., 1860s

MATLACK, WILLIAM: Philadelphia, c. 1780–1790. Watchpaper of this man designates him as clock and watchmaker at 33 N. 3rd. Date, therefore, may be to 1800s

MATTHEWSON, J.: Providence, R.I., 1840s. Clock manufacturer

MATHEWSON & HARRIS: New Hartford Center, Conn., 1830s or 1840s. Made modified pillar & scroll mantel clocks

MATHIAS, J.: Gettysburg, Pa., 1830s or earlier to 1840s

MEAD & ADDY: Boston, Mass., from 1850s. Tower clocks, balances and clock models. At one time had shops at No. 4 Chickering Place

MEARS, WILLIAM: Reading, Pa., 1770s–1780s. Tax lists of 1785 mention man as working at trade of clockmaker

MECKLE, JOHN: Philadelphia, 1840s

MEEK, J. F. & SON: Louisville, Ky., 1860s

MELVILLE, HENRY: Wilmington, N.C., 1798

MEYER, ALBERT: Cincinnati, Ohio, 1850s

MEYLI, SAMUEL: N.d., n.p. Tall case clocks with pewter dial reported. The name Meyli, Meylin, Mylin, Miley, and other variants, is Swiss. Immigrants by this name entered the Conestogo country (Lancaster County, Penna) very early in 18th century, from 1710s. They were all fine mechanics but heretofore have been associated only with making rifled barrels for guns. Clock reported may be a Swiss made example brought in by family and made by a member of the family or, it may be of colonial construction

MILES, E. JR.: Sag Harbor, L.I., N.Y., 1860s

MILLER, CORNELIUS: Very early clockmaker working in New Jersey in 1700s. One tall clock known, reported by Paul Bigelow, Esq.

MILLER, PHILIP: New York City, 1760s

MILLS, ALEXANDER: Brooklyn, N.Y., 1850s. Shop at 41 Atlantic Ave.

MILLS, J. R. & CO.: N.Y. City, 1840s. Manufacturers of Crane's Patent 12 month clock. Advertised in 1845

MITCHELL, PROFESSOR: Cincinnati, Ohio, 1850s. Maker of astronomical electric clocks

MOCKFORD, RICHARD: Medina, N.Y., 1860s

MOORE, NELSON A.: Newark, N.J., 1850s

MORELY, WILLIAM: Bond servant and apprentice to Isaac Pearson of Burlington, N.J., from 1726

MORGAN, GIDEON: Pittsburgh, Pa., 1810s–1830s. was member of firm of Morgan & Hart. Shop on Wood Street between 4th and Diamond. Traditionally one of Pittsburgh's early clockmakers. He is listed in directory of 1819 and 1826 but not in 1837. Tall case clock in inlaid case, 8-day brass movement with time, date and sweep seconds hand, moon phase, swan neck scroll top, cherry carcass, inlaid with curly maple, reported by owner, R. E. Wise, M.D., of Hanover, Pa., in 1949

MORGAN & HART: Pittsburgh, Pa., 1810–1820s. (See Morgan, Gideon)

MORGAN, WALKER & SMITH: New York City, 1830s–1840s. Our research on this firm reveals they were dealers in "clock glasses" and not in clocks

MORRILL, H. C.: Baltimore (label by Hanzsch stamping). Est. 212 Baltimore St., 1830s–1840s

MORRILL, H. O.: Baltimore, 1840s–1850s. The Maryland Institute Exhibition of 1850 included a display of a brass, 8-day repeating and alarm clock by this maker which could be set to sound an alarm at any desired moment and light a lamp

MORRIS, ABEL: Reading, Pa., 1770s. Tax lists of 1774 name him a clockmaker

MORRIS, JOHN: Grafton, Mass., 1760s–1770s. This name in full appears with the name "Simon Willard" on the pendulum of a tall case clock, the pendulum being dated 1770. This would seem to settle the hitherto unanswered query regarding the first name of the Mr. Morris who was Simon Willard's master and teacher. Clock with this pendulum is owned by American Antiquarian, Worcester, Mass.

MORRIS, WILLIAM: This maker worked at following points, at dates given. Carl Williams, Esq., supplies the information. Bridgetown, N.J., to 1816; Bridgeton, N.J., 1816 to 1831; Camden, N.J., from 1831. Died at Philadelphia, 1862. Born in Wales, 1770

MOSS, ______: Rochdale, no state designation. Badly rubbed watch paper with this name and date 1818 owned by American Antiquarian

MOTTS, ______: Manufactory of clocks, chronometers, and watches under this name is listed as operating in New York City in the 1780s

MOUNTJOY, JOHN: N.Y. City, 1810s. Shop at 265 William Street

MOUNTJOY, WILLIAM: New York City, 1850s

MOUTOUX, CARL: Brooklyn, N.Y., 1850s

MUELLER, FREDERICK: Savannah, Georgia, at the Ebenezer Colony, 1736 to 1745. Rudolph Hommel, Esq., (in Hobbies Magazine, July, 1949) cites several pertinent entries in the Saltzberger diaries in respect of this clockmaker who was also a pewterer and cabinetmaker. Said to have made wooden movements and striking clocks of fine quality. An accomplished German craftsman

MULFORD, E.: Princeton, N.J., 1830s

MUNROE, DANIEL & NATHANIEL: Listed in Drepperd as reputed makers, they are now known to have made clocks and marked them with their name

MUNROE, JAMES: New Bedford, Mass., 1840s–1850s. Chronometers

MURPHY, THOMAS: Allentown, Pa., 1830s
MURRAY, ROBERT: Trenton, N.J., 1800s
MYER, GEORGE: New York City, 1840s
MYLE, SAMUEL: Lebanon, Pa., around 1800s

NATION, SYLVAN: New Lisbon, Ind., 1860s
NEGUS, T. S.: N.Y. City, 1860s. Chronometers
NEISER (NEYSER) AUGUSTINE: Moravian clockmaker who first worked in colony of Georgia, from 1736 and removed to Germantown, Pa., 1739. This is extension of entry of same man in Drepperd
NEISER, AUGUSTUS: Bethlehem, Pa., 1780s. May be same man as previously listed as working at Philadelphia, or son of Philadelphia maker
NEMERT, GOTTLIEB CHRISTIAN: Reading, Pa., 1830s–1840s. Mentioned as a clock and watchmaker, jeweler, silversmith and fire gilder in "A Description of the Borough of Reading, Pa., 1841"
NETTLETON, WILFORD H.: Briston, Conn., 1860s
NEWHALL, WILLIAM: Boston, 1850s
NEWHART, ______: Lebanon, Pa., 1840s
NEWLIN, EDWARD G.: Philadelphia, 1848
NEWTON, WILLIAM: New York City, 1840s. This man was not a clockmaker but a clock case maker at 7 Chrystie Street. Any clocks marked by him are in his own cases but movements are by other makers
NEW YORK CLOCK DEPOT: By this name did G. V. House, clock manufacturer of New York City designate his retail store from 1840s
NEW YORK WATCH COMPANY: N.Y. City, 1860s. Reported as making small clock movements. Another firm, American Watch Company was in operation at same time in N.Y. City. This firm also is reported as making 20 size watches for use in small clocks. Neither report verified by an actual clock
NICAISE, GABRIEL: Nauvoo, Illinois, 1848 to 1893. French clockmaker who was member of Icarian sect led by Etienne Cabet. Their socialistic community lasted but 10 years. Nicaise remained at Nauvoo where, in 1850s he made hand wrought iron "bird cage" clocks that are readily mistaken for 17th century examples

NICOLAI, GEORGE: Belleville, Illinois, 1850s–1860s

NICHOLET, JULIAN: Baltimore, Md.; 1820s; Pittsburgh, Pa., 1830s

NOLEN & CURTIS: Painted dials with the name of this firm applied to backs, giving two addresses, 3rd Street, Philadelphia, and 8 Washington Street, Boston, are reported. Dials are for tall case clocks and are of c. 1820–1830. No other clockmakers' insignia appear on the faces or the backs of the dials reported

NORRIS, WILLIAM: n.d., n.p. Tall clock. Around 1810–1820

NOXON, MARTIN: Edenton, N.C.; from early 1800s. Died 1814

OAKLAND CLOCK WORKS: Sag Harbor, L.I., N.Y., 1860s–1870s

OLIVER, D.: Plainfield, New Jersey, n.d., but probably first quarter or first half of 19th century

OLIVER, JOHN: New York City, 1850s. Had shop at 96 John St. and house at 34 Chapel St., Brooklyn

OLIVER, JOHN S.: Reading, Pa., 1830s–1840s

OLMSTEAD, DIGEON: Charlotte, N.C., 1830s

O'NEIL, H.: Philadelphia, Pa., 1860s

OSBORNE: OSBORNE & WILSON: English makers of dials, dial plates, and moon phase parts, many of which bear their marks cast in the plates, imported in considerable quantities by American clockmakers between 1770 and 1825

OTIS, F. S.: Brooklyn, N.Y., 1850s

OWEN, CHARLES F. & CO.: New York City, 1850s

PACE, C.: San Francisco, Cal., 1850s–1860s

PACKARD, ISAAC: North Bridgewater, Massachusetts. This man was working in 1830s and clock papers in clocks of record indicate this period. While listed in American Clocks & Clockmakers as working with Rodney Brace at North Bridgewater, there is now evidence he worked alone from 1820s. Charles Stockman Tarr, Esq., of Wollaston, Mass, reports a wood movement mantel clock with paper marked "Made by Isaac Packard, North West Bridgewater, Mass." This paper bears census figures of 1830 and was purchased in 1832

PARKS, G. D.: Cincinnati, Ohio, 1850s. Probably an agent for Connecticut Clocks

PEABODY, ASA: Wilmington, N.C., from 1820s

PEABODY, JOHN: Fayetteville, N.C., from 1820s

PEALE, CHARLES WILLSON: Annapolis, Md., 1760s. Best known as an artist, Peale's first picture, painted as an amateur, was a self-portrait posed with one of the clocks he made. A biographical notice of Peale in the "Cabinet of Natural History," Philadelphia, 1830, reveals that he was a saddler, then a clockmaker, then a silversmith, and finally an artist

PECK, S. & CO.: New Haven, Conn., 1860s

PENNEPACKER, WILLIAM: Frederick, Pa., 1860s

PERRY, THOMAS: Westerly, R.I., b. 1814–d. 1898. This man, quite definitely was a watch and clockmaker. At one time he employed Leonard Whitney, an expert silversmith and clockmaker

PHILADELPHIA WATCH CO.: Philadelphia, Pa., from 1860s. E. Paulus, President; C. Jacot, Secretary. Made a 20 size watch movement used in some clocks of small size

PIATT, W.: Columbus, Ohio, 1840s. Probably misspelling of PLATT, WILLIAM A., which is in this list

PICKERING, GEORGE: Cincinnati, Ohio, 1850s. Listed as a clock manufacturer in the 1867 directory of his city

PIGGOT, SAMUEL: N.Y. City, 1830s. Clock and silverware manufacturer

PIKE, WILLIAM: n.p., (Pennsylvania) c. 1780–1800s

PITT, W.: New York City, 1850s

PLATT, BENJAMIN: Danbury, Conn., to 1776. Lanesboro, Mass., to around 1779. New Fairfield, Conn., around 1779–1817. Columbus, Ohio, after 1817

PLATT, CALVIN: Columbus, Ohio, 1840s–1870. Probably a clockmaker

PLATT & BROTHERS: New York, N.Y., from 1828. There is evidence to warrant assumption this firm, or its individual members, were clockmakers

PLATT, WILLIAM AUGUSTUS (SR.): Columbus, Ohio, 1830s–1850s or 1860s. Grandson of Benjamin Platt. Was watch and instrument maker. Probably made clocks

PLATT, WILLIAM A., JR.: Columbus, Ohio, 1840s–1870s. Probably a clockmaker

PLUNKETT, R.: Boston, Mass., 1850s–1860s

POOL, DAVID L.: Salisbury, N.C., from 1830s–1850s

POPE, M.: Boston, Mass., 1780s, 1790s. Built a planetarium

POSEY, F. J.: Hagerstown, Md., 1830s

POTTS, THOMAS: Norristown, (Norriton) Penna., from 1760s. (said to have been associated with D. Rittenhouse. Brass dialed tall clock with this name & place designation on boss of dial, and lentil in door is of record)

PRATT, AZARIAH: Marietta, Ohio, 1790s–1800s

PRATT, BETTS & CO.: Alliance, Ohio, 1860s

PRATT, DANIEL & SONS: Reading, Mass., 1860s–1870s. Manufacturers

PRENTISS CLOCK IMPROVEMENT CO.: New York, c. 1870s. Complicated calendar clocks with jump (½ minute) minute hand, single wind toy. Both time and calendar springs. 60 day, iron back plates, brass front plate and movement. No strike

PRICHARD, BUEL: Dayton, Ohio, 1820s. In 1830 he entered into partnership under the name of Prichard & Spining

PRICHARD & MONSON: This name, instead of Prichard & Munson, appears on certain clocks reported to J. L. Ruth, editor of "Timepieces" Quarterly. Papers also designate brass bushings on wooden wheels. Bristol, Conn.

PRICHARD & SPINING: Dayton, Ohio, 1830s–1840s. A clock dated 1830–31 by this firm is reported. It is believed they were established as merchants and dealers rather than clockmakers. It is believed also that the firm was connected in some way with Prichard & Munson of Bristol, Conn. Mostly wooden movement shelf clocks with Pritchard & Spining papers, printed by a Dayton, Ohio, printer

PRIOLLAUD, D.: New Orleans, La., 1850s–1860

PRITCHARD & SPINING: Dayton, Ohio, 1830s–1840s. Wooden movement mantel clocks bearing their clock paper, printed by J. Wilson, Dayton, are known

PROCTOR, G. K.: Beverly, Mass., 1850s–1860s. Inventor of burglar and fire-alarm clock, 1860. This invention was made by Seth Thomas as a regular item of production to c. 1880

PUTNAM, JONATHAN: New York City, 1840s

PYLE, BENJAMIN: Washington, N.C., from 1790s–1810. A son, Benjamin Jr. worked at Fayetteville, N.C., 1830s and 1840s

RAWSON, S. E. F.: Saratoga Springs, N.Y., around 1867–1870. Made solar and globe clocks

RAY, DANIEL: Sudbury, Mass., c. 1790. Authenticity not yet established. Clocks by this maker, marked Sudbury, may be Sudbury, Mass., or Sudbury, England

RAYMOND, FREEMAN C.: Belfast, Maine and Boston, Massachusetts, 1820s to 1870s. Watch & Clockmaker. Worked at Belfast 1825 to 1840; Boston from 1840. Died 1879. Clocks by him are reported from several places, in hands of collectors or institutions

READ, THOMAS: New York, N.Y., from 1840s. This clockmaker invented the sundial on which time was indicated in minutes. An excellent mathematician and craftsman

REED, BENJAMIN: Delete this name from list of makers appearing on pp 185, Volume I, Number 3, of "Timepieces." He did not work at Bristol, Conn. The clock sold at the Reifsnyder sale was not American but English and Benjamin Reed is definitely identified as a maker working in Bristol, England, 1775–1797

REED, ISAAC: Frankford, Pa., 1800s–1810s and later. This is not a new name but an extension of an already listed name in respect of the dates of working

REED, JAMES R. & CO.: Pittsburgh, Pa., 1840s–1850s. Probably dealer only but makers of mathematical instruments

REEVE, BENJAMIN: Philadelphia, Pa., 1750s to late 1760s. Thereafter at Greenwich, N.J. These data in extension of entry on pp 267 of American Clocks & Clockmakers

REEVE, JOSEPH: Brooklyn, N.Y., 1840s–1850s

REEVE, THOMAS: New York City, 1840s–1850s

REEVE & CO.: New York City, 1850s

REEVES, ELIJAH: Bellefonte, Penna., from 1810s or 1820s, to 1830s

REGALLY, M.: Boston, Mass., 1840s. Listed at 4 School Street; advertised as a clockmaker in 1846

RENTZENHEIMER, HENRICH: Allentown, Pa., prior to 1812. Broken arch pine cased tall clock by this maker is known. Name of Allentown was used only from 1800 to 1811, prior to that and after, to 1838, the place name was Northampton. Changed again to Allentown in 1838

RICHARDS & CO., GILBERT: Chester, Conn., 1830. "Manufacturers of patent clocks"

RIDDELL, CRAWFORD: Philadelphia, Pa., 1840s

RIOU & BOELL: N.Y. City, 1830s. Importers of French clocks

RITTENHOUSE, BENJAMIN: "Worcester" on dial of clock owned (1925) by W. E. Montague, Norristown

RITTERBAND, HENRY: N.Y. City, 1830s

Robbins, W. H.: Vandalia, Illinois, from 1830s. Advertised in "Illinois Register & Advocate" as Clock & Watchmaker, December 28, 1838

Roberts, O.: Eaton, Ohio, 1825 and later. Probably Oliver Roberts, one-time journeyman with Henry Lewis Montanden of Lancaster, Pa., who became a partner with Hannah Montanden, widow of Henry Lewis, from 1802 to 1808, when he left the firm of Montanden & Roberts, Lancaster, Pa., and migrated westward

Roberts, Thomas: Easton, Pa., 1812–1840

Robinson, W. F.: Wilmington, Del., 1840s. Probably dealer only

Rodman, John: Burlington, N. J., 1760s–1770s

Rogers, Caleb: Newton, Mass., b.1765, d.1839. Caleb Rogers' shop at Newton, 1785–1835, was marked by a sign in the form of a dial. He issued a delightful engraved watch-paper

Roome, James H.: New York City, 1850s

Rowlands, Henry: Albany, N.Y. Established 1832

Royce, J. C. & Son: Plainville, Conn., 1860s. Dial manufacturers

Rugheimer, Moses: New York City, 1850s

Sargent, Ebenezer: Newbury, Massachusetts, c.1750–1770s. Brass dialed tall clocks

Sayre, Elias: Elizabeth-Town, N.J., n.d. Tall clocks. This maker used dials made by Osborne, England

Schaffer, T. C.: Portsmouth, N.H., 1840s. He invented a clockwork driven cooling fan which operated 2 to 3 hours at one winding

Scharf, J.: Selinsgrove, Pa., (Snyder County) 1810s–1830s. Made pillar & scroll cased 30 hour brass movement mantel clocks

Scharf, John: Ephrata, Lancaster County, Pa., from 1810s; Selinsgrove, Pa., from c.1830. Made fine 8-day brass movement, time & strike mantel clocks in pillar & scroll cases

Scheidt, ——————: Sumneytown, Pa., 1780s–1800s. Probably Daniel Sheidt

Schey, F.: Lewes, Delaware, 1850s

Schoemaker, Peter: New York City, 1810s

SCHULTZ, JACOB: Lancaster, Pa., 1850s–1860s

SCMOLTZ, WILLIAM: San Francisco, Calif., 1850s–1860s

SCOTT, ANNE: Harrisburg, Pa., 1850s–1860s

SCOTT, SAMUEL: Concord, N.C., from 1825

SCRAFTON, WILSON: Wilmington, Del., 1850s–1860s

SCUDDER, JOHN: Westfield, N.J., c.1760s–1790s. It is believed this man was a cabinetmaker who purchased movements and thus made complete clocks by fashioning the cases. A clock marked with the name of John Scudder bearing a label reading "Made and sold by John Scudder, Cabinetmaker, Westfield" has a movement marked "Wilson" on its front plate

SEAMAN, THOMAS: Edenton, N.C., from 1790s

SEARS, JOHN: Chillicothe, Ohio, 1810s

SELLS & SCHOFIELD: Augusta, Ky., 1860s

SERVOSS, BENJAMIN: Philadelphia, Pa., 1830s–1850s

SEYMOUR, SYLVESTER: Pittsburgh, Pa., 1840s–1850s

SEWARD, JOSHUA: Boston, 1830s. Shop at 63 Congress St.

SHAW, CALEB: Kingston, N.H., 1740s–1770s

SHAW, GEORGE: N.Y. City at 18 Maiden Lane, 1840s–1850s

SHAY, MICHAEL: Lancaster, Pa., 1850s–1860s

SHEAM, FRANCIS: New York City, 1810s

SHEIDT, DANIEL: Sumneytown, Pa., c.1790–1820

SHENK, HENRY: Lancaster, Pa., from 1850s

SHERRY & BYRAM: Sag Harbor, Long Island, N.Y., 1840s–1850s. Operated the Oakland Works, producing clocks for churches, courthouses, and public buildings; timepieces for session and vestry rooms, banks, hotels and railroad stations. Made regulators for astronomical purposes and for jewelers. Made illuminated glass dials and other specialties. Advertised extensively in the Scientific American as Sherry & Byram

SHERWOOD, R.: San Francisco, Calif., 1850s. Also BARRETT & SHERWOOD

SHORT, JOHN: Halifax, N.C., 1790s–1819

SHREVE, G. C. & Co.: San Francisco, Calif., 1860s

SIDLE & BARLBERGER: Pittsburgh, Pa., 1840s–1850s

SIDLE, MATTHIAS & NICHOLAS: Pittsburgh, Pa., listed as a partnership in 1850 directory, and also as individual clockmakers at the same address

SIMPSON & JOHNSTON: Hagerstown, Md., 1800s–1804

SINWELL, RICHARD: Pittsburgh, Pa., 1830s. Clock and watchmaker with shop on 5th St., between Liberty & Market in 1837

SITWELL, RICHARD: Pittsburgh, Pa., 1830s. Most likely a variant of Sinwell Richard, listed above. The Pittsburgh directory featuring this man's name had broken type and researcher was unable to state without question whether the name was SINWELL or SITWELL

SMITH, A. D.: Cincinnati, Ohio, 1850s. Probably an extensive dealer doing sufficient business to warrant name on dial and clock papers with his name

SMITH, CLARK & CO.: New York, 1840s–1850s–1860s

SMITH, H. C.: N.Y. City, at 105 John Street, 1840s–1850s. Claimed to be manufacturer

SMITH, JAMES: Philadelphia from last quarter of 18th century. Founder who made blanks for clockmakers

SMITH, JAMES: Philadelphia. Sometimes James S. Smith. Brass, wood and "alarm" clocks; 8-day and 30 hour, from 1840s

SMITH, JESSE: Salem, Mass., 1840s–1850. Chronometers

SMITH, J. L.: N.Y. City, 1840s

SMITH, JOHN: New York City, 1840s. French clock importer and custom maker of clocks at 84 Fulton Street

SMITH, JOHN: Ashford (Mass.?), 1680s–1700s

SMITH, JOHN CREAGH: Philadelphia, from 1830s. Shop at 196 Chestnut Street

SMITH, SAMUEL: Philadelphia, from 1850s

SMITH, S. G.: 1867, Boston

SMITHS CLOCK ESTABLISHMENT: New York City, 1830s. Located at 7½, the Bowery. A clock paper of record and directory listing bracketing the date, constitute the authority for this entry and its chronology

SOLLIDAY, JOHN N.: Advertised in Reading, Pa., newspapers as a clockmaker in 1816. Removed to Bucks County in 1821 or 1822

SOLLIDAY (also SALLATE, SOLLATE) JOHN N. (SR.): Migrated from Canton of Berne, or Appenzell, Switzerland, to Pennsylvania, 1751. Clocks by him may bear place name of Sumneytown, Allentown, Northampton, or Reading. Founder of the Solliday clan of clockmakers in this district of Pennsylvania

SOMERS, ALBERT: Woodbury, N.J., from 1821. He was an apprentice of George Hollinshead at Woodstown, N.J., and there succeeded to his masters business

SOUTHWEST GEORGIA CLOCK CO.: No particular place, probably a clock peddling concern. Their clock was a special calendar type of 1850s or later. May be as late as 1870s and 1880s. Clocks are extant with this designation on dials and papers

SOUTHWICH, A. W.: 1867, Boston

SPENCE, JAMES: Flemington, N.J., from 1800s. Tall case clocks reported from several owners

SPENCER & WOOSTER & CO.: Salem Bridge, Conn., n.d.

SPERRY & GAYLORD: New York City, 1850s

SPOTSWOOD & CLARKE: Philadelphia, 1770s–1787. Thereafter A. Clarke

SPRATT, SAMUEL L.: Elkton, Cecil County, Md., 1820s–1830s. In 1831 he sold his property and tools to Thomas Howard, Jr., who, it appears, was not a clockmaker and did not continue the business

SPYCKER (Speicher), PETER: Tulpehocken, Pa., 1780s

STADT, J.: New York City from 1810s or 1820s

STANWOOD & CO., HENRY B.: Boston, Mass., 1850s, manufacturers and importers. H. B. and J. D. Stanwood and G. D. Low were the company

STARK, W. T.: Xenia, Ohio, 1830s

STAUFFER, SAMUEL: Manheim, Pa., from 1770s or earlier. Clock No. 25 by this maker in Georgian type case, brass dial and chiming movement has been found. This is an extension to name in Drepperd

STEDMAN, D. B.: Boston, Mass., from 1860s

STEPHENSON, HOWARD & DAVIS: Boston, from 1840s. Manufacturers of "superior tower, gallery, public and astronominal clocks and regulators." This firm was composed of Luther Stephenson, Edward Howard and David P. Davis

STEVENS, GEORGE M. & CO.: Boston, Mass., from 1860s. Tower clocks

STEVENS, S.: Lowell, Mass., 1853

STEVENSON, GEORGE: Albany, N.Y., from 1850s or 1860s

STEWARD, D. M.: Shelbyville, Ind., 1860s

STEWART, WILLIAM P.: Funkstown, Md., 1820s. Advertised as clock and watchmaker, 1825

STILES, SAMUEL: Windsor, Conn., n.d.

STILLMAN, BARTON: Westerly, R.I., c.1810–1820s

STILLMAN, PAUL: Westerly, R.I., c.1803-1810

STILLMAN, (DEACON) WILLIAM: Westerly, R.I., from 1786 to 1789 and from 1792 to 1809. Burlington, Conn., 1789–1792. Made wood movement tall clocks at Westerly, 1786–1789; thereafter made brass movement clocks at Burlington and at Westerly

STILLMAN, WILLITT: Westerly, R.I. A magnificently cased tall clock, 8-day, time, strike, seconds hand and day of month slot, is owned by H. D. Green, Esq., of Birmingham, Alabama. On a boss in the tympanum is the legend: Willitt Stillman, Westerly, and the date 1790. Deacon William Stillman of Westerly (b.1767) worked at Westerly 1786 to 1789, removed to Burlington, Conn., to 1792 and then returned to Westerly where he worked to 1809. Willitt Stillman, dating a clock at Westerly 1790 was therefore working at Westerly during the absence of Deacon William in Connecticut. This, then, is another newly discovered name of an American eighteenth century clockmaker

STOLL, GEORGE: Lebanon, Pa., 1850s

STOLL & FUNK: Lebanon, Pa., 1850s

STONE, JASPER: Charlestown, Mass., 1853

STONE, J. W.: East Randolph, Vermont, 1830s–1840s

STOWELL, A.: Charlestown, Mass., 1853

STOWELL, A. & SON: Charlestown, Mass. Watches extant carry the advertisement in cases "made by A. Stowell & Son, watch and clockmakers, 42 Main St., Charlestown, Mass." The date would seem to be c.1800s to 1850s

STREPEY, GEORGE: Salem, Pa., 1800s–1830s. Clock by this maker with name as here spelled, and place designation, owned by a lady of Dillsburg, Pa. This is a cherry cased tall clock. It is believed the name STREPEY is a variant of STREIPY and STREIBY. There were clockmakers by all these names in the vicinity of Greersburgh, Pa.

STRETCH, ISAAC: Philadelphia, advertised in 1752. Watchmaker first but also made clocks, or is so reputed

STRETCH, SAMUEL: Philadelphia, early 18th century to 1732. Nephew of Peter Stretch

STRETCH, WILLIAM: Philadelphia. Early 18th century to 1748. Son of Peter Stretch

STRONG, PETER: Fayetteville, N.C., from 1790 or earlier. Died 1797

STUART, JAMES: Philadelphia, 1830s–1850s

SUNNING, S. V.: n.p. c.1800–1825. Gilded case banjo clock bearing this name in a broad ribbon in neck panel was sold in the S. Serota sale, American Art Galleries, March 8, 1924

TABER, RUBINE: Hingham, Massachusetts, from 1800s or 1810s

TAPPEN, JOHN: Flemington, N.J., 1840s

TAYLOR, ANDREW: New York City, 1850s

TAYLOR, SAMUEL: Worcester, Mass., b.1780, d.1864. One-time partner of Jonathan Barker (see Barker & Taylor). Samuel Taylor worked alone as a clockmaker at Worcester from 1807 to 1856. This man is wrongly designated as Samuel E. Taylor in first edition of American Clocks & Clockmakers. He should not be confused with the Samuel E. Taylor who did work at Bristol, Conn. The man here considered spent his entire active life at Worcester, Mass.

TENNENT, THOMAS: San Francisco, Calif., 1850s–1860s

TERRY, SAMUEL: Bristol, Conn., 1831. At that time he is advertised as a Brass Founder as well as "mfr. of patent 30 hour wood clocks"

TERRY, THOMAS & HOADLEY: Greystone, Conn., 1809. Evidence of this firm, as in business and making clocks so signed, provided by Dana L. Shaw, Esq.

THAXTER, SAMUEL: Boston, 1830s, chronometers. Shop at 125 State St.

THOMPSON, S. N.: Roxbury, Mass., 1853

THOMSON, WILLIAM: Wilmington, N.C., from 1834. Also at Raleigh, N.C., c.1836. Returning to Wilmington 1840s. Died 1850

THORNE, ROBERT: Albany, N.Y., 1850s–1870s

TILDEN, THURBER: See Killam, George R.

TIMBY, THEODORE R.: Baldwinsville, N.Y., 1850s–1860s. Inventor of the Timby solar clock

TIMME, M.: Brooklyn, N.Y., 1840s. Inventor of musical chime clock in tall casing with 12 inch zodiac dial

TISDALE, BENJAMIN H.: Newport, R.I., from 1810s. Clock & Watchmaker. Had a jewelry store. Died 1881 at age of 90 years

TISDALE, EBENEZER DAWES: Taunton, Mass. Born 1821. Worked 1840s to 1860s. This entry corrects that of TISDALE, E. D., on page 282 of American Clocks & Clockmakers

TISDALE, WILLIAM, JR.: Washington, N.C., from 1816. New Bern from 1821

TRAVIS, JOHN: New York City, 1859–1860. One clock, a brass skeleton, fusee, bearing above name is known. John Travis is listed as a cabinetmaker, not a clockmaker in some directories

TROTT, ANDREW C.: Boston, Mass., b.1779, d.1812. Worked as maker c.1799–1812. His obituary notice appears in the Boston "Columbian Centinel," July 8, 1812

TROTT, A. C. & Co.: Boston, Mass., at 28 Marlborough St., 1805–1808. An excellent watchpaper designates this firm as watch and clockmakers

TUCKER, J. W.: San Francisco, 1850s–1860s

TUERLINGS, JAMES: New York City, 1850s–1870s

TURNER, J. S.: New Haven, Conn., 1860s

TURRET & MARINE CLOCK CO.: Boston, 1860s. The firm was made up of Collins Stevens and Moses Crane

TUTTLE, ELIDIA: Owego, N.Y., 1820s–1840s. Wood movement shelf clocks which would seem to be of Connecticut make. Papers in clocks of record designate this man as maker. Name not reported on dials. Probably a representative, dealer, or distributor using local name to promote sale

TYLER, E. A.: New Orleans, 1840s–1850s

UNDERHILL, GEORGE H.: Young America, Illinois, 1860s

UPSON, LUCAS: New York City, 1840s

URLETIG, VALENTINE: Reading, Pa., from 1754. Made town clock of Reading in 1762. Died 1783. First clockmaker of this town. This entry corrects name as in Drepperd "URTELIG" as the spelling here given URLETIG, is according to the records of Reading. Also spelled UHRLE-DIG. Both spellings, as well as the one in Drepperd, are reported on clocks

U. S. CLOCK COMPANY: Austin, Ill., 1866. Chauncey Jerome is said to have made his final come-back bid with this firm. They had a sizable factory but were, apparently, not successful in production and sale of clocks

VAN AKEN, WILLIAM: Philadelphia, 1840s

VAN COTT, A. B.: Racine, Wisconsin, c1850s. Clock and watchmaker. He issued tokens used as one cent pieces during Civil War and later 1860s

VAN DER VEER, JOS: Somerville, N.J., n.d. Probably early 19th century

VERDIN, JACOB: Cincinnati, Ohio, 1850s

VERDIN, MICHAEL: Cincinnati, 1850s. Recorded as maker and manufacturer of town and church clocks

VICKERY, THOMAS: New Lisbon, Ind., 1860s–1870s

VINING, L. S.: Cincinnati, 1830s–1840s. A Connecticut clockmaker who emigrated to the Ohio Country

VOGEL, FREDERICK: Middleburgh and/or Schoharie, N.Y., 1820s–1840s. This is extension of entry in Drepperd. Vogel imported movements and parts from England, cased them in cases made by George Bouck, and sold the finished product as his production. Tall case clocks. Reported a bankrupt in 1840s

VOIGHT, HENRY: Reading, Pa., and Philadelphia, 1770s–1780s. Taxed as clockmaker in Reading, 1780. Associated with John Fitch at Philadelphia, in steamboat experiments. Became chief coiner at first U. S. Mint. As such he would have been known to Rittenhouse. Voight was a Dutch trained clockmaker

VOUTE, LEWIS C.: Bridgeton, N.J., c.1820 to 1833; Philadelphia, Pa., thereafter

WADSWORTH, JEREMIAH: Georgetown, S.C., 1820s

WADSWORTH, LOUNSBURY & TURNERS: Litchfield, Conn., 1830s and 1840s. Pillar & Scroll cased mantel clocks with 30 hour wood movements. Movement vagary is counter clockwise wind for time side and clockwise wind for strike

WAGSTAFFE, THOMAS: English (London) maker who shipped finished movements and parts to Philadelphia makers who cased them, 1750s–1770s. Wagstaffe, while not of record as a visitor to the colonies, was closely affiliated with the Friends, or Quakers and dealt with the clockmaker members of his church

WAHLBERG, VICTOR: Brooklyn, N.Y., established 1849. Maker of tall case and mantel clocks. His clock paper bears a woodcut picture of a Sheraton type tall case clock

WALTERS, CHARLES D.: Harrisburg, Pa., 1850s–1860s

WALTON, HIRAM: Cincinnati, 1820s–1830s

WALTON, S. B.: Livermore Falls, Maine, 1850s. Invented a perpetual motion clock which he claimed would run for a year

WAPLES, NATHANIEL: Philadelphia, from 1820s

WARD, W. D.: Springfield, Illinois, 1850s and 1860s. Clocks made by him reported from central Illinois (Sangamon County)

WARDEN, W. PALMER: N.d. and n.p. but probably Iowa, along Mississippi; with indication of vicinity of Keokuk

WARNER, A. & H. A.: 1867, Boston

WARRINGTON, S. R.: Philadelphia, from 1830s

WATSON, JAMES: Philadelphia, 1820s

WATSON, LUMAN: (additional data on) This clockmaker of Cincinnati, in 1820s, produced a hollow column clock in Grecian style casing. This clock is pictured in the L. Watson advertisement reproduced on page 49 of American Clocks & Clockmakers

WATSON, WILLIAM: Philadelphia, from 1860s

WATTLES, W. W. & SONS: Pittsburgh, Pa., from c.1850. Reported as makers of fine carriage clocks, cut glass and gilt bronze cased clocks. May have used French movements. Most likely energetic and resourceful dealers and assemblers

WATTS, STUART: Boston, Mass., c.1740s. Walnut cased, brass dial, 8-day clock by this maker was once in collection of late Harry Koopman

WEATHERLY, DAVID: Philadelphia, c.1800s–1810s. Tall case clocks

WEHRLE, JOSEPH: Belleville, Illinois, from 1850s. Probably peddler or dealer

WEISS, JEDEDIAH: Bethlehem, Pa., from 1815 when he took over shop of his master and employer, Samuel Krause of

Krouse. These notes in extension of entry in American Clocks & Clockmakers

WELLES, GELSTON & Co.: Boston, 1820s to 1831 when the partnership was dissolved. Silversmiths and importers of parts and movements. Doubtful if they made any clocks

WELLS, CALVIN: Watervliet, N.Y. Shaker clockmaker 1810s–1830s

WELLS & FOSTER: Cincinnati, Ohio, 1830s–1840s. L. T. Wells and J. Foster, owners of this firm, manufactured town and house clocks and mathematical instruments

WELSH, DAVID: Lincolnton, N.C., from 1840s to 1850s

WELTON, H. & Co.: Terrysville, Conn. This firm name is on a clock paper inside a hollow column, one-day, brass movement, time and strike mantel clock in the Shanaberger collection. The designation is "H. Welton & Co., Successors to Eli Terry & Co., Terrysville, Conn."

WENTZEL, H.: San Francisco, Calif., 1850s–1880s. Made the now famed pneumatic impulse clocks and clock systems. This entry is in extension of Wentzel & Co. entry in Drepperd, giving Washington, D.C., as the locale. The Washington business was merely an office

WEST, EDWARD: Lexington, Ky., from 1780s. Born, Virginia, 1757, died, Lexington, 1827. Inventor of an oared steamboat, a nail-cutting engine and gunmaking tools. Also a clock and watchmaker

WEST, ROBERT: Potsdam, N.Y., 1860s

WEST, S. B.: Odessa, Delaware, 1850s–1870s

WESTCOTT, J.: Brooklyn, N.Y., 1840s–1850s

WESTON BROTHERS: Boston, Mass., from 1860s

WESTON, JAMES & SON: 1867, Boston

WETHERELL & MEAD: Montpelier, Vt., 1840s–1850s

WHEELOCK, GEORGE: Wilmington, Del., c.1790s–1800s. Apparently this man was a cabinetmaker who purchased movements from clockmakers and assembled the complete units vending them as his production and with his name on dial or on case

WHITE, J.: Brooklyn, N.Y., 1830s

WHITE, JOHN: Boston, Mass., 1780s–1790s. Tall clocks

WHITEAR, BENJAMIN: Fairfield, Conn., 1770s–1800s. Tall case clocks known

WHITING, L. E.: Saratoga Springs, N.Y., after 1863. Made the Timby Solar Clock. This is a correction of the listing in Drepperd, which is S. E. WHITING

WHITMAN, BENJAMIN: Reading, Penna., from 1770s. Brass dialed tall clock of record

WHITNEY, LEONARD: Boston, Mass., and Westerly, R.I., 1830s–1850s. At Westerly he was employed by Thomas Perry

WIDDEFIELD, WILLIAM, JR.: Fayetteville, N.C., from 1832 to 1840s. Formerly of Philadelphia

WILCOX, ALVIN: Fayetteville, N.C., from 1819. Formerly of Hart & Wilcox, Norwich, Conn. New Haven, Conn., after 1830. Became a silversmith

WILDER, E. E.: Rochester, N.Y., from 1860s

WILIS, JOSEPH: Philadelphia, c.1790s. Brass, 8-day movement, time and strike, with day of month slot and moon phase, brass dial marked "IOS Wilis, Philada." is reported in a case in turn signed by its maker, T. Davis

WILKINSON, ————: "Penrith, Maryland" – – – an error. This is William Wilkinson of Penrith, England, and listed in Baillie as working c.1790. Several clocks by this maker, owned in Maryland, with the place name "Penrith" have lead to assumption of local making at an early place in Maryland known by this name

WILLARD, AARON: Boston in 1834 at 843 Washington

WILLARD, HENRY: Boston, 1834, as clockcase maker. Shop rear of 843 Washington or 673 Washington

WILLARD, SIMON & SON: Boston, 1860s

WILLIAMS, ANDREW L.: Newark, N.J., 1850s

WILLIAMS, BENJAMIN: Elizabeth Town, N.J., 1780s–1790s. Partner of William J. Leslie in firm of Leslie and Williams, also Williams & Leslie

WILLIAMS, N.: Portsmouth, (N.H.?) n.d.

WILLIAMS, WILLIAM: Boston, 1770s

WILLOCK, JOHN: Pittsburgh, Pa., 1830s. An Ohio River trader who is reputed to have made clocks, but probably sold clocks made by Pittsburgh makers

WILLS, JOSEPH: Northampton County, Pa., is place designation on dial of a tall case clock by this maker. Date c.1770s–1780s. May have come from Reading, Pa., to work in Northampton County

WILMARTH, H. M. & BROTHER: Chicago, Illinois. Advertised clocks and bronzes. Probably dealers only

WILMOT, SAMUEL: Savannah, Georgia, from 1850s

WILMOTT, BENJAMIN: Easton, Maryland, 1790s–1800s. Advertised in Republican Star 1797, 1802, 1807

WINGATE, PAINE: Haverhill, Mass., late 1810s or early 1820s. This is an extension of same entry in Drepperd

WINSTON, JONATHAN: n.d., n.p. An 8-day brass movement tall case clock of c.1820 reported in 1949 as having this name and nothing else in the way of designation on dial

WINTERS, CHRISTIAN: Easton, Pa., 1800s

WISTER, CHARLES J.: Germantown, Phila., 1820s–1860s

WITHERILL & CO.: South Bend, Indiana, from 1850s

WITMAN, BENJAMIN: Reading, Pa., 1790s–1840s. Advertised as a clockmaker in 1796 and as a painter of clock faces in 1799. After 1800 he engaged in the manufacture of clock dials. Died 1857

WOHLSCHLANGLER, B.: Carondelet, Missouri, from 1860s

WOLF, THEODORE: Lancaster, Penna., from 1850s

WOLTZ, GEORGE ELIE: Hagerstown, Md., 1820–1840. Son of George Woltz

WOLTZ, JOHN: Sheperdstown, West Va., 1800–1825. Son of George Woltz

WOLTZ, WILLIAM: Oakland, Md., 1825–1840. Son of George Woltz

WOODRUFF, ENOS: Cincinnati, 1820s–1830s

WOODWORTH, F. A.: New York City, from 1840s "Successor to Joseph Bonfanti, Importer of Clocks." Probably neither were actually makers of clocks, but assemblers and casers of French movements

WRIGHT, T. H.: Lancaster, N.H., c.1800–1820s

YATES (also YEATES), EDWARD J.: Freehold, N.J., 1800s–1810. The Yates, or Yeates family seem to have persisted in New Jersey and the Hudson Valley as Clockmakers, Jewelers and Watchmakers down to the present day. It would seem that a contemporary member of this family should research the clock and watchmakers of this name down through the years from the last quarter of the 18th century

YATES, JOSEPH: Trenton, N.J., from 1780s

YATES & KENT: Trenton, N.J., from c.1790 to 1800. Yates was the clockmaker of this firm. Kent is presumed to have been a silversmith. Leslie & Williams took over the business in early 1800s. Yates is believed to have moved to N.Y. State, (Westchester or Dutchess County) and continued clockmaking in the Hudson Valley. Latter data not yet verified

YEAR CLOCK CO.: New York City, 1850s. Made one year clocks under the Aaron Crane patents

YOUNG, JACOB: Elizabethtown, (N.J.) c.1750s to 1760. Believed to be the same Jacob Young who worked in the Manheim section of Philadelphia from 1760s. John Myers, Esq., of New Oxford recently found, at Fort Edward, N.Y., a 30 hour brass movement, pull up, tall case class, brass dialed, with pewter chapter ring and pewter boss in tympanum, bearing the crudely engraved name of Jacob Young and the place, Elizabethtown

YOUNGS, BENJAMIN: b. Hartford, Conn., 1736. Son of Seth Youngs, worked at Windsor, Conn., with father to 1761, alone to 1766, Schenectady, N.Y., to 1806, there, as member of Shakers at Watervliet, N.Y. Died 1818. Made tall case, wall clocks and alarms

YOUNGS, ISAAC: New Lebanon, N.Y. Son of Seth Youngs (Jr.). Wall clocks in the Shaker tradition of casing. From 1810s to 1840s, apprentice of Benjamin Youngs. Was also a tailor

ZAHM, G. M.: Lancaster, Penna., from 1830s or 1840s. Listed in 1st Edition of American Clocks and Clockmakers as working from 1850s, this entry corrects the listing. The man worked in late 1830s and advertised in 1842 directory of Lancaster. He did make clocks, silverware and finally conducted a Jewelry establishment of some size and importance

ZEISSLER, G. A.: Philadelphia, 1848

ZILLIKEN, WILLIAM: Pittsburgh, Pa., from 1850s. Listed as a clockmaker

ZIMMERMAN, C. H.: New Orleans, La., 1850s–1860s